# TEACHING ELEMENTARY ARITHMETIC

Harper's Series on Teaching

Under the editorship of

Ernest E. Bayles

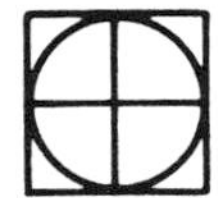 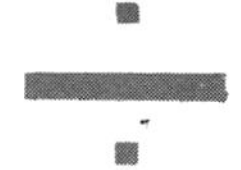   

# TEACHING ELEMENTARY ARITHMETIC

**Cleata B. Thorpe**



HARPER & BROTHERS, PUBLISHERS, NEW YORK

TEACHING ELEMENTARY ARITHMETIC



*Printed in the United States of America*



*For information address Harper & Brothers*
*49 East 33rd Street, New York 16, N.Y.*

*Library of Congress catalog card number:* 62-7142

# Contents



# Part ONE

## TEACHING ARITHMETIC WITH INSIGHT AND UNDERSTANDING

# Part TWO

## REVIEW OF COMPUTATION AND APPLICATION OF ARITHMETIC PROCESSES

### Section A—Computation

# Editor's Introduction

Emerging from the eighteenth century and entering the nineteenth, one of the great teachers of Western culture was struggling to develop, and to acquaint his generation with, a new way of teaching. Johann Heinrich Pestalozzi saw the deadliness of memorization by rote and devoted a lifetime of doggedly pertinacious labor in behalf of what may well be called the developmental method.

Pestalozzi early caught the significance of his idea for the teaching of arithmetic. Then in this country came Warren Colburn's book, *First Lessons in Arithmetic on the Plan of Pestalozzi.* But the past gives way slowly and grudgingly, and by the middle of the twentieth century we are still in the throes of breaking away from memoriter drill.

The author of this book has clearly seen the value of developmental teaching, as is evident in this paragraph from Chapter 10:

> The present-day teaching of arithmetic places much emphasis on the generalization that all four of the fundamental processes are basically processes of regrouping, and all are actually extensions of counting. To help children see these relationships, frequent experiences in counting should be provided to prove the results obtained by the various processes. Thus the child realizes that the fundamental processes are really timesavers—short cuts—that he can use instead of counting.

She has, moreover, gone a step further and recognizes the value of making the development reflective—of getting the pupils themselves to work out arithmetical relationships and thereby reach more effectual understandings.

This therefore is not a book for the self-satisfied. It represents a forward look, but one that is convincingly presented and extensively implemented. It ably takes its place in a line of progressive thinking.

ERNEST E. BAYLES

# Preface

The world has entered a new era. Whether it is called the atomic age, or the space age, or merely the age of giant strides in science, there is every indication of a prevailing emphasis on science in the educational programs of the civilized world. Everywhere there are demands for more scientists and more engineers, and consequently for more mathematicians.

One assumption on which *Teaching Elementary Arithmetic* is based is that in the years immediately ahead there will be an increasing demand upon our schools for more mathematics to be taught and for it to be taught more effectively than in the past.

However, if more proficient students of mathematics are to come out of our schools, our entire mathematics curriculum should be revised, the teaching objectives to which we subscribe should be reevaluated, and our present-day knowledge of child nature and child development and of the psychology of learning should be used more effectively in the teaching procedures.

The matter of reconstructing the curriculum in the area of mathematics is not within the realm of this book; that is left to curriculum experts. Nor is it within the province of this text to set up the content for each grade level in elementary mathematics; that is left to course-of-study specialists and writers of elementary arithmetic textbooks.

Some revision of the mathematics program is now in progress, particularly in the secondary-school curriculum where attempts are being made to modernize the classical mathematics program, even to the extent that the National Science Foundation and other agencies are providing financial assistance for the further training of selected high-school teachers in order to bring them up to date in the fields of science and mathematics.

Revision on the elementary level has thus far consisted mainly of removing from the curriculum certain types of computations and problem material because they were said to lack social utility, and of upgrading most of the arithmetic content. But a new trend is in evidence—a movement to reinforce the arithmetic curriculum by "stiffening" the content but applying methods of teaching which involve more insight and understanding and aid in a better comprehension of arithmetic at every grade level. One of the purposes of this text is to contribute to such a movement.

A second purpose is to point out the ultimate objectives for teaching elementary arithmetic, the procedures by which those objectives can be attained, and ways of determining the extent to which the objectives have become real outcomes. In this connection some attention is given to the historical development of elementary teaching methods and of arithmetic as a subject in the American school curriculum; the application of modern teaching methods to arithmetic also is given attention.

A third and highly important purpose is to give students an understanding and comprehension of arithmetic that will enable them to teach elementary arithmetic with confidence and with a gratifying sense of accomplishment.

Since the book is intended for students in teacher-preparation classes in college, as well as for teachers in service, the need for a clear and readable as well as practical text is recognized as paramount.

Part Two is intended to be used as a review of the computational and reasoning processes usually included in elementary arithmetic textbooks. This should serve as a refresher course for the prospective teacher, as well as a test of his ability to apply the rationale of arithmetic, to which Part One is chiefly devoted.

The Competence Check at the end of each chapter is planned to help fix essential concepts and to aid students in determining to what extent they have mastered the concepts and processes presented in the chapter.

The Optional Assignments, also at the end of each chapter, are included to aid the instructor who wishes to provide additional work for more advanced students.

Such References have been included as add information or contribute to further discussion of the topics dealt with in the chapter, as well as those in the Optional Assignments.

If this book has a dedication, it is dedicated to the fledgling teachers whom it may have inspired to become proficient arithmetic teachers.

CLEATA B. THORPE

*August, 1961*

# *part* ONE

## TEACHING ARITHMETIC WITH INSIGHT AND UNDERSTANDING

chapter 1

# Importance of Arithmetic

## 1. Important Part of Environment

We have but to look about us to become aware that numbers have an important place in all aspects of our environment. Persons as well as things have quantitative characteristics—weight, size, age, degrees of temperature, pulse beats, and so on. The clothes people wear are designated by size from hats to shoes. Time schedules, wages, expenses, games, transportation, food purchases—where can we turn throughout the day without being involved with number? The illustrations are innumerable.

So basic to human existence is number that even primitive man needed some way of reckoning "how many" before he had use for either reading or writing. As civilization advanced, number came into greater and greater use and a system of numbers evolved; without it our modern civilization could never have been attained.

How much arithmetic does the average person use during a normal day? In view of the part number plays in our environment it is clear that everyone needs some degree of competence in the fundamental processes to handle the simple problems of everyday living—When do we eat? What does it cost? How many people will be here? What time does the bus leave? Furthermore, in all spheres of life there will undoubtedly be much greater dependence on mathematics in the future than there is today.

## 2. Basic to Many School Subjects

We hardly need to be reminded that arithmetic is basic to many school subjects. What would history be without dates, time lines, tables, charts, and maps? How could there be geography without land measurement, population figures, elevation, latitude and longitude, production data, and so on? Music, art, the physical and social as well as the biological sciences, economics, and obviously algebra, geometry, and trigonometry, all involve computations of some sort.

### 3. Indispensable for Vocations and Professions

Today vocational success depends to a large extent upon ability to use arithmetic. Farmers, merchants, contractors, printers—for them arithmetic has become increasingly complex. Even the payroll clerk who writes his company's pay checks is involved in numerous tax and insurance deductions, retroactive salary increases, and other complicated computations.

Members of the various professions, technical and others—engineers, chemists, dentists, accountants, psychologists, physicians, geologists—all must have sound arithmetic on which to base the science and mathematics required in their work.

### 4. Integral Part of Man's Cultural Heritage

Regardless of whether one is to *use* arithmetic in the various ways implied in the paragraphs above, it is assumed to be an important part of man's cultural heritage and is therefore an essential part of what is known as general education.

For centuries mathematics has been developed by scholars for the satisfaction of intellectual achievement as well as for the usefulness of the processes. To many people an interest in mathematics comes from intellectual curiosity, the love of problem-solving, and the pursuit of knowledge for its own sake. Arithmetic is more than a mere informational subject. It makes a large contribution to the development of the higher mental processes—discrimination, comparison, analysis, synthesis, and sequential arrangement, in all of which psychologists now grant some possibility of transfer. In that respect it is unsurpassed as a subject in the elementary curriculum.

General education is presumed to assist an individual in coping with life situations which are not in the regular vocational category. Although the ability to do critical thinking is not dependent upon mathematics for its development, and although it has been well proved by psychology that skills do not transfer automatically to other situations, mathematical thinking no doubt helps establish a sort of pattern for clear and critical thinking. Geometry is credited with representing a perfect example of critical thinking.

According to Gates,[1] transfer depends upon understanding. It is not automatic, but involves a deliberate attempt to interpret new situations in the light of past experience and to apply appropriately the meanings and methods previously learned. This sounds decidedly like *application* of a skill or ability learned in one situation to another situation. Teaching for application is a high level of teaching. It is quite possible that a mathematics teacher may teach some ability to do critical thinking in a way so that it may be transferred, or applied, if you will, in another situation.

Religion may be considered to be within the realm of general education. According to Smith,[2] mathematics contributes to religion for it leads to a feeling that the Infinite exists when it induces such questions as: What is the largest number? What is infinity? What lies beyond space, and how far? Writing in the *Sixth Yearbook* of the National Council of Teachers of Mathematics almost thirty years ago, he stated: "A new era is dawning and with it a nobler conception of what all the sciences mean in relation to one another and to the higher ideals of humanity."

## 5. Important Enough to Merit Good Teaching

If arithmetic is of such great importance as has been indicated, and if more youth will be expected to attain more competence in it in the elementary school, what of the teachers who will be responsible for accomplishing those ends? Obviously teachers who have a high degree of competence in teaching arithmetic will be called for, and such teachers will be more important than ever before.

For at least a decade farsighted educators have been pointing out weaknesses in the arithmetic program of the elementary schools in the United States. Most of their criticisms stem from the inability of a large proportion of high-school graduates to comprehend comparatively

[1] Arthur I. Gates, *et al.*, *Educational Psychology*, pp. 536 ff., as quoted by William Betz, "The Teaching and Learning Processes in Mathematics," *Mathematics Teacher*, January, 1949, pp. 49 ff.

[2] D. E. Smith, "Mathematics and Religion," in National Council of Teachers of Mathematics, *Sixth Yearbook*, 1931, pp. 53–61.

simple arithmetic and compute problems in it. According to Wilson, there is general recognition of the problem: "Military men found inductees incredibly weak in basic arithmetic. College teachers found students unable to do the simplest arithmetical operations. Employers complained of employees with lost or unacquired skills."[3]

Such criticisms are not based on opinion alone. A number of research studies, particularly in college classes, have brought forth supporting data. In 1949 Glennon reported that studies show the general development of arithmetic understanding on the part of undergraduates in representative teacher-training institutions to be inexcusably low, and that the weaknesses are common to all types of schools—teachers colleges, liberal arts colleges, and colleges of education in universities.[4]

Schaaf's report in 1953[5] points out that there is no lack of evidence of elementary teachers' need for more knowledge of arithmetic, and indicates that there was probably little change during the immediately preceding five years.

Research since that time seems to corroborate earlier findings of a general lack of arithmetic ability, and indicates that in the five years since Schaaf's study there has been no marked improvement. One of those studies concludes that " . . . *graduate* students in Education show lack of competence in arithmetical computations, accompanied by a lack of confidence, that causes them to fear courses in statistics."[6]

After a test study, Geiselmann[7] in 1956 reported the types of difficulties found when the Cornell Mathematics Test was given to college freshmen. He outlined a remedial course for them, which he indicated was practically all in eighth-grade arithmetic and ninth-grade algebra.

Concluding the series reported here, Weaver's report, also in 1956, substantiates the findings of Glennon's research seven years earlier, and summarizes as follows: "The undergraduates who were sampled appear to have mastered a disturbingly small proportion of the understandings

[3] Jack D. Wilson, "Arithmetic for Majors," *Mathematics Teacher*, December, 1953, p. 560.

[4] Vincent J. Glennon, "A Study in Needed Redirection in the Preparation of Teachers of Arithmetic," *Mathematics Teacher*, December, 1949, pp. 389–396.

[5] William L. Schaaf, "Arithmetic for Arithmetic Teachers," *School Science and Mathematics*, October, 1953, p. 537.

[6] Jacob S. Orleans and Julia A. Sperling, "The Arithmetic Knowledge of Graduate Students," *Journal of Educational Research*, November, 1954, p. 177.

[7] Harrison Geiselmann, "Mathematical Deficiencies of College Freshmen," *Mathematics Teacher*, January, 1956, p. 22.

tested—understandings that are vital to meaningful arithmetic instruction in the elementary-school grades."[8] Weaver tested students on: I. Decimal Systems of Notation; II. Basic Understandings of Integers and Processes; III. Basic Understandings of Fractions and Processes; IV. Basic Understandings of Decimals and Processes; and V. Basic Understandings of the Rationale of Computation. Their mean score on the test as a whole represented only slightly more than 55 per cent of the total items.

In the light of these findings it would seem that in teaching what is generally considered to be arithmetic at the elementary level our elementary schools have failed to develop competence, and that secondary schools have withdrawn from responsibility for developing it further.

The fault on the whole lies not with the freshmen in teacher-training institutions who find themselves ill-equipped to master the technique of teaching arithmetic—for certainly they cannot teach what they do not know—but rather with the schools they attended. Those schools, it appears, are in no particular geographical area; rather, their location follows the general pattern.

In discussing the in-service development of teachers of arithmetic, Wilburn and Wingo say: "In nothing which is taught in the elementary school is it more important that teachers have an adequate understanding of the content itself than in arithmetic. Yet it is probable that elementary-school teachers have less insight into the content of arithmetic than into any other subject. . . . Teachers will not see the importance of changing their methods of teaching unless they have sufficient understanding of the number system to enable them to see the deficiencies in their methods."[9]

Probably their findings, like the many reported above, are due not to the inherent difficulty of arithmetic, but to the way arithmetic has been learned and the way it has been taught.

Writing in this vein, Morton[10] discusses, with many illustrations, the incorrect and confused wording in instructions to children; for example,

[8] J. F. Weaver, "A Crucial Problem in the Preparation of Elementary School Teachers," *Elementary School Journal*, February, 1956, pp. 255–261.

[9] D. B. Wilburn and G. M. Wingo, "In-Service Development of Teachers of Arithmetic," in National Society for the Study of Education, *Fiftieth Yearbook, Part II*, 1951, pp. 261–269.

[10] R. L. Morton, "Low Visibility, or Ideas in a Fog," *Arithmetic Teacher*, October, 1958, pp. 172–176.

"How many more dolls than Ruth has Jane?" instead of the simpler question: "Jane has how many more dolls than Ruth?" Illustrative of another type of poor statement is: "Find $2\overline{)13}$" instead of simply: "$2\overline{)13}$." He comments that pupils may become accustomed to a teacher's faulty language and, in spite of it, succeed in getting correct answers.

Surely if there is any area in which precision of language is desirable, if not in fact essential, it is in connection with arithmetic where precision as such is so important. It is not difficult to supplement Morton's list profusely. For example, in listing things that pupils should understand, the authors of one recently published article have such "foundational meanings" as: "When a digit in any place-value position in the minuend is smaller than the digit in the same place-value position in the subtrahend, the numerical order of the minuend must be changed by substituting for one unit in the next higher place-value position ten units in the next lower place-value position."[11] This article also includes the statement: "Division as a physical act may involve: a. . . . b. Finding how many units in an equal group when the quantity is changed into a given number of equal size groups."[12]

A student preparing to teach in an elementary school should have a right to expect his teacher-training program to provide an opportunity to acquire competence in arithmetic that will enable him to feel confident of being prepared to teach arithmetic with security and assurance. However, with the rather widespread inadequacy in arithmetic which has been pointed out at the elementary-school level, and, according to some surveys,[13] with only about half the prospective teachers having any mathematics at the high-school level, if elementary teachers are to be adequately prepared to teach arithmetic, teacher-training institutions must provide a more concentrated program of preparation in mathematics.

These institutions have in the past taken too much for granted regarding competence in arithmetic when their students enter college. Teachers have gone into service poorly prepared to cope with arithmetic; and a vicious circle is created, for their pupils are no better prepared than they themselves were in elementary school.

[11] E. T. McSwain and Ralph J. Cooke, "Essential Mathematical Meanings in Arithmetic," *Arithmetic Teacher*, October, 1958, p. 188.

[12] *Ibid.*, p. 189.

[13] For example, Foster E. Grossnickle's national survey on the training of teachers in arithmetic reported in National Society for the Study of Education, *Fiftieth Yearbook*, 1951, and William L. Schaaf, *op. cit.*, p. 552.

Mueller seems to concur when he says: "What is needed is coursework specifically designed to meet the specific mathematical demands of the elementary classroom; coursework that will provide the elementary teacher with a mature awareness and appreciation of the foundation elements, of the diversity and interrelatedness of the myriad parts which go to form the structure of arithmetic; coursework that will provide a consciousness of the whole against which one may, with security and understanding, teach the segments of the subject pertinent to the given grade level."[14]

## COMPETENCE CHECK

1. List some reasons why modern civilization could never have been attained without a system of numbers.
2. Itemize one day's use of number and of the fundamental processes of arithmetic in your own experience.
3. Give illustrations of arithmetic's contribution to the processes of discrimination, comparison, analysis, synthesis, and sequential arrangement.
4. Do you as a college student have a fear of arithmetic and a feeling of inadequacy in it? If so, to what do you attribute this weakness, and when were you first aware of it?
5. Collect illustrations from your college textbooks of wording that you think is obscure and pedantic and serves no purpose that simpler language would not serve.

## OPTIONAL ASSIGNMENTS

1. Read and prepare to discuss Newsom's chapter, "Mathematical Background Needed by Teachers of Arithmetic." How much of what he proposes do you think is needed?
2. List Morton's illustrations of faulty language and unnecessarily involved wording and write them in improved form.
3. Cite four or five definite weaknesses of the Army Air Cadets in arithmetic that Henderson pointed out.
4. Report on Dutton's or Grossnickle's article.

## REFERENCES

Dutton, Wilbur H., "Attitudes of Prospective Teachers Toward Arithmetic," *Elementary School Journal*, October, 1951, pp. 84–88.

[14] Francis J. Mueller, "Arithmetic Preparation for Elementary Teachers," *Education*, January, 1959, pp. 299–302.

Henderson, Kenneth B., "Weaknesses in Arithmetic Teaching," *Elementary School Journal*, June, 1946, pp. 579–581.
Grossnickle, Foster E., "The Training of Teachers in Arithmetic," in National Society for the Study of Education, *Fiftieth Yearbook, Part II*, 1951, pp. 203–231.
Newsom, C. V., "Mathematical Background Needed by Teachers of Arithmetic," in National Society for the Study of Education, *Fiftieth Yearbook, Part II*, 1951, pp. 232–250.

chapter 2

# Arithmetic in the American School Curriculum

## 1. In Colonial Schools

Arithmetic as a subject in the curriculum of American schools has had a long and somewhat erratic history. It was made a required subject in Massachusetts schools by act of the legislature in 1789, just when the Constitution of the United States was being ratified. Up to that time English arithmetic books were in use in the colonies; these naturally dealt with English measurements (3 barleycorns = 1 inch, etc.,), English coins, and the English environment in general. These books were largely replaced in American schools by a ponderous volume by Nicholas Pike published in 1788. By this time arithmetic as a school subject had found its way into the elementary curriculum.

Early in the colonial period arithmetic was an essential tool in the market place. The earliest texts were designed to be useful in business computations, and this was the chief purpose of teaching arithmetic in the schools.

## 2. Mental Discipline an Early Aim

In the early nineteenth century a prevailing aim of education was *mental discipline*, or the development of mental power, which, according to the "transfer of training" theory of the day, would automatically transfer mental skill in arithmetic, for example, to mental acumen in other subjects. The mental discipline theory held to two assumptions (which some people say are still with us), namely, all processes must be studied on a drill mastery basis, and verbal "problems" of the usual textbook sort must be solved. These processes and problems constituted the content of arithmetic.

The study of arithmetic in schools consisted largely of copying worked examples and memorizing rules and definitions, practically all of it done on an individual basis.[1] There were many involved and complex problems, and computations with large numbers; for example, such a number as $16\frac{1277}{15425}$. In those early schools the rigorous logic of arithmetic, with its orderly and systematic arrangement, was considered one of its chief virtues.

The "ciphering-book" method prevailed until the rise of the public schools in the early decades of the nineteenth century, when class instruction became more common. Even then there was little explanation by the teacher. Pupils did their work on slates or on the blackboard and it was examined by the teacher or an older pupil.

## 3. Theory Influenced by Colburn's Book

In 1821 Warren Colburn's text, *First Lessons in Arithmetic on the Plan of Pestalozzi*, was published. It was one of approximately a hundred published by that time, and was much less widely used than many of the others. Although his book was frankly devoted to the development of the mental powers, it had considerable influence on later books in the matter of content and method, particularly the latter.

The Swiss educator, Pestalozzi, was attracting international attention by advocating more activity on the part of the pupil, more learning by doing and experiencing—an *inductive* approach to learning, of which the *developmental* approach is typical in modern procedure. Although Colburn still proposed to discipline the mind and develop mental power, adhering to the theories of Pestalozzi he sought to do this by inductive procedures. Therefore, defying traditional practice, he did not begin new processes with rules; he claimed that for rules to be useful they must be understood, and to be understood they must be formulated through a developmental approach. In all this Colburn had more of the marks of a modern educator than many a hundred years after him.

Colburn's *First Lessons* popularized mental arithmetic and made it parallel with written arithmetic. Today educators are trying to bring

[1] Cecil B. Read, "A Century Old Arithmetic Work Book," *School Science and Mathematics*, June, 1940, pp. 516–517.

back an interest and efficiency in mental arithmetic, which has been all but lost from school lessons through the years.

Late in the nineteenth century an arithmetic text series by Joseph Ray brought *some* encouragement for pupils. Problems and explanations were briefer and simpler and more readily understood by elementary-age children. For a generation or two Ray's *Arithmetics* almost matched McGuffey's *Readers* in extended use.

## 4. Questions About Content and Method

Early in the present century questioning and debating began on such problems as: What should be the content of the arithmetic curriculum? What is the place of drill in teaching arithmetic? What should be the grade placement of various topics like decimals and percentage? What aims or purposes should arithmetic serve? How much time should be given to arithmetic in the daily schedule? To what extent can arithmetic be made functional in the lives of pupils? Why have so many American children grown up without adequate competence in arithmetic?

Research in the form of surveys, experimentation, and tests has sought answers to these questions. Theories wax and wane, especially those relating to *what* arithmetic should be taught and *how* it should be taught. Back of each theory lies a philosophy—a series of value assumptions about the purposes of teaching arithmetic and what arithmetic should be taught to serve those purposes. In a more scientific vein divergent schools of psychology propose principles which reputedly can make teaching most effective. On the basis of observation and investigation, educational psychologists have collected and analyzed a tremendous amount of information about growth and learning. This evidence has served as a guide to methodology.

We can touch only briefly upon the numerous theories that have claimed the limelight in the teaching of arithmetic since the beginning of the twentieth century.

## 5. S-R Bond Theory

Before 1930 the stimulus-response or association theory of learning was prevalent. Also known as the Thorndike theory, the S-R Bond theory, and the connectionist theory, it set the pattern of teaching and learning for many years. Drill was the procedure which by the law of exercise would fix the bonds or connections and induce learning. Speed and accuracy in computation were the *aims*. Opponents called this theory the atomistic theory because it broke arithmetic, or any other subject to which it was applied, down into minute, unrelated parts for drill; and the mechanistic theory because the responses came from repeated mechanical drill, with understanding playing little or no part in the learning experience.

## 6. Advancement of the Gestalt Theory

By 1935 another theory of psychology, the organismic—or, as it was generally called, the Gestalt—theory of learning was making some impression on educators. Key ideas in this theory were: (1) The whole is greater than the sum of its parts; (2) the organism as a whole reacts to the situation as a whole; and (3) insight and understanding have an important role in learning.

Translated into classroom procedures, these ideas would have the following results. (1) They would treat number facts and computations as part of the whole logical system of arithmetic and bring about comprehension of number relationships. (2) They would remove pressure for the memorizing and mechanical figuring of number operations, in view of their recognition of the pupil's inability to concentrate his mental power on recall items when other aspects of his organism—physical, social, and emotional—were in need of the teacher's attention. (3) They would emphasize basic concepts, including an understanding of the number system and of fundamental operations, and the development of principles and generalizations. (4) They would recognize the fact that material that is organized is learned and remembered more readily than unrelated items, and that material which the learner understands and which has meaning for him is more easily learned and remembered than that which doesn't make sense to him. (5) They would recognize the important part that insight, discovery, and creativity play in the learning process.

## 7. More Attention to Social Utility

Since 1920 there has been a continuing demand on the part of some educators, among whom Wilson has been prominent, for more attention to *social* arithmetic. The utility theory would weed out the deadwood from arithmetic textbooks, retaining only such material as is definitely "useful" and for which pupils see a need. This idea led to extensive research, chiefly surveys of what "can be shown to have a plain relation to some real need in life."

Some of these investigations attempted to determine content on the basis of adult social use—what arithmetic does the "average man" use? On this basis fractions with denominators larger than 2, 3, and 4, and possibly 8 and 12 were taken out of the arithmetic content. It was claimed that decimals, aside from United States money, were not used except in the statistical departments of industry and some engineering departments; accordingly they also were removed from elementary arithmetic. Denominate numbers, their tables and reductions, came under the social utility ax, and factors and multiples were no longer found in elementary textbooks.

Some proponents of social utility advocated that content be determined on the basis of *child* usage. They sought inclusion of the arithmetic which the child used both out of school and in school. This theory was an element of the contemporary progressive education movement, with its child-centered schools, activity programs, and experience units which frequently involved the incidental teaching of arithmetic.

Critics of the social utility theories have been numerous. Wheat,[2] for example, says that social situations are part of the child's expanding world and give him a chance to apply his number thinking in the complex and concrete realities of everyday life. However, he maintains that instead of social situations supplying meaning to number, as the utilitarian theory holds, exactly the reverse is true; and he illustrates this by saying that percentage as an arithmetic learning should precede, not follow, a lesson on installment buying.

In discussing the social point of view in arithmetic Buckingham has this to say:

> The teacher who emphasizes the social aspects of arithmetic does well. But, in the sense in which the term is here used, he is not teaching the meaning of arithmetic. He may, and indeed he should, use a socially significant approach, but his teaching of a given point is not complete until the goal of mathematically meaningful ideas has been reached. These ideas should then find their application in social situations, either actual or described, for it is the application of number to the affairs of life which justifies arithmetic in the

[2] H. G. Wheat, "The Fallacy of Social Arithmetic," *Mathematics Teacher*, January, 1946, pp. 27–34.

common school. Since, however, the facility with which one may apply arithmetic depends squarely upon one's apprehension of the meaning of arithmetic, it is clear that significance and meaning are indispensable to each other. . . . Meaning and significance are attributes external to the learner who, as he reorganizes his experience, merges them and attains insight.[3]

In a similar vein, Betz[4] says that frequency studies have helped to eliminate some traditional, useless material, but at the same time a purely utilitarian emphasis on an immediate and wide application has done an enormous amount of harm in all fields, to the detriment of our national culture.

## 8. Research on Unit Skills and Order of Difficulty

Meanwhile another group, among whom Brueckner and Knight were prominent, were using an analytic approach to determine curriculum. They maintained that the unit skills or types involved, rather than the use of fractions in life, should determine the curriculum and teaching plans for fractions. In 1930 the first report on arithmetic by the National Society for the Study of Education (*Twenty-ninth Yearbook, Part II*) put a good deal of emphasis on the minute analysis of subject matter and the identification of unit skills and their order of difficulty as a guide to instruction.

Spitzer compared that approach to teaching with approaches advocated by himself and others during the last decade: "Specific aspects of arithmetic, practically isolated from other aspects of the subject, received attention. Today, with emphasis on securing a grasp of facts and processes, related facts and processes are considered without regard to order of difficulty."[5]

## 9. Meaning Theory

Widely acclaimed during the last two decades is the meaning theory to which Spitzer and many other arithmetic authorities now subscribe. This theory was first publicized in the *Tenth Yearbook* of the National

[3] B. R. Buckingham, "The Social Point of View in Arithmetic," in National Society for the Study of Education, *Fiftieth Yearbook, Part II*, 1951, p. 279.

[4] William Betz, "The Place of Mathematics in Human Affairs, and Related Curriculum Problems," *Mathematics Teacher*, February, 1952, p. 81.

[5] Herbert F. Spitzer, "Learning and Teaching Arithmetic," in National Society for the Study of Education, *Fiftieth Yearbook, Part II*, 1951, p. 140.

Council of Teachers of Mathematics in 1935. It holds that arithmetic is a closely knit system of understandable ideas, principles, and processes. It adheres to the Gestalt theory of psychology, which emphasizes wholes, in connection with which meanings, relationships, and whole-part patterns take on significance.

One psychologist,[6] writing in the *Tenth Yearbook*, advises teachers to forget drills, prepare their work logically, and concentrate on relations. He holds that the whole purpose of arithmetic is to discover number relations and be able to reason with numbers—not to learn tables.

Later writers have been less likely to tell teachers to forget drills. Even those who subscribe wholeheartedly to the Gestalt theories say there is a place for drill, but they put much emphasis on the idea that drill should *follow* understanding. After a pupil understands what 6 × 8 means and how the answer is arrived at, and also what use it can serve, they would have him learn it for quick recall. That would involve drill.

The meaning theory relies heavily on the Gestalt theories of learning discussed earlier in this chapter, with learning seen as a continuous process of integrating new concepts and skills with those previously learned. The term "meaningful teaching" may be said to imply that such teaching reveals to the learner the concepts and rationale of the processes in arithmetic, and the relationship of the processes to each other. This revelation the Gestaltists call **insight.**

Many psychological experiments confirm McGoech's statement: "The conclusion that there is a high positive correlation between meaningfulness of material and rate of learning holds under a very wide range of conditions."[7]

Since about 1940 much has been said and written about meaning and its place in learning. However, the present writer is inclined to agree with Van Engen when he says, "The literature on the meaning of 'meaning' is extensive and much of it is hard to read."[8] Furthermore, it seems doubtful whether the concept of "meaning" as applied to the meaning theory has been completely clarified since his statement in 1949.

[6] R. H. Wheeler, "The New Psychology of Learning," in National Council of Teachers of Mathematics, *Tenth Yearbook*, 1935, chap. 12.

[7] John A. McGoech, *The Psychology of Human Learning*, Longmans, Green, New York, 1942, p. 159; quoted by W. A. Brownell in "The Place of Meaning in the Teaching of Arithmetic," *Elementary School Journal*, January, 1947, pp. 256–265.

[8] H. Van Engen, "An Analysis of Meaning in Arithmetic II," *Elementary School Journal*, March, 1949, p. 400.

Certain arithmetic authorities maintain that for a process to have meaning for a pupil (he sees sense in it) and for him to understand the process (he knows why he does what he does) are not identical experiences. At any rate, it seems reasonable to assume that understanding is a product of experiences. Concepts are not transferred directly from teacher to pupil; they develop from a sequence of explorations by the pupil which lead to conclusions and generalizations. This series of activities we may refer to as developmental experiences. From such experiences insight is acquired.

This sequence of experiences is the backbone of teaching for meaning and understanding. As a first step experiences with concrete materials relate the new learning to the familiar. Here experimentation and discovery may be employed to arrive at new concepts. Generalizations are formulated and procedures are translated from manipulative activity to a recording of symbols. This record takes the form of an **algorism,** which though abstract in itself will have meaning for the learner.

Advocates of the developmental method say pupils may require more time to learn that way than by the rule and drill method, but as they progress, the need for teacher direction becomes less and less. Increasingly they learn to depend on their own resourcefulness, and to develop insight. At the same time, retention is good and less review is required.

## COMPETENCE CHECK

1. Explain the meaning of mental discipline as an aim in instruction.
2. How has the theory of transfer of training changed from the early period of education in the United States to the present?
3. What is meant by content in arithmetic teaching? What is meant by method?
4. If possible, find some arithmetic textbooks used long ago and note some of the differences between them and modern texts.
5. What does methodology mean? Be precise in your definition or explanation.
6. In what way was Warren Colburn more than a hundred years ahead of his time in arithmetic methodology?
7. Explain and illustrate the developmental method of teaching.
8. Define philosophy as applied to arithmetic teaching.
9. Explain the relationship between psychology and arithmetic.
10. List several of the identifying tenets of the two theories of psychology with which teachers are most concerned.

chapter 3

# Arithmetic in a New Era

## 1. The Road Traveled in Arithmetic Teaching

Current thinking about the importance of arithmetic as a subject in the American elementary-school curriculum and the ineffectiveness of learning in that area was discussed in Chapter 1. Chapter 2 traced the progress of arithmetic as a subject in the elementary curriculum and indicated the continuing search for a better arithmetic program in terms of both content and method. This search points to the meaning theory as portending more effective teaching and brings us to the point where scientifically prepared elementary arithmetic textbooks, copiously and beautifully illustrated and supplemented by teaching manuals, would seem to leave little to be desired in the way of materials.

## 2. Rapid Development of New Conditions

Rapidly occurring world events, involving an element of fear and anxiety, have recently thrown the spotlight on our schools in a search for more and better-trained scientists, and also for a means of identifying the bright and gifted segment of the population and developing its full potential. Scientific education demands mathematical proficiency, which in turn calls for adequate arithmetical foundations. So it is that the usually casual educational research and experimentation, suddenly prodded by public concern, have taken on some overtones of urgency. There seems no doubt that arithmetic teaching is entering a new era.

## 3. Significant Changes in the Making

No one can predict with certainty the direction that arithmetic teaching will take in the decade ahead, but what some of the changes will be seems fairly certain. These will likely involve grade-by-grade content, methodology, teaching materials, and a search for more differentiated programs.

## 4. Proposed Changes in Grade-by-Grade Content

In accordance with the decidedly diluted and upgraded arithmetic curriculum of recent years, educators have attempted to justify the program in two ways. First, they said that the unsatisfactory arithmetic learning of so many pupils was due to the fact that the material was too difficult; and second, that if material was presented slowly and very gradually, less remedial work would be necessary. In line with that philosophy, some schools gave no formal arithmetic instruction in the first and second grades. In all textbooks the various processes eventually were moved up and some material—e.g., factors and multiples—was removed completely. To make the learning easy enough much repetition of content was provided.

The rigor that once characterized elementary arithmetic in the form of difficult, unduly complex, and impractical computations and verbal problems was done away with completely. This type of content was replaced by problems related to the children's experiences and interests and those having social value. Pictorial material occupied increasing amounts of space in textbooks; the abstract elements of arithmetic, proportionately less and less.

Newer ideas hold that with more meaningful, developmental teaching procedures children are entirely capable of learning formal arithmetic in the primary grades and of acquiring some division and fraction concepts at least as early as the third grade. Teachers have realized that average and better pupils were bored into listlessness by getting to no more challenging concepts than $2 + 2$ by the middle of the first grade.

There will be a pushing down of content; some that has been taken out, such as factors and multiples, will be put back; repetition will be decreased because better understanding at the first exposure will make it less necessary. Furthermore, if some of the curriculum planners attain their goals, the seventh- and eighth-grade content will go beyond the prevalent social applications of percentage and life and family problem materials, and will deal largely with preparatory mathematics in areas of algebra and geometry to pave the way for a more advanced high-school mathematics curriculum.[1] Most of this, however, will be for accelerated groups.

Probably upper-grade arithmetic will include more concepts basic to contemporary mathematics—the theory of sets, topology, and the like. More attention could well be given to comprehension of the historical and cultural development of arithmetic, and there could be more understanding of our number system and of systems with bases other than 10. Statistics and approximations, areas of arithmetic which are coming increasingly into the average person's experience, may be introduced. And there is what the old-time arithmetics called involution and evolution; these quite probably will be restored to the elementary curriculum, especially since enlightened nations have to deal with numbers of ever-increasing size.

Such a program will give more attention to the mathematical aspects of arithmetic and to mathematical concepts, principles, and relationships. There will be a better balance between the concrete and the abstract in arithmetic, made possible by meaningful procedures and attention to rationale. More attention will be given to the derivation of generalizations.

## 5. European Influences

The Council for Basic Education has recently published a comparative study[2] of American and European textbooks which points to the fact that most European children study arithmetic content on an average of one to two grade-years earlier than American children. Although many educators accept this study in support of the movement to stiffen up our elementary arithmetic program, we should not be pushed too abruptly into a crash program by these facts; instead we should give some consideration to their background.

For decades there has been prevalent in Europe an approach to learning number concepts that is more mathematical and less based on real life situations. Dr. Maria Montessori, an Italian, created a considerable flurry of interest in America about 1912 with her Montessori Method for kindergarten and nursery schools. Though she was most concerned with retarded children, her methods were also adapted to

[1] Francis J. Mueller, "Building Algebra Readiness in Grades Seven and Eight," *Arithmetic Teacher*, November, 1959, pp. 269–273.

[2] Charles H. Schutter and Richard L. Spreckelmeyer, *Teaching the Third R*, Council for Basic Education, Washington, 1959.

normal children. Contrary to American practice, she taught reading and writing and arithmetic as part of the school arts in kindergarten. There is space here for only a few of the highlights of her method that pertain to the development of number concepts. She emphasized didactic apparatus that could be used by the children themselves (her auto-education). Much of it was used for sense training and individual occupation.

William Heard Kilpatrick, spokesman for the American progressive education movement of the early twentieth century, commented as follows on Dr. Montessori's method:

> As to arithmetic, there is little to be said. About the only novelty is the use of the so-called long stair. This consists of ten blocks, of lengths varying from one to ten decimeters, alternate divisions being painted in like colors. These blocks are used in teaching the various combinations which sum ten. On the whole, the arithmetic work seemed good, but not remarkable; probably not equal to the better work done in this country. In particular there is very slight effort to connect arithmetic with the immediate life of the child. Certainly, in the teaching of this subject, there is for us no fundamental suggestion.[3]

Other of his conclusions include: "The scientific conception of education is certainly valid." . . . "Her doctrine of education as unfolding is neither novel nor correct." . . . "Her doctrine of auto-education will at most provoke thought; the term is good, the idea old." . . . "The sense training which to her seems most worth while, we decline to accept except in a very modified degree. The didactic apparatus we reject in like degree." Typical of the progressive point of view is his statement, "Really necessary concepts will come in the normally rich experience of child life. Those that do not so come are not then necessary."

About two decades later Catherine Stern brought her structural arithmetic program to America from Germany. She too used cubes and elongated blocks for developing number concepts; and as the title of her book, *Children Discover Arithmetic*,[4] indicates, her theory was similar to Dr. Montessori's auto-education. But America was not yet ready. Mrs. Stern's kindergarten and first- and second-grade materials had only limited use. However, with the current new interest in arithmetic, Mrs. Stern is now developing her text material for use through the elementary grades.

[3] William Heard Kilpatrick, *The Montessori Method Examined*, Houghton Mifflin, Boston, 1914, p. 58.

[4] Catherine Stern, *Children Discover Arithmetic*, Harper, New York, 1949.

Recently, another European teaching device, this one from Belgium, has been put on the market following experimentation with it in the United States. This device which has the trade name of "Cuisenaire rods," consists of colored rods that are somewhat similar in form and use to the blocks and rods used by Montessori and Stern. The rods are graduated in length from one to ten. The University of Illinois Arithmetic Project has been making effective use of them in its demonstrations, and other experiments with them are now in progress. They have extensive possibilities for teaching number relationships, place value, and the fundamental processes.

## 6. Possible Grade-by-Grade Content Changes Anticipated in This Text

Readers will become aware as they use this book that the author has confidence in the ability of children at successive grade levels to understand and master specific content in grades lower than those in which such content is now presented in elementary arithmetic textbooks.

Certain computational and problem-solving techniques described in this text lead into readiness for algebra and geometry. For example, the value of learning to use equations is stressed consistently, from the simple primary-grade equations in addition and subtraction ($4 + 3 = ?$; $4 + ? = 7$; $7 - 3 = ?$; $7 - ? = 4$) to those taught in the higher grades and frequently written as formulas ($l \times w = A$; $l = A \div w$). The authors of elementary textbooks in arithmetic seem to be realizing more and more the value of equations on this level in both computational and problem-solving processes. The use of equations and formulas in arithmetic, including some use of letter symbols, is excellent preparation for the abstract nature of algebra; furthermore, the equation is a basic process of algebra.

A formula is merely a shorter and more convenient statement than a principle written as a sentence. For example, in words, one principle is: The dividend equals the product of the quotient and the divisor, plus the remainder. As a formula it is: $D = dq + r$. Here, too, the pupil learns the algebraic practice of indicating multiplication without the multiplication sign ($abc = a \times b \times c$; $dq = d \times q$).

Pupils in the upper grades should be given much practice in converting a sentence to a formula, and vice versa; for example, "Write the rule indicated by the formula $prt = i$" (for finding interest); "write the formula for: The area of a triangle equals one-half the base times the altitude." With such practice, pupils will learn that a formula is a generalized statement of the number relationships in a given situation, and will be able to comprehend that algebra is likewise a way of dealing with generalized relationships. Having learned to apply such principles as commutation and association, as advocated in this text, they will see that many of the principles they have learned in arithmetic apply to algebra as well.

Similarly, many types of problems, particularly measurement, that this book suggests will lead pupils into geometry. These problems are of the type referred to as intuitive geometry, and are more readily comprehended as early concepts than the deductive type used in geometry textbooks. The arithmetic work presented here acquaints pupils with many geometric forms (circles, triangles, rectangles, etc.) and with various geometric relationships (diameter to circumference, etc.) which they can verify by measurement. With this basic experience they will be ready to comprehend better what they will later obtain by the logical deductions of geometry.

### 7. Proposals for Improved Methodology

Expansion of the content of the elementary arithmetic curriculum is predicated on improved methodology. As we saw in Chapter 2, Pestalozzi long ago advocated more learning by doing and experiencing; and Colburn, an inductive approach to learning arithmetic. But those theories were lost in the advance of civilization and culture. On the whole, during the past generation it was the drill method (without regard to understanding), along with a content that gave attention to social values and children's interest, that dominated arithmetic teaching.

Gradually, however, the meaning theory developed and challenged meaningless drill, and the developmental method pioneered by Spitzer more than a decade ago initiated methodology of a different type. Although the acceptance and use of this new type of procedure—call it a developmental method, a discovery method, reflective teaching, or what you will—has made limited progress, the progress has been persistent.

The idea that arithmetic can make a contribution to the higher mental processes is not new. In the Preface to Ray's *New Intellectual*

*Arithmetic*[5] dated May, 1877, we read: "... Intellectual Arithmetic [apparently mental arithmetic] ... when properly taught, is one of the most useful and interesting studies in which pupils can engage. By its study, the pupil is taught to reason, to analyze, to think for himself; while it imparts confidence in his reasoning powers and strengthens the mental faculties." Perfectly good aims, but the procedure involved formal analysis and memorization. As an illustration, a section on addition begins with the principle or definition: "Addition is the process of uniting two or more numbers. The result is called the *sum* or *amount*." Every pupil memorized this. Next comes an illustrative "problem" and "solution": "Two and 4 and 1 are how many? *Solution:* Two and four are six; six and one are seven." This is followed by a series of practically identical examples. As soon as concrete numbers are used, a new solution is stated: "I have in one basket 8 dozen eggs, in another 4 dozen, in another 3 dozen: how many eggs in all? *Solution:* I have in all 8 dozen and 4 dozen and 3 dozen eggs. 8 dozen and 4 dozen are 12 dozen; 12 dozen and 3 dozen are 15 dozen." Logic? Yes. Memorization? Yes. Reasoning? None. Compare these procedures with those that introduce addition in your textbook and note the contrast.

Though we subscribe to the principle that much of the success of an arithmetic program depends upon classroom procedures, we recognize that there is no procedure that guarantees successful learning in itself. An interested and understanding teacher who uses a certain procedure because he believes it to be effective in a given situation is the keystone to success in teaching arithmetic. A traditional type of teacher who firmly believes in an arbitrary drill procedure gets some results in teaching arithmetic; but by today's standards he does not get the *best* results in terms of understanding, permanent learning, and interest in arithmetic. For such types of outcomes a pattern of developmental—or, in current terminology, reflective—teaching in both computational and problem-solving situations is widely accepted among competent teachers today. And so far as plans for future methodology are concerned, these procedures seem to be gaining support as the best way to obtain the learning of the proposed content in arithmetic. This does not say that there will be no place for drill. On the contrary, extensive practice to acquire proficiency in computation will be essential, but not until understanding has been established.

[5] Ray's Mathematical Series, American Book Company.

## 8. More Adequate Teacher Preparation Required by New Content and Methodology

If new and higher-grade content is to be brought into the elementary arithmetic curriculum, together with a methodology that requires competent management, the preparation of teachers of arithmetic will become increasingly important. In view of this situation there are widespread proposals that individuals preparing to teach elementary arithmetic have a college-level basic mathematics course as well as an arithmetic methods course; textbooks for such a course are now being published.[6] Since a rapidly increasing number of states now require four years of preparation for elementary teaching, it seems probable that a course of this kind may become part of the required general education area of teacher preparation. At any rate, such a course may become necessary for all students who want to be mathematically literate in this age of infinite space and correspondingly infinite numbers.

## 9. Materials for the New Arithmetic Teaching

It is not the intent of this book to be concerned with elementary textbook content for each grade level. But it is obvious that new content and new procedures such as have been mentioned in preceding sections of this chapter call for the development of new materials. Especially are new materials required if the proposed differentiated programs for accelerated groups are to become effective. Some research has been done on the preparation of such materials, especially on the upper-grade levels. Garstens sums up some of the current work in this field as follows:

> There is fairly wide experimentation with materials prepared by three groups: the University of Illinois Committee on School Mathematics, School Mathematics Study Group, and the University of Maryland Mathematics Project (junior high school) known as UMMaP.
>
> The University of Illinois Committee is examining the possibility of teaching its ninth-grade algebra course to eighth-grade students and possibly to seventh-grade students. The School Mathematics Study Group is trying out units, written last summer, in seventh- and eighth-grade mathematics classes in 12 centers throughout the nation.
>
> UMMaP has a seventh-grade experimental course being taught in 45 classes from Connecticut to Washington and expects to prepare an experimental eighth-grade course for the 1959–60 year. In all three major projects

[6] For example, William L. Schaaf, *Basic Concepts of Elementary Mathematics*, Wiley, New York, 1960.

changes being considered are concerned with both content and methodology, often inextricably intertwined in the writing of materials.[7]

Some additional new materials now in experimental use have been developed in the Madison Project[8] at Madison Junior High School in Syracuse, New York; the project was started in 1957.[9] A number of educators are undoubtedly working on the production of new elementary arithmetic textbooks, or the revision of others, in line with the changes in content and method which seem imminent.



### 10. The Search for a Differentiated Program

Mentioned earlier in this chapter as one of the significant changes due in the immediate future in teaching arithmetic is more adequate provision for a differentiated program involving early identification of pupils with high ability, and provision of a program suited to their needs. More will be said on this subject in Chapter 5.

## COMPETENCE CHECK

1. Why are some textbooks in arithmetic said to be scientifically prepared?
2. Examine some elementary arithmetic textbooks and evaluate the illustrations by a check list you make yourself.
3. Enumerate some of the ways in which the spotlight was thrown on the schools in the 1950's and later.
4. What is your own opinion as to the need for or desirability of changes in grade-by-grade content in arithmetic? Find some factual support for your opinion, or some research that supports it.
5. What types of computation are classified as involution and evolution? Do you favor including them in elementary arithmetic? Why or why not?

## OPTIONAL ASSIGNMENTS

1. Review *Teaching the Third R*, by Schutter and Spreckelmeyer, and state your opinion about what effect it should have on teaching arithmetic in our schools.

[7] Helen L. Garstens, "Experimental Mathematics in the Junior High School," *Journal of the National Education Association*, May, 1959, pp. 42–44.

[8] Marie Lutz, "The Madison Project," *Arithmetic Teacher*, December, 1959, pp. 320–321.

[9] John Chamberlain, "The Third 'R'," *Wall Street Journal*, Midwest Edition, February 9, 1960, p. 12.

2. Make a survey of college catalogues to determine what percentage of the colleges in your area offer prospective elementary teachers a basic mathematics course or a college arithmetic course, in addition to a course in arithmetic methods.
3. Find cases of experiments in the new arithmetic teaching, in addition to those mentioned in this chapter.
4. Report on Brownell's article, "Arithmetic in 1970."
5. In his article, "Distinguishing Between Basic and Superficial Ideas in Arithmetic," what does Hartung set forth as basic and what as superficial?
6. Report on Spitzer's article, "How Will the New Emphasis on Science Affect Arithmetic Teaching?"
7. What are Van Engen's ideas as presented in his article, "Twentieth Century Mathematics for the Elementary School"?

## REFERENCES

Brownell, W. A., "Arithmetic in 1970," *National Elementary Principal*, October, 1959, pp. 42–45.

Hartung, Maurice L., "Distinguishing Between Basic and Superficial Ideas in Arithmetic," *Arithmetic Teacher*, March, 1959, pp. 65–70.

Spitzer, Herbert F., "How Will the New Emphasis on Science Affect Arithmetic Teaching?" *The Instructor*, April, 1959, p. 6.

Van Engen, H., "Twentieth Century Mathematics for the Elementary School," *Arithmetic Teacher*, March, 1959, pp. 71–76.

chapter 4

# Reflective Teaching in Arithmetic

## 1. Lack of Progress with Old Methods

As was previously pointed out, arithmetic teaching in the past has been less effective than it should be. In seeking reasons for this lack of efficiency we may say that materials and content have been somewhat at fault, but certainly the *methods* of teaching arithmetic have also been an important factor. A growing interest in improving arithmetic learning readily gains supporters for a more effective type of teaching procedure. We saw in Chapter 2 that the meaning theory and the developmental method seem to point the way to a better understanding of arithmetic and to more efficient means of acquiring that understanding.

Critics of our schools say that reasoning and independent creative thinking are neglected areas in education today, and that children and youth alike are frustrated by situations, especially mathematical situations, which involve reasoning. If this is a true indictment—and few will deny that it frequently is—arithmetic teachers have a responsibility to teach that subject in a way that will challenge pupils, even on the elementary level, to think and reason creatively. It is the intent of this book to support claims that arithmetic can be so taught, and to set forth procedures for this kind of teaching.

## 2. Reflective Teaching as a Developmental Procedure

Although "showing" and "telling" have characterized too much of our teaching in the past, the writer believes that there are some appropriate occasions for their effective use. Pupils can profit a great deal from learning to observe and listen and to follow demonstrations and explanations carefully and thoughtfully (an ability not all college students have). But in attaining permanent learning, with understanding, there is little doubt that the most effective procedures provide opportunities for pupils to *think* (by working out exploratory proposals built on familiar concepts); and *do* (by using manipulation or dramatization, or making diagrams to aid in structuring a problem situation, and doing the necessary computation to obtain the solution); and *tell* (by sometimes analyzing a problem situation orally, describing how it is structured, identifying the number processes required, and formulating generalizations). Such procedures are recognized as components of reflective teaching. Many teachers, however, are obsessed with the "cover-the-material" idea and give their pupils few such opportunities.

Reflective teaching involves certain basic assumptions.

1. Children are capable of learning and understanding, step by step, the arithmetic processes and the purposes they serve.
2. With guidance they can build on known concepts and develop new ones.
3. With encouragement they can acquire a spirit of exploratory curiosity and enjoy the satisfaction of discovering processes and principles.
4. With guidance they can reason out new processes on their own.
5. They can acquire confidence in their own ability to attack a problem situation with reflective thinking and to know when they have a satisfactory and correct solution.

Building this confidence in independent reasoning and problem-solving ability is the teacher's chief responsibility in teaching arithmetic by the reflective method. Such confidence comes gradually, as pupil insight develops, but it is cumulative in effect.

The general steps in a reflective teaching procedure are:

1. An introductory situation is presented which points to the need for obtaining a quantitative answer. This may be an unstructured environmental situation, either computational in nature or of the problem-solving type, or it may be the common structured textbook type of computational or problem-type material.
2. Pupils discover that a new and unfamiliar aspect of arithmetic is involved in obtaining the answer.

3. Building upon familiar concepts and known arithmetic principles and processes, they experiment and explore possibilities for finding the solution.
4. Working either individually or as a group, they propose procedures or solutions and try to prove them either correct or incorrect.
5. They may reject several proposals, and perhaps find several others that prove to be correct.
6. They select the simplest and most practical procedure or solution as the most useful and therefore the best one.
7. They may do several computations or problems of the same type and then formulate a generalization by which such operations can be done.
8. With these experiences pupils acquire a sense of arithmetical conquest which increases their confidence and encourages them to "try some more like that."

### 3. An Illustration of Reflective Teaching in Computation

To illustrate a computational situation for which reflective teaching is appropriate, suppose pupils in the third grade have learned to multiply by simple two-digit multipliers with no reduction involved, and have some knowledge of zero combinations, but are now confronted with a new situation: $\begin{array}{r} 16 \\ \times 10 \\ \hline \end{array}$. Without demonstration, the teacher asks them to find the answer, perhaps by more than one procedure. They now embark on an exploratory group experience. They employ reasoning.

Ron suggests that you could multiply by half of 10 (5) and then do it again and put the answers together. (He has been well taught, and either consciously or unconsciously is applying a basic arithmetic principle; instead of multiplying by the number 10 he is multiplying by its factors.) He gets 160 and the pupils discuss whether that is a reasonable answer; they conclude it is, because 10 × 10 is 100 and 10 × 16 is more than that.

Mike says they can do it like $\begin{array}{r} 16 \\ \times 10 \\ \hline 160 \end{array}$ and just put the numbers down in a row because that's the way his dad showed him when they did one like that. The answer is the same as the one Ron got, but Alice says: "How can you do that—multiply by 1 and just put down the 0?" No one is sure whether you can do that. The teacher does not explain but merely puts it aside and says, "We'll look at that one again later."

Janet says, "Well, you could add 16 and 16 and 16 and so on until you had ten 16's." But everyone agrees that takes too long. At any rate Janet has applied another basic arithmetic principle—that multiplication is equivalent to a series of additions.

Kathy suggests they write it

$$\begin{array}{r} 10 \\ \times 16 \\ \hline 60 \\ 10\phantom{0} \\ \hline 160 \end{array}$$

; then 6 × 0 is 0 and 6 × 1 is 6, and go on with 1 × 0 and 1 × 1, and that gives 160. Then Sally says 0 × 6 is the same as 6 × 0, and 0 × 1 is the same as 1 × 0; she writes it

$$\begin{array}{r} 16 \\ \times 10 \\ \hline 00 \\ 16\phantom{0} \\ \hline 160 \end{array}$$

and again the answer is 160.

They conclude that 160 is correct. Mike says his way is the shortest, and wants to know whether it is a correct way. More than one teacher has been confronted with the question of *his* way vs. Dad's way. This teacher does not say what many others have said, "Well, maybe your father's way is correct, but I want you to work it *this* way." Here there is no conflict. After several examples like

$$\begin{array}{r} 12 \\ \times 20 \\ \hline 00 \\ 24\phantom{0} \\ \hline 240 \end{array} \qquad \begin{array}{r} 31 \\ \times 10 \\ \hline 00 \\ 31\phantom{0} \\ \hline 310 \end{array}$$

the pupils find that the answer always ends in 0 and the part of the answer preceding the 0 is the tens figure of the multiplier times the multiplicand. They decide Mike's way is a good short cut—just put down the 0 and find the rest of the answer; or better yet, multiply by the tens figure and add the 0, as in

$$\begin{array}{r} 45 \\ \times 10 \\ \hline 450 \end{array}$$

. Mike goes home elated and tells his father that they tried several ways of multiplying those numbers and found his way was the shortest and it was correct too.

Now the class wants to know whether this procedure works for 100 and for 200. It seems to:

$$\begin{array}{r} 16 \\ \times\ 100 \\ \hline 1600 \end{array} \qquad \begin{array}{r} 16 \\ \times\ 200 \\ \hline 3200 \end{array}$$

. After a few more such examples, the pupils are ready to generalize: To multiply a number by 10, just add 0 to the number; e.g., $6 \times 10 = 60$; $25 \times 10 = 250$. They find that this is even quicker than Mike's way, and they practice with more examples so they will remember the procedure.

In class activities such as this, pupils make suggestions, ask questions, challenge the views of others, and test each proposal—a genuinely scientific method. This is in sharp contrast to the long-used nonreflective teaching pattern in which the pupils are shown *how* to multiply by numbers ending in one or more zeros, and then given zealous practice to fix the computational procedure in mind; the *why* of the procedure and the value of short cuts receive little if any attention, and the class as a whole acquires attitudes of indifference or disinterest.

Skeptical teachers may ask: "Wouldn't it be better to show them one correct procedure instead of their having several procedures and perhaps being confused?" After all, Ron and Mike and Kathy and Sally all have correct solutions; but when the group sees why Mike's way works they will probably choose to do it his way because it is the shortest way, and they will remember it as Mike's—not the teacher's—way. And because Mike found the best way on this problem, the other pupils will be eager to find the best way on later problems; thus creativity is encouraged. Now they are ready and willing to apply the new principle, and they practice mental computations like $16 \times 10 = 160$ and $25 \times 10 = 250$.

## 4. An Illustration of Reflective Teaching with Problem Material

An **arithmetic problem,** as the term is used in this text, is a situation stated in words and numerals which calls for a quantitative solution and involves number relations new to the problem solver. The example used here for illustration is a problem in measurement.

When pupils are introduced to square measure, they make square-inch and square-foot patterns of cardboard, and they see that *square* units of measure are necessary to describe surface measurement and the quantities of materials needed to cover those surfaces. With such measuring units they are prepared to learn how to find, for example, the number of square feet in a given area, perhaps the classroom floor.

When a genuine discovery method is employed, pupils are motivated by a useful purpose to determine the area of a given surface. If they want to describe the size of the classroom floor, they see that their problem is to figure out the number of square feet required to cover the floor. This poses a true problem, an aspect of arithmetic with which they have not previously been acquainted or concerned. After some reflection they see that their problem involves how to determine the number of squares of the given size required to cover the floor.

Some of the pupils may laboriously mark off all the squares on the floor with the square-foot pattern, and almost as laboriously count them. But some of the more alert will discover that by using multiplication, which they have previously learned to use, instead of counting all the squares, they need only to count the number of squares in one row and multiply it by the number of rows (building on earlier concepts). After they have done that, they find that the number of square feet they get by computing agrees with the number obtained by counting. They have *discovered* a much faster procedure than counting.

Soon they discover that they do not need the measuring square because the length and width of the room in feet tells them how many squares there are in a row and how many rows there are, and multiplication gives the answer. Now they are ready to make up a short-cut rule or formula or principle, $l \times w = A$, and they will apply it to all rectangular figures or surfaces whose area they want to find. This represents the discovery procedure which leads to a generalization, no doubt accompanied by understanding. This is the developmental or reflective method.

If the teacher in this case had used the procedure commonly used in most elementary classrooms, he would have given the pupils the rule, or formula, for finding the area of a rectangle, $l \times w = A$, instead of giving them an opportunity to develop the rule. Then he would have asked them to find a number of areas with the rule, probably a page of them in the textbook, and after that he would have had frequent reviews of the process to maintain the learning.

A teacher using the discovery method will also from time to time have the class compute areas to keep in practice; but when understanding is established at the beginning, much less reviewing is necessary.

Class procedures such as these provide interest, enthusiasm, and learning accomplishment as well. Obviously, however, every day's lessons cannot be handled in this way; they must be followed by periods of practice and application. But at intervals, especially when new operations or procedures are being introduced, there will be opportunities for pooled thinking and exploratory procedures.

With such experiences, pupils find arithmetic coming alive, and they readily enter into the experimental spirit of it. Reflective teaching, judiciously employed, will yield outcomes of the kind we seek in arithmetic learning—interest, ability to reason, self-confidence, and the capacity for independent, exploratory thinking in problem situations.

As a matter of fact, teachers use arithmetic content with three basic purposes in mind; they want their pupils (1) to acquire comprehension and understanding of new computational or problem-solving procedures; (2) to keep in practice on these acquired learnings; and (3) to transfer and apply these learnings to related situations. The floor-area problem and many others like it will be used later as computational exercises to keep the pupils in practice. Later on, when areas of triangles and parallelograms are to be found, the floor-area problem will serve as a basic concept in area, and pupils comparing the floor area with triangular areas will discover a means of finding areas of triangles.

In addition to knowing which of the three purposes is involved at any given time, the teacher should enable pupils to determine whether they are working out a new problem situation (a true problem), or doing exercises to keep in practice, or applying previously learned concepts to new computational or problem situations.

As has been pointed out, there is a place for reflective teaching, or reasoning processes, in purely computational work; but it is in the solving of true problems that this developmental type of teaching reaches its greatest potential. This will be discussed further in a later chapter.

This book illustrates a number of reflective procedures. But there are many additional possibilities for using some of the constructive thought, exploration, and discovery experiences in various types of arithmetic situations. Suggested occasions and ways of using these reflective techniques are indicated by asterisk-marked notes; many of them are appropriate for college classes as well as for elementary pupils.

## 5. Understanding and Insight as Aids to the Art of Teaching

It is knowing when and why to use particular methods, recognizing that no one method is all good or all bad, and being sufficiently creative to devise illustrative materials and situations appropriate for present needs, that distinguishes the master teacher from the ordinary teacher. And when appropriate methodology is combined with insight, along with an understanding of pupils and their respective needs and abilities, teaching becomes an art, characterized both by skillful technique and by rewarding results. Is it not possible that as the result of the new era of arithmetic teaching there will be many more classrooms where the *art* of teaching arithmetic prevails?

## COMPETENCE CHECK

1. List several terms comparable to developmental teaching in arithmetic.
2. Write a lesson procedure in which pupils *think*, and *do*, and *tell.*
3. Make a diagram that will aid in finding $\frac{1}{3}$ of $2\frac{1}{4}$.
4. In what respects is the reflective procedure like the scientific method?
5. Write a problem and make a diagram that will help in comprehending the problem situation.
6. Show how the following problem might be (1) the content for a true problem-solving situation; (2) material for an exercise to keep in practice; and (3) a foundation for new concepts: "How many quart bottles will be required to hold 5 gallons of milk?"

## OPTIONAL ASSIGNMENTS

1. From Bayles or other sources, give a report on the theory of reflective teaching and the values associated with it.
2. Report on Eads' article, "Let's Think About Arithmetic."
3. Report on Hart's article, "Critical Thinking—Where Does It Begin?"

## REFERENCES

Bayles, Ernest E., *Democratic Educational Theory*, Harper, New York, 1960, Chaps. 1, 12.

Eads, Laura K., "Let's Think About Arithmetic," *Grade Teacher*, March, 1958, p. 55.

Hart, Murlee, "Critical Thinking—Where Does It Begin?" *Grade Teacher*, September, 1958, p. 54.

chapter 5

# Adjustment to Individual Abilities of Pupils

## 1. Lock-Step System of Long Standing

In early American schools the lagging learner was consigned to the dunce stool; he usually dropped out of school at an early age. The apt student went on with the drills, and if he memorized readily he went to the head of the class and "made the grade."

With the enactment of compulsory attendance laws, pupils had to stay in school; the slow learners eventually reached the age at which they could leave school, regardless of grade level of accomplishment. Little attention was given to their individual problems.

As psychological study began to give teaching a more personal relationship, and attendance laws kept pupils in school for a longer period of time, educators became more conscious of and more considerate of individual differences among pupils. This created a sense of duty toward the slow learner; as a result, until the last decade he was every teacher's chief concern, whereas the very bright were left to shift for themselves. It also brought some realization of the impossibility of lock-step accomplishment. The means commonly used for dealing with this problem of individual differences was remedial work for those who were not keeping up with their class.

## 2. Diagnostic and Remedial Work

Remedial work was expected to strengthen the weak spots and bring pupils up to grade average. Many types of diagnostic procedures were developed for identifying the weak spots. Whole books were written on the subject of diagnostic and remedial work,[1] and diagnostic tests were scaled to fine degrees of "unitary analysis." Extra classes were established and sometimes special teachers were employed for remedial work in arithmetic. But in spite of these procedures, it never proved possible to bring all the pupils in a class up to a class-average level of accomplishment.

In recent years more attention has been given to preventive procedures and, in general, less to remedial work. New textbooks and the teachers' manuals which accompany them have given much attention to slowed-down presentation and the establishment of meaning in an effort to make the introduction of each new step a comprehensible experience for pupils. This necessarily slowed down the bright pupil to the point of boredom. But, to repeat, no group is sufficiently homogeneous in ability to grasp each step with equal ease; hence the need for further differentiation has continued.

In the meantime the extra-bright pupils were left to their own devices. They always made progress and required little instructional attention. Unfortunately they worked on a class-average level much below their ability, acquired lazy work habits, and were never challenged to attain greater proficiency. The slow pupils presented a new problem; for with more research in the areas of child development, the nature of learning, and human personality, psychologists began to convince educators that successive retardation has detrimental effects on all aspects of pupil development.

### 3. New Promotional Policies in Effect

In accord with the new theories, more and more schools began promoting all or practically all pupils even though they were not up to grade standards in certain subjects or, in some cases, in any subjects. This procedure complicated the work of classroom teachers because it resulted in classes that varied widely in abilities. As a matter of fact, the higher the grade the greater was the range of abilities. The idea of expecting all pupils, even with extra remedial assistance, to attain a given class-average level of work was of necessity discarded.

[1] L. J. Brueckner, *Diagnostic and Remedial Teaching of Arithmetic*, Holt, Rinehart & Winston, New York, 1930.

## 4. Adapting Arithmetic Instruction to Individual Needs

Up to the present, few schools have made any marked progress in adapting instruction in arithmetic to individual needs. Most schools, however, have set up at least three ability groups for reading instruction. But if a teacher is to have six periods for reading and arithmetic alone, the question of scheduling is raised at once. What is to be curtailed? Or should the school day be lengthened?

Some schools are administratively organized for homogeneous grouping, mostly on the junior and senior high school levels. Few have found it feasible on the elementary level. Likewise, junior and senior high schools are departmentalized, but few educators approve departmentalization in grades below the junior high. The heterogeneous, self-contained classroom remains as the general elementary-grade pattern of organization, and thus far most of the procedures for adjusting arithmetic teaching to individual needs have been used in this type of situation.

Most prevalent among such procedures has been one referred to as *enrichment*. Although it takes many forms, it generally implies differentiated content and materials, rather than differentiated teaching procedures. Its value ranges from very low to high.

One teacher may simply give a larger amount of the same type of work and call it enrichment (which it is not). Through the years a common practice among teachers has been to give such an assignment as, "Everyone work the first ten problems, and those who complete them and still have time, do the next five." In some textbooks the "next five" are labeled, "For the fast workers," but are no more difficult than the first ten. This plan provided little motivation to be a fast worker—just the opportunity to do five more problems. Actually the only purpose in having pupils work a series of examples or problems is practice in learning the procedure. The fast workers quickly learn the procedure and do not need additional practice in it. However, some of the newer textbooks include additional problems of a more challenging nature, perhaps labeled, "For the good thinker." Pupils take pride in accomplishing this work.

In a somewhat different plan, teaching manuals of some current arithmetic series give suggestions for work for both slower and more accelerated pupils. But it must be admitted that many teachers themselves have too meager a background in arithmetic to venture into some of the more challenging pupil activities suggested by way of enrichment.

Unfortunately also, in far too many classrooms the mathematical wings of the very bright pupils have been clipped by the common practice of giving special privileges to those who finish their arithmetic quickly—perhaps reading library books, or doing extra work on the social studies unit, or assisting a slow learner. Although all are good in themselves, none of these activities contribute any arithmetic enrichment.

Theoretically, enrichment may be either the horizontal or the vertical type. In the horizontal type rapid learners are given a much broader and deeper program than slower learners have; such programs are referred to as programs of more scope and depth. In this type of program the entire class works on the same curriculum topics—for example, addition of common fractions—at the same time, but the more accelerated group moves on quickly to more complex computational forms and more advanced problem applications.

In the vertical type of enrichment, more advanced topics are introduced than are called for by the text or course-of-study requirements for the particular grade. This plan has a disadvantage in that certain pupils cover in one grade some of the work outlined for the next higher grade; hence the next year they may have to mark time when the same types of problems are being covered as part of the class work.

In another form of the vertical type, some pupils are given double promotions, a practice generally frowned upon by educators today because of omissions of subject matter. Consequently for some years horizontal enrichment, and not vertical in the form of double promotion, has been advocated. This keeps every pupil within the established curriculum content for his grade and limits his grade content.

## 5. Nationwide Attention to Needs of the Gifted

Before school officials had found entirely adequate ways of coping with the group work necessary if each pupil was to have materials and instruction suited to his level of ability, a nationwide movement calling for more attention to the very bright and gifted pupils got under way. This was mentioned in Chapter 3 in connection with the new arithmetic program.

As was said earlier, all through its history American public education had given this group of pupils little guidance and little incentive to work up to their intellectual capacity. This situation attained greater significance as new theories upgraded many arithmetic processes and, in general, eased the arithmetic curriculum load in the elementary grades. Furthermore, the rapid advances in science and its related areas of mathematics called for students of more than average intellectual ability and accomplishment if progress was to be maintained. Accordingly, society began to look anxiously to the schools for leadership.

Prompted by these circumstances, more and more public criticism has been directed toward the schools, in particular for the lack of an early and adequate fundamental education for the able students who will go on to college with a serious purpose in mind and to whom we must look for the intellectual and technical competence required in this scientific age. Coupled with those criticisms has been increasing recognition of the fact that many pupils have ability and talent that, from the elementary school on upward, remain undeveloped and therefore wasted because of the lack of motivation and challenge.

Whether as a result of these criticisms and observations, or for other reasons, some progress has recently been made toward developing in students, at both the secondary and college levels, better attitudes toward high academic accomplishment than have prevailed through the past several decades.

Under present competitive circumstances in international affairs the balance of power, both economic and scientific, seems to depend in large measure on scientific and mathematical advancement. Faced with this need, both industry and government have urged early identification of and accelerated education for students capable of becoming outstanding and creative scientists and mathematicians. More than that, these agencies are willing to subsidize the education of such people in order to procure the statisticians, laboratory technicians, and other specialists so urgently needed.

All of this is related to the teaching of arithmetic. If there is to be an accelerated program of mathematics for the gifted, it will have to begin on the elementary level. It will involve several factors, among them administrative provisions, identification of high-ability pupils, suitable instructional materials, and competent teachers.

## 6. Proposals for Meeting New Needs

For any extensive program revisions, administrative provisions will be necessary, but that will be a local and institutional matter. Identifying pupils with high ability is relatively easy. By general acceptance, the term "highly gifted" is applied to the top 1 per cent of the population, those with IQ's above 137. The next 10 per cent are called "moderately gifted;" their IQ's range from 120–137. We do not mean to imply, however, that the IQ should be the only criterion by which to select pupils of high ability.

To help upgrade teaching competence, various types of fellowships enable interested and capable teachers to further their mathematical education and be up to date with modern mathematics.

As for the type of program to be developed and the preparation of suitable materials, some experimentation has been going on and some progress has been made, as we saw in Chapter 3.

Some schools are experimenting with a plan that is not new in its pattern of organization, but is like the platoon system. For some years it has been used by a few schools but never widely adopted. Under this plan pupils of a given grade spend a half-day with a homeroom teacher on language, arts, social science, and the like; the other half-day is spent in classes such as art, music, arithmetic, and science, for which it is assumed that teachers need more specialized preparation. When all the grades in a building are on this plan, homogeneous ability groups in arithmetic become possible. According to McMeen,[2] this plan is being tested experimentally in the schools of Ossining and Long Beach, New York, under the direction of Dean George Stoddard of New York University.

A different approach points out the widespread feeling among mathematics-minded educators today that there is a fundamental need to reevaluate the entire elementary arithmetic curriculum to provide a suitable program for the gifted. Its adherents maintain that the grade-by-grade content in most schools today is leveled down to the needs of the average pupil, with provision for the very bright and gifted being far from adequate.

In the opinion of the present writer, more will be heard about this type of reorganization of the arithmetic curriculum in the years immediately ahead. In effect, it will involve vertical differentiation which will reorganize the arithmetic curriculum for fast learners into a six- or seven-year program that will cover what is now taught throughout the entire eight grades. More experimentation in this area is needed, as is

[2] George H. McMeen, "Differentiating Arithmetic Instruction for Various Levels of Achievement," *Arithmetic Teacher*, April, 1959, pp. 113–120.

also a whole new series of teaching materials for the accelerated group. Much less space would be given to pictures and other types of visual and manipulative aids in the textbooks, and there would be considerably less repetition of content from grade to grade; furthermore all the processes would be covered far more rapidly.

For the new needs discussed in this section to be met, the first and simplest step is identification of the very bright and gifted pupils. More difficult to accomplish, but now underway to some extent, is reorganization of the curriculum and the preparation of materials to fit it. Of equal importance, and also receiving attention at the present time is giving teachers adequate proficiency in arithmetic to enable them to teach the accelerated program.

### 7. Improving Prevailing Practices

The accelerated programs that have just been discussed will not immediately find a place in average schools across the country, especially in the smaller systems. However, even in those schools, alert teachers can make many improvements along the lines of adapting arithmetic teaching to the needs of pupils with varied abilities.

Psychologists tell us that slow learners follow approximately the same mental processes as the fast learners, but at a much slower pace. They need a longer time for visual and manipulative aids, they are unable to comprehend abstract symbols and procedures as quickly as the fast learner can, and they do not master generalizations as quickly.

Every classroom teacher needs to take these psychological characteristics into consideration. In some cases he may adopt some type of two-track program of horizontal enrichment. Under such a program, while the slower group spends more time on manipulations, visual aids, practice, and games, the very bright will be discovering several ways to solve many types of problems, be doing problems and computations that are more challenging, be developing more mathematical principles, formulas, and equations, and be investigating supplementary areas of interest—for example, other number systems, money exchange and foreign money, powers, roots and exponents, computations with approximate numbers, and numerology. The Optional Assignments at the end of each chapter in this book take into consideration differences among college students.

As soon as the teacher determines the characteristics of his class, he should set up appropriate plans for differentiation. Some teachers may decide to organize a mathematics club for volunteer members who want a real challenge.

From the administrative point of view, instead of leaving the entire responsibility to individual classroom teachers, some school systems might employ a full-time teacher-consultant to help plan and implement the arithmetic program for the very bright group. In general, however, every classroom teacher with a sufficient background in arithmetic, a measure of interest, and some resourcefulness, can find many ways to improve arithmetic teaching and adapt it to some extent to individual needs at his particular grade level.

## COMPETENCE CHECK

1. What is meant by the lock-step system?
2. Prepare a short diagnostic test in arithmetic for any grade you choose, and explain its diagnostic features.
3. Outline remedial work to cover what your diagnostic test may point out as needing remedial treatment.
4. Explain and illustrate horizontal enrichment.
5. Explain and illustrate vertical enrichment.
6. Can you give an illustration of either one used in any school you attended?
7. Examine some elementary arithmetic textbooks and manuals. What provision do they make for individual differences?

## OPTIONAL ASSIGNMENTS

1. Report on Price's reasons for the need for more first-rate mathematicians.
2. What program for the able does Price propose?
3. List some of Schaaf's proposals for teaching arithmetic concepts and understandings that will be a basis for later mathematics.
4. Discuss Buswell's proposed changes in the arithmetic program at the primary and upper-grade levels.
5. How does Buswell propose to improve the teaching materials?
6. Evaluate Parsons' proposals for arithmetic for the gifted in the fourth and fifth grades.
7. Hawthorne says that until recently music was generally considered a branch of mathematics. What illustration does he give involving the use of the mathematical symbols for "less than" and "more than"?
8. List Junge's characteristics of gifted children.
9. Report on Junge's suggestions for types of learning experiences that will challenge the able learner.

10. On the basis of Marks, Purdy, and Kinney and other sources, list in a notebook what seem to you to be good supplementary procedures for a slow group, and also some procedures for the very fast learners.
11. Browse through National Society for the Study of Education, "Education for the Gifted."
12. How does Schwartz propose to challenge the rapid learner?
13. Compare Glennon's and Grossnickle's proposals for arithmetic for the very bright.
14. What is your opinion of the dual progress plan in the elementary school?

## REFERENCES


Buswell, G. T., "The Content and Organization of Arithmetic," *Arithmetic Teacher*, March, 1959, pp. 77–83.

Clancy, Jean C., "An Adventure in Topology—Grade 5," *Arithmetic Teacher*, November, 1959, pp. 278–279.

Glennon, Vincent J., "Arithmetic for the Gifted Child," *Elementary School Journal*, November, 1957, p. 91.

Grossnickle, Foster E., "Arithmetic for Those Who Excel," *Arithmetic Teacher*, March, 1956, pp. 41–48.

Hawthorne, Frank, quoted by Ray Bengston in "The 'Make 'Em Run' Theory," *Mathematics Teacher*, January, 1958, p. 11.

Heathers, Glen, and Pincus, Morris, "The Dual Progress Plan in the Elementary School," *Arithmetic Teacher*, December, 1959, pp. 302–305.

Junge, Charlotte, "The Gifted Ones—How Shall We Know Them?" *Arithmetic Teacher*, October, 1957, pp. 144–146.

Larsen, Harold D., *Enrichment Program for Arithmetic*, Row, Peterson, Evanston, 1956. (Eight 16-page booklets for Grades 3 through 6.)

Marks, John L., Purdy, C. Richard, and Kinney, Lucien B., *Teaching Arithmetic for Understanding*, McGraw-Hill, New York, 1958.

National Society for the Study of Education, "Education for the Gifted," *Fifty-Seventh Yearbook, Part II*, 1958.

Parsons, Cynthia, "Arithmetic for the Gifted," *Arithmetic Teacher*, March, 1959, pp. 84–86.

Price, G. Bailey, "A Mathematics Program for the Able," *Mathematics Teacher*, October, 1951, pp. 369–376.

Schaaf, William L., "Arithmetic Taught as a Basis for Later Mathematics," *School Science and Mathematics*, May, 1946, pp. 413–423.

Schwartz, A. N., "Challenging the Rapid Learner," *Arithmetic Teacher*, December, 1959, pp. 311–313.

Spitzer, Herbert F., *Practical Classroom Procedures for Enriching Arithmetic*, Webster, St. Louis, 1956.

Swain, Robert L., *Understanding Arithmetic*, Holt, Rinehart & Winston, New York, 1957, chap. 2.

Taylor, E. H., and Mills, C. N., *Arithmetic for Teacher Training Classes*, Holt, Rinehart & Winston, New York, 4th ed., 1955, chaps. 22, 23.

chapter 6

# Organized Planning in Arithmetic

## 1. Broad Perspective of Arithmetic Important

When teachers have a broad perspective of arithmetic, they are able to set up satisfactory patterns for both content and method. Most teachers, however, use a course of study developed by someone else—by a state department of education or, in the case of a city school, by supervisors and committees of teachers. The question of *what* is to be taught and *when* is very rigidly stated in courses of study classified as traditional. In some schools the textbook series and the accompanying teachers' manuals serve as a course of study and no other is provided. In other localities the course of study is much more flexible; it outlines broad areas to be covered during the year but leaves the allotment of time largely to the teacher. This is the case in more progressive school systems.

If he must use a rigid course of study, a teacher with a breadth of learning in arithmetic material and arithmetic methodology will know the over-all needs of his pupils, and hence will know where concentrated work is needed and how to compensate for poorly distributed time.

Teachers without such background plod along, covering the material because "we have to get over the work." Their pupils acquire a shallow, easily forgotten kind of learning, and the teachers themselves make arithmetic "the sum of its parts" without any vision of the whole.

## 2. Purposes and Aims Basic to Teaching

An earlier chapter discussed the various theories of what arithmetic should be taught and how it should be taught, and the wide differences of opinion in these aspects of arithmetic teaching. However, both content and method evolve from the purposes and aims basic to teaching a subject.

Every society attempts to provide for its youth a form of education that will presumably perpetuate that society—its form of government, its ideals, and its mores. Hence when we consider the purposes and aims of teaching any subject in the American school curriculum, we must look first to the needs of our society as a whole. Local needs are somewhat secondary.

The United States does not have a centralized system of education as some countries do, but has left the organization and conduct of education almost solely to the individual states; in such a case national purposes are more difficult to establish. However, nongovernmental groups and organizations, the latter frequently educational, have seen the need for nationwide educational policies with purposes and aims that are national in scope, and have from time to time formulated such purposes for education in this country.

In 1938 the Educational Policies Commission, made up of members of the National Educational Association, formulated a series of general objectives for education which have served as a beacon for national educational guidance for the last two decades. Briefly stated, these objectives are: (1) self-realization, (2) better human relationships, (3) economic efficiency, and (4) civic responsibility. Is it unreasonable to believe that arithmetic, when efficiently taught, should contribute to these general objectives?

More specific purposes to be served by arithmetic in the curriculum may be stated as follows: (1) It should provide the arithmetic needed for a general education. (2) It should lay the foundation for the mathematics needed in scientific and technical pursuits. (3) It should enable an individual to deal with number ideas and symbols as easily as he deals with the language ideas and symbols in his environment.

A course of study, whether formulated by a state department of education or a city school system, usually provides general objectives for the teaching of arithmetic, and frequently also a series of guiding principles which reflect the philosophical and psychological theories of its makers. These objectives and principles serve as an organizing element or unifying theme for the subject.

If we accept the above four general objectives of education and the three more specific purposes for arithmetic teaching, our next step is to draw up some principles of action. The eleven guiding principles in the following section constitute a "charter" upon which this book is based, and outlines what the writer considers an acceptable guide to the teaching of arithmetic.

## 3. Guiding Principles for the Teaching of Arithmetic

1. *There should be a place for the social applications of arithmetic, for the rationale of arithmetic, and for drill.* Most people have no need for arithmetic except as it helps them live in their environment. We saw in an earlier chapter the large part that number plays in our daily life. Social situations in which the arithmetic processes are applied furnish one of the most logical reasons why elementary pupils should learn these processes.

When we subscribe to the meaning theory, we are making a place for the rationale of arithmetic. This implies understanding the number system, seeing meaning in number relationships, and resolving problem situations by first thinking the process, then using the appropriate algorism, and finally judging the reasonableness of the answer obtained.

After some ability in computation with meaning is attained, drill on arithmetic facts and processes is desirable for the eventual acquisition of speed and accuracy, and for convenience.

2. *Arithmetic should be considered a social study.* Since our number system was inherited from peoples of ancient times and far-off places, some knowledge of those origins will induce greater interest in and more comprehension of our number system, as well as greater appreciation of our cultural heritage. As we shall see in a later chapter, civilization progressed largely as mathematical knowledge, and the sciences based upon it, paved the way.

International understanding requires cooperation in terms of numbers—production, imports, exports, tariffs, money systems, international loans, and so on. Both nationally and locally, government, economics, and sociology would be only husks if statistics, averages, and money were removed from them.

Since arithmetic is held to be a social study, one of its chief purposes is the application of its processes to the problems faced by the individual in the society in which he lives.

3. *Content should be presented on a spiral plan of development that*

*provides for expanding concepts at successive grade levels with corresponding summaries of learning.* This means, for example, that fractions in simple oral form will be introduced in the first grade. Then step by step through succeeding grades will follow reduction and the four fundamental processes with fractions, their relationship to decimals and to percentages, and problem-solving involving fractions.

Textbooks of a generation ago, or perhaps even later, "started classes on fractions in fifth grade" as if this were a new language; the ensuing difficulties were almost as frustrating as though a new language *was* being begun. But simple division concepts can be introduced in the first grade and gradually spiral into real division, thereby easing that abrupt "Now-we-are-starting-long-division" nightmare of teachers.

4. *Problem-solving is an evolving process, to be developed from the first grade on.* At the first-grade level, "How many books do we need for our reading class today?" presents a problem and uses concrete materials in its solution. On a slightly higher scale an average boy sees a realistic problem situation in: "John has 6 marbles, but he can't get into the game unless he has 10 marbles. How many more will he have to gather up?"

The quantitative problem situations gradually become more complex; but if the problems provide a setting for the introduction of each new phase of arithmetic, problem-solving will not be set off as "the part of arithmetic that pupils fall down on."

5. *Arithmetic can make definite contributions to the development of the higher mental processes.* The pupil learns to think a situation through and to recognize what process is needed by visualizing the actions indicated by the wording of the problem; for example, having 50 cents and losing 10 cents requires a separation, a taking an amount away from the whole amount.

He learns to concentrate his attention on the essential elements of a situation and to disregard the nonessential in such a problem as: "Tom and Bill walked a mile and a half to the lake to fish. By ten o'clock Tom had 6 fish, and two hours later Tom had caught 2 more and Bill had the same number. How many fish did both boys have?" Call it reading for meaning if you will, but it also involves analyzing the situation and sorting the relevant from the irrelevant information. Such an analysis also requires discrimination; and if the pupil is taught to judge whether his answer makes sense, he is learning to make comparisons.

None of the mental processes indicated—thinking, analyzing, comparing, discriminating—are outcomes of mechanical drill or of reliance on cue words in a problem.

6. *No standard conceptual attainment can be assumed for children when they enter school.* Preparatory to the introduction of each new step readiness tests and teacher observations are needed to determine whether individual children have adequate concepts.

Some authorities favor grouping children for arithmetic in primary grades much as they are grouped for reading in most schools. Few subscribe to a plan of completely individual progress either in the first or in higher grades.

7. *There are marked differences in the individual members of any class.* As pupils proceed from grade to grade the gap between those of high ability and those of low ability widens. It is the teacher's responsibility to give pupils at each level of ability the kind of work they are capable of accomplishing.

More attention has recently been called to the very bright pupils. For them the teacher has the responsibility of providing interesting and challenging work beyond the general class level. This does not mean just an extra amount of the same kind of work.

8. *Children should be given more opportunities to think and talk and do in arithmetic learning situations.* In traditional methods of teaching arithmetic the usual procedure was demonstration of a process by the teacher, followed by a period of practice for the pupils for fixation and developing speed.

Modern procedures give children an opportunity to think creatively, to propose and try solutions, to discover and express orally their solution before they begin to "figure." In this kind of procedure manipulation of counters and measures will be helpful and will prepare them for written algorisms.

9. *Extensive use should be made of concrete materials, visual aids, and community resources.* A child should have a clear concept of an idea before he is introduced to a symbol that represents the idea.

In his first experiences with numbers—counting, putting groups together (addition), and taking them apart (subtraction)—counters should always be within reach. They may be checkers, sticks, toothpicks—anything that will attract him and keep him from using his fingers for counters. They will be a tool—or a crutch, so to speak—that is near him ready for use until he no longer needs it.

Number lines, fractional parts, and all kinds of measuring units can be used as he progresses. Such community resources as blank forms from a bank, road maps, and so on, can be used in many connections.

10. *Children will be better motivated and will have greater success in arithmetic if they are conscious of steady progress.* Individual progress charts have been widely used to measure speed and accuracy in computation.

More should be done about determining pupils' rate of progress in understanding, in using sensible procedures for solution, and in knowing why the process they use is the right one. It is far more difficult to chart progress in these attainments than in speed and accuracy of computation.

11. *Much of the success of an arithmetic program depends upon classroom procedure (method).* According to John Dewey, it is not the end product we seek in learning; it is rather the chain of experiences which a child undergoes that has educative value. Many say we have put too much stress on the *product* of learning in arithmetic and not enough on the *process* of learning.

Little in arithmetic content readily interests most elementary-age children, as exciting scientific experiments or "history made real" might. Therefore, the teacher of arithmetic must so present and direct learning in this field as to challenge the pupils' interest and thinking and motivate them to want to succeed.

## 4. Grade Goals for a Year

When teachers have a broad perspective in arithmetic, and a general knowledge of content and method, they are prepared to plan the year of teaching arithmetic at their respective grade level. This means that a fourth-grade teacher, for example, *knows* elementary arithmetic. He knows something about spiral development and about what fourth-grade arithmetic can and should contribute to the over-all elementary program in the subject. He knows what comes, or *should* come, in the arithmetic curriculum of the first three grades and whether his pupils have adequate background and readiness for the work of the fourth grade. He knows for what upper-grade processes and understandings fourth-grade arithmetic should be preparing his pupils. In short, he has established goals for his fourth-grade teaching. He will do well to write down the goals for the year, and consult the list frequently to help him keep on the right track and evaluate his progress.

## 5. Need for Specific Working Plans

A teacher must do some rather specific lesson planning from day to day or week to week, or in some cases for much longer periods, if he is to make consistent progress.

Lesson plans vary according to the curriculum program of the school. One school's curriculum may have a rigid separate-subject plan. Another school may have a correlated plan which calls for two or more subjects to be taught together; for example, reading, spelling, language, and writing may be taught together as language arts. A more progressive type of school may use integrated units, often called activity units or experience units, which cover larger areas of material and require an extended period of time. Such a unit might be "How We Tell Time"; in the middle grades it might involve history, geography, science, arithmetic, language, and so on. Arithmetic might be a major element in the unit, or in some cases merely incidental.

In summary, a teacher's plans must fit into the curriculum organization of the school, and accordingly may vary from brief daily plans to long-range unit plans.

## 6. Three Basic Teaching Steps

In general, teaching involves three basic steps: (1) setting up objectives, (2) organizing procedures to accomplish those objectives, and (3) evaluating the outcomes to determine to what extent the objectives were accomplished.

Necessary for these steps is a lesson plan; this may be a daily or weekly plan, or one that provides for a longer unit. Many lesson plans in the past have included these three steps, but have had only one main objective—rapid and accurate computations; have used only one procedure—drill; and have had only one evaluation technique—testing for speed and accuracy.

## 7. Modern Arithmetic Objectives

Modern arithmetic teaching recognizes the need for many other types of objectives, which in turn call for appropriate types of procedure and for adequate evaluation techniques.

The efficient teacher today commonly sets up six types of objectives: *knowledge*, *understanding*, *habits*, *skills*, *attitudes*, and *appreciation*. Instead of concentrating on knowledge (*knowing* the tables) and computation with *skill* in a *habitual* way, as the lesson was laid out under the ultratraditional plan mentioned above, he now gives attention to the *understanding* of the processes, and the acquisition of *attitudes* of interest, curiosity, experimentation, and so on, along with *appreciation*—perhaps of the place arithmetic has in our cultural heritage and in modern progress. In most cases, all these six types of outcomes would not be expected in any one lesson. *Habits* and *skills* are acquired gradually.

## 8. Avoidance of Undesirable Outcomes

William H. Kilpatrick is credited with a diagram similar to that in Fig. 1, which illustrates the fact that teachers sometimes unknowingly and indifferently allow undesirable outcomes to develop, unless they make a conscious effort to prevent their appearance. For example, in terms of the figure, the *primary* outcome sought in a certain arithmetic lesson might be for every pupil to know the multiplication table of 9's. These pupils no doubt have had previous experience with multiplication and therefore, as a secondary or *associate* outcome they will probably be able to multiply a three- or four-digit number by 9.

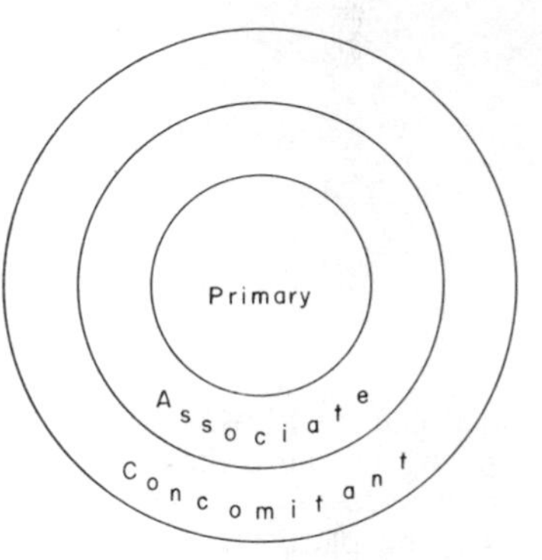

**Fig. 1.** Types of Outcomes.

Though this teacher seeks nothing further in the way of outcomes, there are certain to be some *concomitant* outcomes. These are likely to be of an emotional type; they occur even if the teacher gives this aspect of the pupil's learning no thought whatever. If the child is progressing well in arithmetic, if the teacher is congenial and friendly, and if the atmosphere of the arithmetic class is pleasurable to him, he will develop good attitudes toward arithmetic, toward the teacher, and toward school, even though no special effort is made to help him acquire those attitudes.

But for another pupil who is struggling less successfully with the 9's and the computations, the concomitant outcomes will be of a different sort—a dislike for arithmetic, for the teacher, and for school, a situation of which the teacher is entirely unaware if the pupil is good at covering up. Perhaps he does accomplish the teacher's primary objective—learning the 9's—and the teacher will breathe a sigh of relief and say to his colleague, "At last, even Willie finally knows the 9's." But, in spite of the teacher's assumption of success, Willie in the meantime has become one of the many people who "never did like arithmetic."

## 9. Procedures to Fit Objectives

If other outcomes than knowledge and skill are admitted as objectives, other procedures than drill must constitute the activities by which the teacher hopes to accomplish them. The following outline lists the various objectives with appropriate procedures:

| Objectives | Procedures |
|---|---|
| 1. To *know* the names of the places to the right of the ones (units). | 1. Discussion and demonstration that this is an extension of our decimal number system in which each place has only one-tenth the value of the place to its left. Show by means of common fractions that .01 is $\frac{1}{10}$ of .1, and so on; find the names of each place by taking $\frac{1}{10}$ of the preceding one; then practice reading and writing them (this really is drill following understanding). |
| 2. To *understand* why, when multiplying by more than one figure, each successive partial product is set one place farther to the left than the one before it.* | 2. In the process $\begin{array}{r} 2416 \\ \times\ 241 \\ \hline 2416 \\ 9664\phantom{0} \\ 4832\phantom{00} \\ \hline 582256 \end{array}$ show that $\begin{array}{rcr} 2416 \times 1 &=& 2416 \\ 2416 \times 40 &=& 96640 \\ 2416 \times 200 &=& 483200 \\ \hline 2416 \times 241 &=& 582256 \end{array}$ and that the zeros would keep the figures in their proper columns. But we remember the columns and as short cuts omit the zeros. |

* Pupils who understand the decimal system should be able to explore possibilities and discover the reasons for these positions.

| | |
|---|---|
| 3. To acquire the *habit* of arranging arithmetic work so as to make it easy to read and to check. | 3. From the beginning of the year, pay consistent attention to arrangement of work and to the development of pride in work well done. |
| 4. To acquire *skill* in rapid and accurate computation. | 4. Have frequent but well-distributed practice that gives attention first to understanding the process and to accuracy, then gradually increases the attention given to speed. |
| 5. To acquire *attitudes* of perseverance, interest, enjoyment of problem-solving, and so on. | 5. Have the pupil work at a level that suits his capability; commend good—particularly creative—work and individual initiative. |
| 6. To acquire an *appreciation* of the difference modern mathematics has made in the progress of civilization. | 6. Find information about and discuss computation by the Roman system as compared with our system. |

## 10. Evaluation That Matches Objectives

Along with the broader objectives and the corresponding procedures must go adequate evaluation techniques, some of them used as part of the day's lesson but many of them used at intervals as tests.

When the chief outcome sought was skill in computing both quickly and accurately, evaluation was easy. A short test was simple to make and simple to mark. When knowledge is the outcome sought, checks and tests to determine whether a pupil has acquired the knowledge can be readily devised.

But when attempts are made to evaluate the understanding or appreciation a pupil has acquired, or his ability in reflective learning, or the quality of the attitudes he has developed, the teacher is faced with greater difficulty. Paper-and-pencil tests are entirely inadequate for evaluating these types of outcomes. To evaluate his learning satisfactorily, the teacher needs to watch the pupil work, question him about his procedures, and encourage him to make oral explanations. Only with such techniques can he know to what extent the pupil has attained real understanding. He will need to observe the pupil in both formal and informal class situations to detect attitudes and degrees of appreciation. These evaluations become complex and difficult when done conscientiously.

## 11. Appropriate Levels of Teaching and Learning

There are four commonly recognized levels of teaching and learning, and likewise of testing: (1) *recognition*, (2) *recall*, (3) *interpretation*, and (4) *application*. These levels are applicable to social studies, science, and other subjects as well as to arithmetic. The following arithmetic questions illustrate each of them:

1. Recognition: $16 - 2 = (18;\ 4;\ 14;\ 8)$
2. Recall: What is the formula (or rule) for finding the area of a triangle?
3. Interpretation: Show why dividing a number by $\frac{1}{3}$ gives the same answer as multiplying the number by 3.
4. Application: A family on receiving an assessment notice learned they had a 15 per cent tax increase. If their tax the previous year was $140, what will the amount of the new tax be?

Some pupils do arithmetic computations very well but have difficulty with questions involving interpretation, and with problem-solving in general; the latter is always on the application level, for previously learned principles and processes must be applied to a new situation of a similar nature. There is no doubt, in the writer's opinion, that too much teaching is done on the two lower mental levels in other subjects as well as in arithmetic. Adequate teaching should enable pupils to interpret learning and apply it; and adequate evaluation should determine to what extent they can interpret and apply learning, as well as recall it. Most of the learning for interpretation and application falls into the understanding type of objective, and is definitely tied in both with the theories mentioned in an earlier chapter relative to teaching arithmetic for meaning and for understanding, and with the use of reflective procedures.

## 12. Systematic Progress

Lesson plans, then, should (1) give consideration to a broad set of objectives such as the six listed earlier in this chapter, (2) provide for procedures that will accomplish those objectives and give depth to learning instead of being concerned merely with shallow recognition and recall, and (3) provide for evaluation procedures that will appraise all types of learning called for in the objectives.

According to Buswell,[1] the basic content of arithmetic is old and is not likely to change rapidly in any major fashion, but there are new ideas as to ways to use arithmetic, new ideas as to ways to learn arithmetic, and new ideas about methods and materials of instruction in arithmetic. If teachers are alert to some of the new ideas to which Buswell refers, they will broaden their objectives and reconstruct their procedures somewhat along the lines that were pointed out above. As was indicated in Chapter 3, it is possible that content entirely new to the elementary level may before long become part of the arithmetic curriculum at that level. Whatever the content, however, it is the classroom activities—what the pupils and the teacher do—that motivate learning and lead to success in teaching.

## COMPETENCE CHECK

**1.** Consult the course of study for your state and indicate which of the following elements it contains: (1) objectives for teaching arithmetic, (2) objectives for teaching each grade in arithmetic, (3) guiding principles, (4) outline of content for each grade, (5) content specifically set up for each six-weeks period, (6) procedures to be used.

**2.** Write a paragraph stating how arithmetic can contribute to each of the four general purposes formulated by the Educational Policies Commission.

**3.** In a paragraph explain how arithmetic can serve the three acceptable purposes mentioned in this chapter.

**4.** Discuss the eleven guiding principles listed in this chapter. Which of them do you find easiest to accept? Which most difficult?

**5.** Explain the statement: We put too much stress on the product of learning, and not enough on the process of learning in arithmetic.

**6.** Write a lesson plan for one day's lesson in arithmetic at any grade level you choose; use the following outline and adapt it to your needs:

1. Objectives (for pupil attainment)
   a. To know ..........................
   b. To understand ..........................
   c. To increase skill in ..........................
   d. To acquire attitudes of ..........................
   e. To acquire some appreciation of ..........................
2. Materials
   a. For teacher use
   b. For pupil use
3. Procedures appropriate for the stated objectives (activities to be carried on by teacher and pupils)

[1] G. T. Buswell, "Introduction," National Society for the Study of Education, *Fiftieth Yearbook, Part II*, 1951.

4. Evaluation
   a. Of pupil attainment (extent to which objectives were accomplished)
   b. Of teaching efficiency (critical notes after teaching, indicating strongest and weakest parts of lesson procedure)

**7.** Could you expect any learning to be on the level of interpretation or application in first-grade arithmetic? Explain your answer.

## OPTIONAL ASSIGNMENTS

**1.** Is the Educational Policies Commission still in existence? Give evidence to support your answer.
**2.** List several of its publications.
**3.** Summarize Buckingham's discussion of how arithmetic influences social institutions, and how social institutions influence arithmetic.
**4.** Read Eads' article and explain how more "listening to children think" would result in less verbalism.
**5.** Study Hart's chart and list the items she identifies with critical thinking in numbers. Write your own interpretation of them.
**6.** Olander says that supervisors see much poor teaching. Report on his criticisms.
**7.** What are some of the weaknesses in our total arithmetic program according to Hartung?
**8.** Report on Jones' article on Australian criticisms of the teaching of mathematics in the United States.

## REFERENCES


Buckingham, B. R., "The Social Point of View in Arithmetic," National Society for the Study of Education, *Fiftieth Yearbook*, *Part II*, 1951.

Eads, Laura K., "Let's Think About Arithmetic," *Grade Teacher*, March, 1958, p. 55.

Educational Policies Commission, *The Purposes of Education in American Democracy*, National Education Association, Washington, 1938.

Gates, L. B., "The Spiral Development of Arithmetic," *School Science and Mathematics*, April, 1949, pp. 273–280.

Hart, Murlee, "Critical Thinking—Where Does It Begin?" *Grade Teacher*, September, 1958, p. 54.

Hartung, Maurice L., "Mathematics in the Total School Program," *Mathematics Teacher*, May, 1958, p. 336.

Jones, A. W., "Mathematics Teaching in American Classrooms," *Mathematics Teacher*, May, 1958, p. 344.

Olander, Herbert F., "Supervising the Teaching of Arithmetic," *Education*, February, 1958, p. 374.

State Course of Study for Elementary Subjects.

chapter 7

# Development of Our Number System

## 1. Hindu-Arabic System

The perfected Hindu-Arabic system of notation is one of the most important inventions of all time. It ranks with the invention of the wheel in its value to the development of civilization. The system that we use today, with the digits: 0, 1, 2, 3, 4, 5, 6, 7, 8, and 9, and a base of 10, took many centuries to develop.

A brief survey of the development of the number system we take so much for granted will enable us, in a measure, to appreciate it.

## 2. Roots in Primitive Life

When primitive people reached a stage in civilization where they began to acquire possessions, both personal and tribal, they found a need for some means of keeping account of those possessions. Though they had no written language, some means was needed by which they could establish claim to the correct number of sheep for their flocks. They did this not by counting and using names for the numbers as we do—for example, twenty-four sheep—but by using a collection of pebbles that had a one-to-one correspondence to their sheep; in other words, a pebble for every sheep and a sheep for every pebble. Today three-year-old Tommy uses the one-to-one correspondence when he hands out cookies to his friends and says, "One for Mary, and one for Susie, and one for Jack, and one for me." How many cookies there actually are makes little difference to him so long as the cookies go around. Whenever early man checked up on his flock and found there were extra pebbles, he knew some sheep were missing. His contact with other men often involved bartering, but when he "traded even" no computation and no recording were required.

There were other early means of recording, too; for example, a notch was cut in a stick for every day that passed—again a one-to-one correspondence procedure. In this way men could estimate how many more days must pass before another full moon, a possible advantage for hunting.

## 3. Need for Names and Number Symbols

With the advance of civilization systems of naming developed along with the counting—all of them crude in the beginning. For example, urapun (1), okosa (2), okosa urapun (3), okosa okosa (4) has been reported as the naming system used by one tribe.[1] Such a system of naming a series of numbers is cumbersome, to say the least.

**Notation** is a method of writing numbers. This requires a set of symbols, one to represent each number. The very early tribes had not devised such a system. Marks, Purdy, and Kinney[2] suggest that one of the early plans might have involved the use of tallies[3] (1, 11, or 1111) to represent the respective number of fingers, with symbols like 1, 11, and 1111 used for them; when all the fingers on one hand were thus represented, some agreed-upon mark—the symbol H, for example—could be written. Thus HH would indicate two hands (10); HH111, two hands and three more fingers (13) and so on. In this system the additive principle was used and 13 could be written 111HH as well as HH111. In other words, place value had no part in the system. Consequently, a long series of symbols would be required to write even as large a number as 265.

## 4. Early Egyptian System

The most significant of the systems of notation developed in ancient times were those of the Egyptians, the Greeks, and the Romans.

[1] E. H. Taylor and C. N. Mills, *Arithmetic for Teacher Training Classes*, Holt, Rinehart & Winston, New York, 4th ed., 1955, p. 14.

[2] John L. Marks, C. Richard Purdy, and Lucien B. Kinney, *Teaching Arithmetic for Understanding*, McGraw-Hill, New York, 1958, p. 63.

[3] Our word *tally* is derived from the Latin word *talea*, meaning stick, on which notches were cut to keep a record in counting.

Probably the most elementary system of which there is a record is that of the ancient Egyptians, whose hieroglyphic numerals date back to 3300 B.C. Larsen[4] presents a clear and interesting table of these numerals and their use in notation. In writing numbers the Egyptians used two principles: (1) repetition and (2) addition. Thus in the number 29 the symbol for 10 (∩) is written twice to indicate 20 (∩∩), and the symbol for 1 is written nine times to indicate 9 (111111111). Written together (∩∩111111111), they are added and their sum is 29.

Of interest is the fact that the Egyptian system is based on the scale of *ten*, as is also the Hindu-Arabic system. Apparently the fact that human beings have ten fingers accounts for the use of the *ten* system by different peoples. When a man had enumerated by a one-to-one correspondence as many objects as he had fingers, he needed a symbol to indicate that group number. Hence the Egyptians used a vertical staff ( | ) to represent 1, a heel bone (∩) to represent 10, a scroll (୨) to represent 100, and so on. Ten staffs became a heel bone, 10 heel bones a scroll, etc.

## 5. The Greek System

The Greek system has been traced back to about 450 B.C. Though it was used for many decades, it has been called one of the most awkward systems. The Greek symbols for the numbers were the twenty-four letters of the Greek alphabet, along with three obsolete letters and the symbol *M*.[5] The first nine letters stood for the numbers from 1 to 9, the next nine for the decades from 10 to 90, and the last nine for hundreds, 100 to 900. *M* denoted the number 10,000, or myriad. In order to distinguish numerals from words, a line was drawn above each letter used as a numeral.

## 6. The Roman System

The Roman system of notation is more familiar to us because it is often used in our country. Too cumbersome for modern computation, Roman numerals are frequently used for chapter numbers and the introductory pages in books. Because they are more easily carved than Arabic numerals, they are often used on buildings and cornerstones to indicate dates. They have long been used as numerals on clock faces, although Arabic numerals have to a large extent replaced them.

[4] Harold D. Larsen, *Arithmetic for Colleges*, Macmillan, New York, 1954, p. 3.
[5] *Ibid.*, p. 5.

In the Roman system the symbols are the capital letters I, V, X, L, C, D, and M. Since English uses the Roman (Latin) alphabet, these symbols are familiar. They are combined to form numbers by means of four principles: (1) repetition, (2) subtraction, (3) multiplication, and (4) addition. By repetition, for example, three I's (III) represent 3. By subtraction, IV indicates 1 subtracted from 5, or 4. A bar over a number multiplies it by 1000; for example, $\overline{\text{XXV}}$ is 25,000. By addition, VI indicates 5 and 1, or 6. When the symbol having the smaller numerical value precedes a symbol that has a greater value, as in IV, the smaller value is subtracted from the greater in determining the numerical value of the symbol. However, when the symbol having the smaller numerical value follows one having a greater value, as in VI or XII, the smaller value is added to the greater.

With the following table as a guide, any number can be expressed in Roman numerals. The seven letters that are starred are the only symbols used in this system.

| | | | |
|---|---|---|---|
| 1 = I★ | 11 = XI | 21 = XXI | 300 = CCC |
| 2 = II | 12 = XII | 30 = XXX | 400 = CD |
| 3 = III | 13 = XIII | 40 = XL | 500 = D★ |
| 4 = IV | 14 = XIV | 50 = L★ | 600 = DC |
| 5 = V★ | 15 = XV | 60 = LX | 900 = CM |
| 6 = VI | 16 = XVI | 70 = LXX | 1000 = M★ |
| 7 = VII | 17 = XVII | 80 = LXXX | 31,000 = $\overline{\text{XXXI}}$ |
| 8 = VIII | 18 = XVIII | 90 = XC | 2,100,000 = $\overline{\text{MMC}}$ |
| 9 = IX | 19 = XIX | 100 = C★ | |
| 10 = X★ | 20 = XX | | |

The Roman numerals fall into an interesting pattern of value: multiply by 5; double; multiply by 5; double; multiply by 5; double. Thus I stands for 1, V for five times as much (5), X for double that (10) L for five times as much (50), C for double that (100), D for five times as much (500), and M for double that (1000).

Note that V is never repeated, but that I, X, C, and M are. Also, to express reduced value, only one symbol is ever used before a symbol of larger value—e.g., IX and XC—and only I, X, and C are thus used.

Different theories have been advanced regarding the origin of the symbols used for Roman numerals. One theory holds that I represents one finger and V the hand (the space between the thumb and the index finger), that C stands for the Latin word *centum* (hundred) and M for the word *mille* (thousand), and that X represents the two crossed arms with all the fingers. Whether or not such theories have historical foundation, they may well provide clues to the numerical meaning of these symbols.

### 7. The Counting Table and Abacus

Though we read the Roman symbols with comparative ease, we would find them extremely difficult for computations. But, according to authorities, the use of a counting table enabled the Romans to become rapid computers. That the use of pebbles for counters was common in

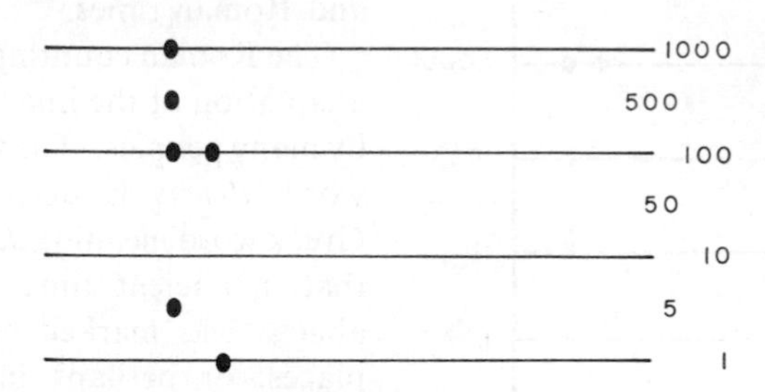


**Fig. 2.** Roman Counting Table.

Roman life is indicated by the fact that our word *calculate* is derived from the Latin *calculus*, meaning pebble. It is probable that pebbles were used as counters on the counting tables.[6] As shown in the diagram of a counting table (Fig. 2), each line, from lower to upper, increases tenfold in numerical value. Each space represents five times the value of the line below it, and the spaces also increase tenfold in the upward direction. Thus a "handful of counters" (5) on the lower line may be replaced by a single counter on the space above it, and a pair of counters on a space may be replaced by a counter on the line above it.

This moving of a counter to a line of higher order probably accounts for our use of the word "carry" in addition with reduction. For example, in the addition of 36 and 45 as shown here, 36, with 11 as

$$\begin{array}{r} 36 \\ +45 \\ \hline 81 \end{array}$$

the sum of the units, we mentally convert 11 to one 10 and one 1, write the 1 in the ones column and *carry* the 10 to the tens column,

[6] No doubt our word *counter*, the table over which sales are made in stores, came from the Roman counting table.

The counters in Fig. 2 indicate the number 1706. When this number is written in Roman numerals, MDCCVI, the fact that there are no tens is evident because no ten symbol appears in this number. Hence no place holder was called for in the Roman system. It would be possible with some practice to manipulate the counters so as to perform any of the fundamental operations with integers, but it has been said that with our Hindu-Arabic system a ten-year-old can do computations which were impossible for the greatest mathematicians in Greek and Roman times.

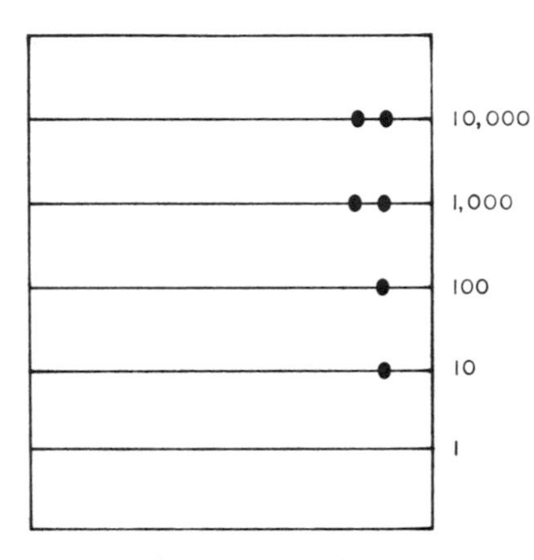


**Fig. 3.** Line Abacus.

The Roman counting table is an adaptation of the line abacus used by many peoples. The fact that the word *abacus* is derived from a Greek word meaning *dust* indicates that in ancient times a form of abacus was marked out in dusty places, or perhaps in purposely prepared dust-covered areas. The line abacus (Fig. 3) is made with ruled lines and loose counters. The count indicated by the placed counters in the figure is 22,110, since two ten-thousand positions are registered, two one-thousands, one one-hundred, and one ten. Note that positional value entered the abacus computation, though there was not yet a notation system for recording it.

Fig. 4 shows what is commonly called a rod-and-bead abacus. Based on much the same principle as the line abacus, it is frequently seen in primary classrooms today. It consists of wires, on which beads are strung, attached to a frame; each wire has either nine or ten beads. In preparing to use the abacus, all the beads are moved to the left end of the wire; they are then moved to the right to register value. Fig. 4 shows the number 159.

Some abacuses used for early computation, particularly during the Middle Ages, were more complicated. In the abacus in Fig. 5, a bead in the left section has five times the value of a bead on the same line in the section to the right. The number registered on the abacus in the figure is 6378. These types of abacus assign no value to spaces; in general, they are simpler than the Roman counting table.

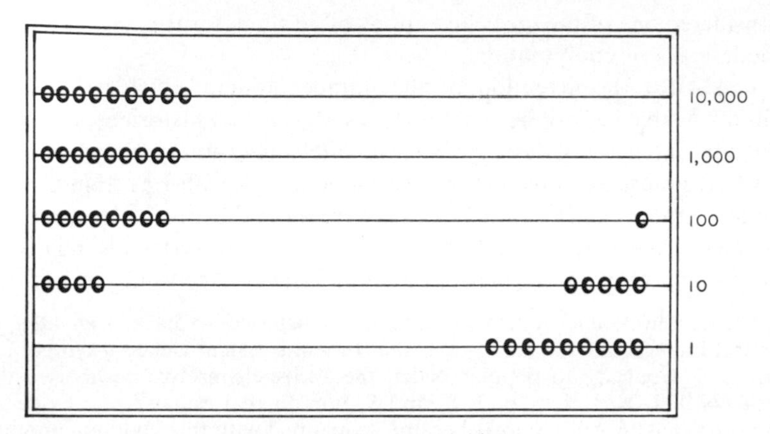


**Fig. 4.** Rod-and-Bead Abacus.

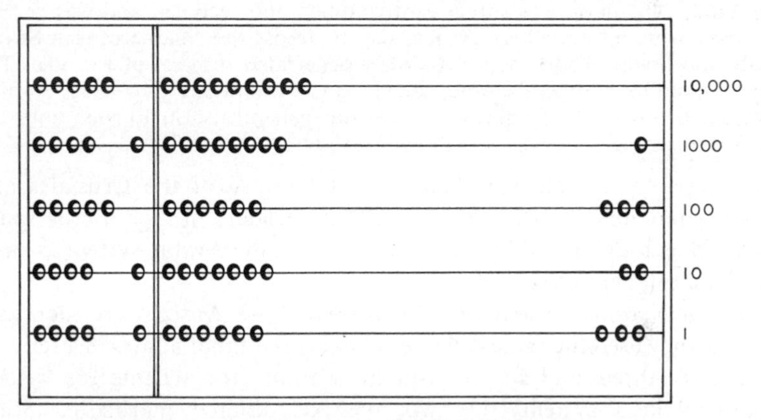


**Fig. 5.** More Complicated Rod-and-Bead Abacus.

In American classrooms the abacus is being dusted off and used more and more as a concrete visual aid in connection with primary numbers.

## 8. Zero and the Modern Era of Computation

Though the abacus was an early aid in computation, there was some difficulty in writing numbers using the symbols 1, 2, 3, 4, 5, 6, 7, 8, and 9 when some of the rods or lines were empty. The zero symbol was probably not "invented" until several centuries after the other digits; it appeared as a tenth digit some time before 600 A.D. The zero is considered one of the great inventions of all time, for it inaugurated the modern era of computation.

Credit for the invention of the number system which we call the Hindu-Arabic has not been definitely established by historians, nor have the time and place of its origin been definitely determined. Some scholars say that a more exact name for it would be Babylonian-Egyptian-Greek-Hindu-Arabic, since contributions were probably made by all these peoples. As to time, the history of our number system is relatively brief when compared to that of the human race. According to Larsen:

> The Hindu-Arabic system of notation is believed to have originated in central India about 500 B.C., but at that time the system lacked a symbol for zero. . . . Contrary to popular belief, the Arabs themselves never used the symbols 0, 1, 2, 3, 4, 5, 6, 7, 8, and 9, nor do they today.[7] . . . Evidence indicates that an Arab scholar became acquainted with this Hindu method of writing numbers and incorporated the system into an arithmetic he wrote by hand. The book was subsequently copied and recopied and was carried by merchants into northern Africa, thence across the Mediterranean Sea to Italy and Spain, from whence it slowly penetrated the rest of Europe. The new unfamiliar numerals were called Arabic numerals by virtue of their presumed origin. They did not come into general use in Europe until the sixteenth century.[8]

However, some historians believe that because of the Crusades and other intercourse between East and West, traders in such a crossroads country as Italy probably knew something of the Arabic system as early as the ninth century.

The *numeration* systems of the Romans and Arabs were identical; that is, they used the same ordered scheme of number names in a series—one, two, three, and so on. But in *notation* (the scheme for writing numbers in a system) the two methods differed markedly. Some characteristics of the Roman system have been pointed out, and more will be said in a later chapter about the Hindu-Arabic system.

## 9. Impact of Modern Mathematics on Society

By the sixteenth century, with the rise of the commercial class in Europe, mathematics had come into its own and the way was paved for

[7] In this he is at variance with some other writers on the subject. According to Marks, Purdy, and Kinney, "Details of the development and spread of Hindu-Arabic numbers are incomplete, but certain fragmentary evidence reveals the pattern. Originating with the Hindus, it soon was widely used by Arabic peoples at the eastern end of the Mediterranean" (*op. cit.*, p. 65).

[8] Harold D. Larsen, *op. cit.*, p. 11.

the development of modern mathematics. Thanks to the facilities for measurement which this new mathematics made possible, the physical sciences were making corresponding progress.

Arithmetic had begun to make a real impact on society. According to Buckingham,[9] astronomy was first used by the Babylonians. The Egyptians developed a system of surveying which helped the farmers of the Nile define their land boundaries and maintain them through the annual floods. Calendars were devised, chronology began to be recorded, coins were minted, and taxes were levied. All these advancements followed the development of a workable and practical system of numbers. As a result of these mathematical advances governments arose. Business and trade replaced barter and pillage, and mapmaking became a science. These mathematical foundations enabled civilization to make marked progress.

By 1600 arithmetic had attained substantially its present form and the digits with which we are familiar were in use. Larsen[10] gives an interesting discussion of the changes that took place in the form of the Arabic number symbols from the tenth to the sixteenth centuries. By that time, with the printing press in fairly general use, these symbols became standardized in their present form. By that time, too, the abacus and counting table had given way to the use of algorisms in computation, at least in the areas of most advanced civilization, and "calculation advanced from a manipulative activity to a process of thinking."

## COMPETENCE CHECK

1. Construct a Roman counting table on paper or a board, provide some type of counters for it, and demonstrate its use.
2. Make a line abacus and provide loose counters for it. Show how difficult it was, before the zero came into use, to write in Hindu-Arabic numerals those numbers indicated on the abacus by an empty line or rod.
3. Why did the Romans not need a zero in their system of notation when using an abacus or counting table?
4. By demonstration explain how, with the use of algorisms, "calculation advanced from a manipulative activity to a process of thinking."
5. Write in Roman numerals: 8749; 122,650; 1,000,602.

[9] B. R. Buckingham, "The Social Point of View in Arithmetic," National Society for the Study of Education, *Fiftieth Yearbook, Part II*, 1951, p. 272.

[10] Harold D. Larsen, *op. cit.*, p. 12.

6. Explain Wheat's statement: "Some four hundred years ago the art of calculation came tumbling from its lofty perch among the courses of the university to land in its present position as one of the common branches of the elementary school."

## OPTIONAL ASSIGNMENTS

1. Consult Larsen or other sources and study the characteristics of the Egyptian system of notation. Using their symbols, write: 1461; 125,000; 1001.
2. Read Larsen or other sources concerning the Greek numerals and how in their system of notation the Greeks used both addition and multiplication.
3. Compare the Greek system with the Egyptian system of using repetition and addition.
4. On the basis of Wheat or other sources, describe how primitive man evolved the principle of positional (place) value in counting.
5. Obtain from an encyclopedia information for a more complete history of the Hindu-Arabic number system.
6. Solve the puzzle problems based on Roman notation on pages 10–11 in Larsen. Try to construct some of your own.
7. Following Swain, do some computations with Roman numerals; e.g., add CXLVII and CCXLVIII, or subtract DCLXV from DCCCXLVI.
8. Write the number 1959 in as many forms as you can (Egyptian, Roman, and others).

## REFERENCES

Swain, Robert L., *Understanding Arithmetic*, Holt, Rinehart & Winston, New York, 1957, chap. 1.

Wheat, H. G., *How to Teach Arithmetic*, Row, Peterson, Evanston, 1951, chaps. 1, 13.

chapter 8

# Basic Concepts of Our Number System

## I. Concepts Acquired, not Transmitted

We saw in the preceding chapter that what had been accomplished by 1600 served as a springboard for the development of modern mathematics, which in turn made modern science possible.

Although modern mathematics is based on human experience, mathematical concepts, and the ability to think in quantitative terms are not innate in a child; they are acquired only when he has received well-planned guidance and direction, and has had adequate opportunity for creative thinking. Concepts are not transmitted from teacher to pupil; they are acquired—by insight, a Gestalt psychologist would say—as a result of the pupil's own experience and effort. Only by thinking for himself can a pupil learn arithmetic and gain mathematical insight.

In other words, understanding is not acquired by rote learning, nor is it an innate part of a pupil's consciousness. Rather it develops gradually; it is a product of experience combined with mental activity. In a measure at least, it can be acquired during the study of elementary arithmetic. Hence, the responsibility for providing the necessary guidance and opportunities rests primarily upon elementary teachers. The nature of this responsibility is the main theme of this book, which is based on the assumption that the chief purpose of teaching arithmetic is to help pupils understand our number system and enable them to use number as a constant aid in the quantitative aspects of their lives.

## 2. Importance of Readiness

According to psychologists,[1] readiness in arithmetic is now recognized as a function not only of mental maturity and inner growth, but also of previous experience, methods of learning, interests, attitudes, and purposes. Therefore, it is the teacher's task to appraise the child's background for learning a new concept, provide foundational experiences, and establish a purpose for the new learning in the learner's mind. Although this idea was expressed almost thirty years ago in the *Fiftieth Yearbook* of the National Society for the Study of Education, the evidence apparently indicates that not all elementary teachers have accepted those tasks as goals.

Arithmetic is a *logical* subject. It builds one mathematical concept on another, following a recognized sequence. For example, a child is not expected to be able to add *unlike* fractions until he has learned how to add *like* fractions. Because of this sequential nature, there is a more or less fixed order of presentation, which makes readiness very important.

In spite of the logic and sequence of arithmetic, however, the *logical method* of teaching it has given way to the *psychological*. The latter, which recognizes relative learning difficulty, has developed into the so-called *spiral method* which provides an expanding concept of learning.

## 3. Importance of Basic Concepts

No one will assume that elementary-school children can acquire a complete understanding of our number system including sets, subsets, factorials, irrational numbers, and such topics. But certainly these children can acquire foundational understandings for developing this comprehension later, and a readiness to advance to further mathematical learnings.

As was mentioned previously, it is not the purpose of this book to set up the curricular content for arithmetic on a grade-by-grade basis. Usually each school prepares its own course of study or follows some other accepted one, perhaps that made by the state education department. Instead the purpose is to help the teacher acquire a thorough understanding of the basic concepts which are generally assumed to be within the field of elementary arithmetic, and to encourage him to "go the

[1] Arthur I. Gates, *et al.*, *Educational Psychology*, Macmillan, New York, 1942, p. 344.

second mile" and attain an understanding of arithmetic that is considerably beyond the content of the elementary textbook. What, then, are some of these foundational learnings—basic concepts, if you will—which teachers should help children acquire in elementary school? The remainder of this chapter concerns the concepts which, in the writer's opinion, are basic.

## 4. Characteristics of Our Notation System as Basic Concepts

The characteristics of our notation system are surely among the concepts to be acquired by both teachers and pupils. The four characteristics set forth by de Milt[2] are significant: (1) a decimal system; (2) the principle of position or location which makes it possible to use only nine symbols and the zero to represent numbers of any size; (3) representation of the numbers 1 through 9 by symbols which stand for things counted, and for nothing else; and (4) the use of zero as a symbol for *none* or *not any*.

### *A decimal system as a basic concept*

Because our number system has a base of 10 and is a system of tens we call it a **decimal system**, from the Latin word *decem* (ten). Ten is the standard to which all numbers larger than 10 are related. We refer to the places occupied by figures, that is, their position in the numeral, as **orders** and give them distinguishing names. The order names reading from right to left are ones (units), tens, hundreds, thousands, and so on, each order representing ten times the value of the order to its right.

| Thousands | Hundreds | Tens | Ones |
|---|---|---|---|
| 2 | 2 | 2 | 2 |

The above number is read two thousand two hundred twenty-two. Two in the tens place indicates 2 tens and has ten times the numerical value of the 2 in the ones place. The 2 in the hundreds place has ten times the value of the 2 in the tens place, and so on.

Although our number system has a base of 10, number systems may have other bases than 10, as we shall see later. The base is the first collection in a number series. When we count objects in groups up to and

[2] Clara de Milt, "The Origin of Our Numeral Notation," *School Science and Mathematics*, November, 1947, p. 701.

including 9, we use a single digit to represent a group of 7 or 5 or 9; but as soon as the group has 10 objects (or units) we indicate it by putting a 1 in the tens place and a 0 to indicate there are no additional units (10). We continue the collection; and as soon as there are ten 10's, we collect the ten 10's into 1 hundred, put the 1 in the hundreds place and 0's in the tens and ones places to hold those places and indicate that there are no tens and no ones. This collection procedure illustrates the position or location principle and also the use of 0 to mean "none."

Ten as a base is used in combination with the smaller numbers to form the next numbers in the series; i.e., 10 and 1 is 11. As was mentioned earlier, we have 10 digits on both hands, and our base probably developed from using both hands as the first collection. When the collection idea is properly employed, 12 is not 12 separate entities; it is 3 entities consisting of a collection of 1 ten and 2 ones. Forty is 4 entities—4 tens. The collection idea makes adding 2000 and 4000 as easy as adding 2 and 4.

Since a numeral increases tenfold in value with each successive move to the left in accordance with the place value system, this increase in value may be indicated exponentially thus:

$$10^6 + 10^5 + 10^4 + 10^3 + 10^2 + 10^1 + 10^0$$

The little figure is called an **exponent**; it tells how many times the base is taken as a factor. The figures above are read 10 to the 6th power, plus 10 to the 5th power, plus 10 to the 4th power, plus 10 to the 3rd power, plus 10 to the 2nd power, plus 10 to the 1st power, plus 10 to the 0 power. Their values are:

$$10^0 = 1$$
$$10^1 = 10$$
$$10^2 = 10 \times 10 = 100$$
$$10^3 = 10 \times 10 \times 10 = 1000$$
$$10^4 = 10 \times 10 \times 10 \times 10 = 10{,}000$$
$$10^5 = 10 \times 10 \times 10 \times 10 \times 10 = 100{,}000$$
$$10^6 = 10 \times 10 \times 10 \times 10 \times 10 \times 10 = 1{,}000{,}000$$

No extensive comprehension of powers and exponents is necessary to interpret these values. Note that the exponent for any power of 10 is equal to the number of zeros after the 1 when the indicated power is written as a natural number, e.g., $10^4 = 10{,}000$* In our number system the successive powers of 10 are of great importance. It is evident that

* This is something for pupils to discover.

large numbers can be expressed with far fewer figures by writing them as powers of a smaller number.

One further point needs to be explained. Even before a pupil has had any algebra he can acquire some understanding of the zero power of a number without too great difficulty. Since $10^4 = 10{,}000$ and $10^2 = 100$, $\frac{10^4}{10^2} = 10{,}000 \div 100 = 100 = 10^2$, it is clear that when the base of the numerator (dividend) and of the denominator (divisor) are the same number, the division can be accomplished merely by subtracting the respective exponents. Hence $\frac{10^3}{10^3} = 10^0$. But it is obvious that $\frac{10^3}{10^3} = \frac{10 \times 10 \times 10}{10 \times 10 \times 10} = 1$. Though more complicated algebraic proof is involved, we can conclude that any integer with a zero exponent is equal to 1; e.g., $10^0 = 1$; $6^0 = 1$, etc.

Looking again at our table of orders:

$$10^4 \quad + \quad 10^3 \quad + \quad 10^2 \quad + \quad 10^1 \quad + \quad 10^0$$

| 10,000's | 1000's | 100's | 10's | 1's |
|---|---|---|---|---|
| | 3 + | 3 + | 3 + | 3 |

| | | | |
|---|---|---|---|
| 3 | 1000's | = | 3000 |
| 3 | 100's | = | 300 |
| 3 | 10's | = | 30 |
| 3 | 1's | = | 3 |
| | | | 3333 |

and remembering the additive property of our decimal system, we arrive at the value of the 3's in the first four orders.

### *Principle of location as a basic concept*

It is evident that each digit represents a product of two factors; one, the intrinsic factor, is indicated by the digit itself, and the other, the local factor, is indicated by the position of the digit in the row. The use of the word local here will be clearer if we remember its derivation from the Latin word *locus* meaning "place." The local factor is the power of the base. The number 356 may be represented as $3(10)^2 + 5(10)^1 + 6(10)^0$ or $300 + 50 + 6$.

The number of orders is infinite; they go on and on to infinity, and names are devised for them as the need arises. The twentieth century has created an unbelievably rapid need for larger and larger numbers.

In very early times it was found convenient to group the digits of a number in some manner for greater ease of reading and greater accuracy of writing. Accordingly the orders have been organized into **periods.** We are accustomed to seeing the figures grouped by three's. These periods are not always set off by the same kind of mark. Although we use commas (246,189), dots, bars, and colons have been used in other countries—e.g., (2/681/246).

Actually two different methods are currently used for setting off periods; they are commonly referred to as the American and the English methods. In the American pattern, commas are used to set off the digits of a number into groups of three, counting from right to left—for example, 1,206,142. (However, the comma is sometimes omitted in four-place numbers, e.g., 7294, not 7,294.) Each of these groups is called a **period**, and each period has a specific name: the first period on the right is the **units** period; the second is the **thousands** period; the third is the **millions** period; the fourth is the **billions** period, and so on. In the following tabulation the words above the figures are the names of the first twelve *orders*; those below the figures are the names of the corresponding four *periods*.

| hundred billions | ten billions | billions | hundred millions | ten millions | millions | hundred thousands | ten thousands | thousands | hundreds | tens | units |
|---|---|---|---|---|---|---|---|---|---|---|---|
| 2 | 3 | 1, | 1 | 0 | 5, | 6 | 2 | 4, | 8 | 0 | 0 |
| billions | | | millions | | | thousands | | | units | | |

Just as the number of orders is infinite, so is the number of periods. Names can be devised for periods as needed and the system of order names can be extended to fit the periods. For practical purposes names of the first twelve periods (sufficient to represent a 36-figure number) are adequate for understanding the system. From right to left in the following tabulation they are: units, thousands, millions, billions, trillions, quadrillions, quintillions, sextillions, septillions, octillions, nonillions, decillions.

| 12th | 11th | 10th | 9th | 8th | 7th | 6th | 5th | 4th | 3rd | 2nd | 1st |
|---|---|---|---|---|---|---|---|---|---|---|---|
| decillions | nonillions | octillions | septillions | sextillions | quintillions | quadrillions | trillions | billions | millions | thousands | units |

Students who have a Latin-language background may be disturbed by the fact that though the names of the periods are obviously based on the Latin names for numerals—*unus* (1), *duo* (2), *tres* (3), *quattor* (4), *quinque* (5), *sex* (6), *septem* (7), *octo* (8), *novem* (9), *decem* (10)—the names do not apply to the respective periods. This is also true of the names of some of the months of the year; the ninth month is named as if it were the seventh (September), the tenth (October) as if it were the eight, and the twelfth (December) as if it were the tenth. Strangely enough, the ninth period in numeration is named as if it were the seventh. These two misnomers have entirely different causes. In the case of the months a change in the calendar upset the order of naming. In the case of the numeration, the confusion is due to the American system of setting off periods; it is not present in the English system.

In the American system a collection of 1000 in one period becomes 1 in the next higher period; thus 1000 units make 1 thousand, 1000 thousands make 1 million, 1000 millions make 1 billion, and so on. The Latin prefix *bi-* indicates 2, and *tri-* means, 3; but *bi*llions is not our second period, nor is *tri*llions our third. In the English system six orders make a period. Hence a million is 1000 thousands (1,000,000), as in the American system; but a *bi*llion is 1,000,000 millions (1,000,000,000,000), requiring *two* six-figure periods, and a *tri*llion is 1,000,000 billions. The English system may be represented thus:

$$
\begin{aligned}
\text{1 million} &= 1{,}000{,}000^1 \\
\text{1 billion} &= 1{,}000{,}000^2 \\
\text{1 trillion} &= 1{,}000{,}000^3 \\
\text{1 quadrillion} &= 1{,}000{,}000^4
\end{aligned}
$$

In this system the names have true significance.

It should by now be obvious that we have a number system, and that comprehending it as a system should make for more effective learning than the too prevalent memorization of unrelated and unmeaningful computational procedures. Unless teachers have this comprehension, pupils can hardly be expected to acquire it.

### *Number symbols as a basic concept*

To understand our number system it is necessary to understand our number symbols. Because values are represented by symbols our number system is said to be *abstract*. Number names and number symbols are the "vehicles for our number thinking." They constitute a language of arithmetic in which we can transmit quantitative ideas to others. For example, when a small boy says to his mother, "I had half a dollar and a quarter and one of those big boys took my fifty-cent piece and now all I have left is twenty-five cents," she understands his quantitative problem.

Written language uses symbols which are unintelligible to a six-year-old until he learns to interpret them so they become meaningful concepts. The symbol *dog* bears no resemblance to the animal it represents. But with satisfactory guidance the child acquires a mental image of some kind of dog when he sees the symbol *dog*. The breed and size and color he visualizes depend upon his past experience with dogs.

Numerical symbols also have no resemblance to the concept they represent. The figure 5 looks not at all like ||||| (pencils) or **ooooo** (pennies). But here again, with satisfactory guidance, a child comprehends the collection represented by the symbol 5 and can arrange a group to match the symbol, e.g., 5 chairs or 5 books.

These number symbols make arithmetic a universal language, just as music scores speak a language by means of symbols that are universally understood, though the names applied to the symbols differ in various languages. The figure 2 means the same thing everywhere, though in Latin it is called *duo*, in English *two*, and in German *zwei*.

As we saw earlier, the Hindu-Arabic system of arithmetic provides an inexhaustible series of numbers—a number scale—by means of only nine digits and the symbol 0 (zero). These ten symbols stand for things counted, and for nothing else. They can be combined so as to represent a number of any size, largely because of the system of place value already discussed.

The word *digit* comes from the Latin *digitus* (finger), perhaps based on the early use of the fingers as counters. The digits represent numbers and we commonly refer to them as numerals. Each group of things counted—each *collection*, or *set*—up to and including 10 has a separate and distinct name. Beyond 10 compound names are used: sixteen (six and ten), twenty-three (twenty and three), and so on. **Place value** is the property of our number system that enables us to think of and write these compounded number concepts in terms of tens, and the additive characteristic of the system enables us at once to comprehend the total numerical value of the number expressed by the several figures.

### *Use of zero as a basic concept*

The zero is a very important element because it makes the system of place value possible. In the number 3002, the position of the 3 indicates that it means 3 thousands, and 2 indicates 2 units; the zeros keep the 3 and the 2 in the correct positions (or orders) to indicate their proper value. At the same time the zeros show that no hundred collections and no ten collections are recorded. Without doubt this placeholding function of zero is its most important use. The zero symbol should never be called anything but zero, except in certain cases when it is part of a telephone number or house number; in these cases it is called "oh."*

Just as the zeros in the number 3002 are interpreted as "not any," indicating not any hundreds and not any tens, zero also means "not any" in the score of a game. Thus a score of 6 to 0 means that one team scored 6 points and the other "not any." So also, if John had 8 marbles and lost all of them, the answer to how many he had left is "none;" the computation is written $8 - 8 = 0$. This illustrates a *second* function of zero, namely, to serve as a number in a set.

A *third* function of zero is its use as a time (0 on a stop watch) at which a test or game or race begins, the clock then running until the time is up.

A *fourth* function, closely related to the preceding one, is the use of zero as the point (line or mark) at which a race begins. "On your mark" means "Get on the zero line." The finish line is 40 or 440 yards or some other predetermined distance beyond the zero (starting) line.

A *fifth* function is similar in that zero is used as a point of reference. For example, a ruler or a tape measure begins with zero, and inches, feet, or any other linear units are measured from it. In this case we may refer to zero as a number in a sequence. It may also be a point on a circular measuring instrument—e.g., a speedometer—at which the indicator shows no movement of the vehicle but moves away from the zero point to show increasing speed.

A *sixth* function of zero is its use as a point on the thermometer; on a centigrade thermometer this indicates the temperature at which water freezes. Zero is less significant on a Fahrenheit thermometer; however, temperatures are said to be a certain number of degrees above or below the zero point on both thermometers. Zero temperature obviously does not mean "not any" temperature, nor does zero time on a stop watch mean it is *no* time of day.

A *seventh* function of zero is its use as a division point between positive and negative numbers. Integers form a two-way sequence

* Give pupils opportunity to discover other functions of zero.

$\cdots -4, -3, -2, -1, 0, +1, +2, +3, +4 \cdots$. If arranged in vertical form these would correspond to the temperature scale on a thermometer. Hence it is by reference to a thermometer that positive and negative numbers are likely to have most meaning for pupils encountering them for the first time. The use of positive and negative numbers (signed numbers) will be discussed in a later chapter.

### 5. Number Structure

The study of number *structure* is a complex and highly technical area of mathematics. According to Swain, "Under the rational approach, the study of the structure of the natural numbers and of the special relationships found within this structure has become the field of pure mathematics called 'Number Theory.' Specialists in the field have claimed it to be the most abstruse and difficult of the many branches of mathematics—'the most brilliant gem in the diadem of the Queen of the Sciences'."[3]

It is not the purpose of the present book to enter the "abstruse and difficult" realms of higher mathematics. That is the domain of such a text as *Number Theory and Its History*.[4] However, some additional mathematical concepts are within our sphere and should be given some attention—an acquaintance with the terminology, if nothing more. These are discussed in the next chapter.

## COMPETENCE CHECK

**1.** Explain: "A number is to its numeral as a person is to his name."

**2.** To be sure you have adequate concepts for these terms, define and give an illustration of each:

1. A number system
2. Creative thinking in arithmetic
3. Quantitative experiences
4. Sequential nature of arithmetic
5. Notation system
6. Decimal system
7. Numerical symbols
8. Principle of place value
9. Number system on base 10
10. Orders in our notation system

[3] Robert L. Swain, *Understanding Arithmetic*, Holt, Rinehart & Winston, New York, 1957, p. 116.

[4] Oystein Ore, *Number Theory and Its History*, McGraw-Hill, New York, 1948.

11. Periods in our notation system
12. Digit
13. The base as the first collection
14. The collection procedure on a base of 10
15. Powers and exponents
16. Successive powers of 10
17. Natural numbers
18. Additive property of our number system
19. Numeration
20. Number scale
21. Computation
22. Calculation
23. Integer
24. Positive and negative numbers
25. Basic sequence of numbers
26. Number
27. Algorism
28. Function of zero

**3.** Consult Larsen or other sources for the evolution of form that took place in the Hindu-Arabic numerals, and check the numerals that changed most and those that changed least.
**4.** When and why did these numerals become standardized in the form in which we use them?
**5.** Name several advantages of the Hindu-Arabic system over earlier systems.
**6.** Why does annexing a zero to the right of a Hindu-Arabic numeral multiply it by 10?
**7.** What number names should be hyphenated?
**8.** Marks, Purdy, and Kinney list the following four characteristics of the Hindu-Arabic system: (1) only nine digits required, (2) place value, (3) base-10 system, and (4) additive property. Explain how each of these characteristics serves a purpose in the number 6341.
**9.** Read the following numbers and write them in words:

1,265,409. 468,000,011,200,156. 100,000,000,001,100.

**10.** Write and read a number having twelve periods and name the periods.

## OPTIONAL ASSIGNMENTS

**1.** Read Larsen or other sources to learn the English method of setting off and reading numbers.
**2.** Consult the same sources and write the names of the first twenty-two periods in the Hindu-Arabic system; trace their derivation from the Latin.
**3.** Find the names used for the numbers from 1 to 10 in several languages.
**4.** Were any number systems ever organized on a base of 10 before the Hindu-Arabic system? Cite sources to support your answer.
**5.** Wheat says that for a generation teachers have been trying to teach what they call the "zero combinations." What is his contention regarding these combinations?"

## REFERENCES

Larsen, Harold D., *Arithmetic for Colleges*, Macmillan, New York, 1954, chap. 1.

Marks, John L., Purdy, C. Richard, and Kinney, Lucien B., *Teaching Arithmetic for Understanding*, McGraw-Hill, New York, 1958, chap. 4.

Taylor, E. H., and Mills, C. N., *Arithmetic for Teacher Training Classes*, Holt, Rinehart & Winston, New York, 4th ed., 1955, chaps. 1, 2.

Wheat, H. G., *How to Teach Arithmetic*, Row, Peterson, Evanston, 1951, chap. 13.

chapter 9

# Basic Concepts of Our Number System *(Continued)*

## 1. Concepts Basic to Meaning

As was pointed out in earlier chapters, teaching arithmetic for meaning is being stressed in modern education. Actually arithmetic can have no meaning for children, or for teachers either, unless they acquire step by step the necessary concepts on which to base their mathematical thinking. The present chapter continues the discussion of those concepts which was begun in Chapter 8.

## 2. Number and Counting as Basic Concepts

Before our science of counting was developed, man used tallies and other primitive means of enumerating and recording his possessions. A system of counting fulfills a basic human need. Counting to find the answer is a process in which everyone has confidence; for example, a teacher thought she had lost some money, but when she counted, she found it was all there. Many an argument is settled by counting—"I have more marbles than you have." "You have not!" "OK, let's count and see." Counting settles it.

We make almost constant use of counting, even at the adult level. Have I enough money for lunch? Have I enough apples to go around? and so on. Children in our environment acquire a sense of the value of counting, even in preschool experiences. An efficient teacher takes them from where they are when they enter school and helps them develop further counting ability. But more about that later; the immediate purpose is to discuss concepts for teachers, not for pupils.

Many children begin school with some ability in rote counting, and a few have acquired a measure of ability in rational counting. Although there is some difference of opinion, authorities are generally agreed that **rote counting** is a necessary first step because it involves only memorizing the number names in order. The ability to use these number names to identify specific objects as in counting four apples—1, 2, 3, 4—is a more advanced ability called **rational counting;** in reality this sets up a one-to-one correspondence, a basic mathematical concept.

In rational counting the last number named (four in the above example) is said to be the **number** of objects in the group; it is also said to be the **cardinal** of the group. Actually the word *four* is one kind of symbol for that number. Rational counting is a means of determining *how many* or *which one.* Counting to determine how many—1, 2, 3, 4 apples—is **cardinal counting;** here the number names are used in serial order to find the total number. **Ordinal counting** identifies the place of any number or object in a series—the *first* apple or the *fourth* apple. Sometimes the distinction between the ordinal and the cardinal use of a number is not this clear. For example, in an index, page 65 means the 65th page in the book; the quantity 65 is hardly involved in the concept. Rote counting is merely a memorized, parrotlike repetition of words with no meaning attached. Rational counting is meaningful and useful. **Enumeration** involves rational counting.

**Number** represents the magnitude or amount of things—a hundred miles (an extensive amount); an ounce of gold (an intensive amount). Since rational counting determines an amount of something in some kind of unit, it is allied to measuring. **Measuring** is the process of finding out how many times a given quantity contains another quantity of the same kind, called **a unit of measure.** Like counting, it answers the question, "How many?"

A number not applied to any entity is called an **abstract number,** such as *five.* A number that designates identified objects or entities is called a **concrete number**—for example, *six children* or *four days.* An abstract integral number may be said to answer the question "How many?" and a concrete number, "How many balls?" or "How many flags?" Guided experience should enable a pupil to move eventually from concrete number concepts, such as *one-half an apple,* to abstract number concepts, such as *one-sixteenth of one-half.*

A true concept of number involves experience with (1) objects, (2) the spoken language, (3) the written language, and (4) the written number symbol. Number also has other aspects. Taylor and Mills[1] list four: (1) *Series meaning* indicates relative position—*four* comes after *three* and before *five*. (2) *Collection meaning* is very distinct for small numbers—for example, *five fingers*—but is vague for large numbers—4,000,000 people. (3) *Ratio meaning* indicates a comparison developed by measuring—*ten* is *twice five*, *ten* is *ten times* as much as *one*, and *half* of *twenty*; it is closely related to multiplication and division and also to fractions. (4) *Relational meaning* is the meaning of a number compared with other numbers in a *more* or *less* relationship; it involves addition and subtraction—*seven* is *two more* than *five* and *eight less* than *fifteen*.

Pupils at the elementary-school level are usually given only two general classifications of numbers, **integers** and **fractions.** Integers are defined as whole numbers, and fractions as numbers that represent parts of a whole and are in either *common fraction* or *decimal fraction* form. More attention will be given to fraction concepts in later chapters.

### 3. Signed Numbers as a Specialized Basic Concept

Integers and fractions as defined above provide only a limited concept of number. Teachers need at least a glimpse into additional areas of mathematics; for example, they should have some knowledge of signed numbers. **Signed numbers** are integers that are preceded by a plus or minus sign and form a two-way sequence from zero; they are known as positive (+2) and negative (−2) numbers. It was not until the sixteenth century that mathematicians began to accept negative numbers as legitimate numerals and developed rules for their use. Signed numbers are of special importance in algebra. Teachers should be able to compute with them in ordinary processes, not only by knowing rules for combining signed numbers but by knowing *why* the rules work. When we have a simple problem such as 12 − 8, we are accustomed to visualize it as involving laying down 12 counters and removing 8 of them; 4 remain. But signed numbers require different procedures.

One rule is: "To subtract a number, change its sign and add." Thus if A's score is 8 points and B's is minus 4 (that is, B is four in the hole),

[1] E. H. Taylor and C. N. Mills, *Arithmetic for Teacher Training Classes*, Holt, Rinehart & Winston, New York, 4th ed., 1955, p. 12.

the difference between their scores is $+8 - (-4)$, difference being determined by subtraction. According to the rule, the $-4$ becomes $+4$ and is added to $+8$. The difference between their scores is 12 points; that is, A is 12 points ahead of B.

Another rule is: "To add two minus numbers, add their absolute values and give the result a *minus* sign." For example, two debts of \$5 each make a total debt of \$10: $(-\$5) + (-\$5) = -\$10$.

A third rule is: "To add a plus and a minus number, write their absolute values, subtract the smaller value from the larger, and give the result the sign of the larger value." If we have \$12 in our pocket and owe \$8, we have a total of \$4; that is, $(+\$12) + (-\$8) = +\$4$.

Algebraic rules govern multiplication and division with signed numbers. These processes should come later, for though the rules are simple (to multiply or divide two numbers, multiply or divide their absolute values; use a plus sign for the result if the two numbers have like signs, and a minus sign if they have unlike signs), the explanation cannot be shown so readily with arithmetic.

The plus and minus integers just referred to are only a part of a much larger concept of number. If we can conceive of this tally (/) and "one more" (//) as becoming a succession of tallies that go on and on, we will be setting up an unending *basic sequence* of numbers represented as 1, 2, 3, 4, 5, · · · . The numbers in such a sequence are called **natural numbers** and the following principle is fundamental: Every natural number in a basic sequence is the number of the set (or collection) of all the natural numbers up to and including it.

Natural numbers and integers are not identical. As indicated above, natural numbers are all positive. Integers include signed numbers and form a two-way sequence: $\cdots, -4, -3, -2, -1, 0, +1, +2, +3, +4, \cdots$. For any given relation involving positive integers such as $(+3) + (+1) = +4$, there is a like relation involving natural numbers, $3 + 1 = 4$, and vice versa. When we write a number like 5 we may think of it either as an integer or as a natural number.

## 4. Sets as a Basic Concept

Modern mathematicians are advocating more attention to the idea of *sets*, a term which may be interpreted as *collections*. According to Breuer: "The subject of set theory may be considered as originating with Georg Cantor about 1878, who attempted to organize concepts on collections of objects into a structure which could serve as a basis for a mathematical theory of the infinite."[2] This theory, Breuer says, has become the basis of structure in algebra, geometry, and analysis. However, some unresolved mathematical problems associated with the set theory still remain to be formulated satisfactorily, but we need not be concerned with them.

Duren[3] says that the idea of *set*, together with logic, has become almost the symbol of modern ideas in mathematics, that the introduction of sets into the curriculum has recently come to the forefront in the "ever-present border wars" between traditionalists and moderns, and that this may bring about a full-scale revolution in the teaching of mathematics. But, he goes on, both sides are still vague as to what makes up this elementary mathematics of sets whose introduction into the curriculum is proposed; moreover, some conservatists insist that sets are only a fad. However, he maintains that the set theory has both mathematical substance and cultural values, that it has caused a revolution in the language of all mathematics and in thoughts regarding the foundations of mathematics, and that it is involved in statistics, science, and engineering, as well as in mathematics.

To illustrate how the set theory has changed the language and the thinking about mathematics, Duren uses the following two examples: (1) What is meant by $x$? The old explanation that the variable $x$ is "a quantity whose value changes in a given discussion" is now regarded as nonsense, according to him. Rather one current view holds that $x$ is a symbol which stands for any one of a *set* of numbers. (2) What is a line? To quote Duren, "It is an insult to modern intelligence to say 'a line is the shortest distance between two points.' A line is a *set* of points with certain geometric properties."

Swain comments: "Our aim is to base the idea of number upon the idea of *set*. Two sets that *match* will have the same number associated with them."[4] He says that mathematicians prefer the simple term *set*, but may use a synonym, especially the word *collection*. The notions of sets and matching of sets are basic or primitive conceptions, part of everyone's experience from babyhood on. A label associated with a set

[2] J. Breuer, *Introduction to the Theory of Sets* (trans. by Howard F. Fehr), Prentice-Hall, Englewood Cliffs, 1958, p. v.

[3] W. L. Duren, Jr., "The Maneuvers in Set Thinking," *Mathematics Teacher*, May, 1958, p. 322.

[4] Robert L. Swain, *Understanding Arithmetic*, Holt, Rinehart & Winston, New York, 1957, chap. 7.

is called a *number*, and we regard a natural number (1, 2, 3 · · · ) as a kind of "size tag" that labels such a set. He points out that hands have always been convenient basic sets with which to compare other sets.

Objects making up a set are said to be in it or to belong to it, and they are called *elements* or *members* of the set. In describing a set we may list its elements (2 apples, 1 orange, and 3 bananas may constitute a *set* just as well as 6 apples would). *Subsets* may constitute elements of a set. (All the textbooks a teacher owns belong to a set; his arithmetic texts are a subset.) Two sets with a one-to-one correspondence are said to match or to be matching sets. (The five children in the Jones family and the birth certificates of the children in that family constitute matching sets with the same number, 5, attached to each set.) Breuer defines set as "a collection of definite distinct objects of our perception or of our thought, which are called elements of the set."[5]

Instead of thinking of numbers as the basic element of arithmetic, the advocates of the set theory would have us think of sets as basic to all mathematics, and numbers as labels attached to given sets, the same label being attached to all the sets that match the given set (1–1).

The number of an empty set is called zero. An empty set is a set that has no elements—e.g., the set of cookies in Mother's cookie jar after the boys have eaten all the cookies, or in Swain's words, "all the 200-year-old men in the United States."

A person has some concept of the set idea when he can conceive of the set of all men in the United States, with the red-haired men forming one subset, the men six feet seven inches tall another subset, and so on indefinitely.

After this brief discussion of sets, you may well ask, "What practical help does this give me in arithmetic?" The answer would probably be, "Very little specific help." However, even these few concepts associated with the idea of sets open the mind to new approaches in thinking of and dealing with numbers. Perhaps even this brief glimpse into the realm where the mysteries of mathematics unfold may cause some teacher, or even a pupil on the elementary level, to penetrate farther and farther into this realm of number and of number theory.

Swain follows his section on sets and numbers with this statement:

> The purpose of this section has been to give the student [college level] some inkling of the variety of ways in which set conceptions are applied in mathematics and in everyday language and thinking activity. In learning about

[5] J. Breuer, *op. cit.*, p. 4.

sets, he is acquiring a mental tool of wide utility, useful to him not only in connection with the understanding of numbers and with the teaching of arithmetic, but also in connection with the understanding and the use of language, of scientific method, and of common reasoning.[6]

As we saw earlier in this chapter, Duren paired the idea of set with logic as potential symbols of modern ideas in mathematics.

## 5. Generalization as a Basic Concept

What is called the *rationale* of arithmetic is likewise receiving much more attention than in past years. It involves knowing *why* we multiply in a given situation, not merely *how* to multiply, and *why* in multiplication the partial products are set in from the right, not merely the pattern for doing this.

Stressing the rationale of arithmetic means stressing the logical foundations of arithmetic which too often have been overlooked and for which rules without meaning to the pupil have been substituted. It also means acquiring generalization concepts following adequate manipulative experience, and establishing well-understood principles of working with numbers.

Some people maintain that all students of arithmetic should know the commutative, associative, and distributive laws of arithmetic by name. When pupils have had manipulative and computational experience with adding and multiplying numbers and have come to understand the recurring situations and results, knowing these laws will be almost incidental. The laws will take form because they have meaning for the pupil; they will not be meaningful simply because he has been asked to memorize them.

Since these laws are a good illustration of a type of generalization that should eventually be acquired, we shall see how they are developed. Addition and multiplication are operations which build up. Their work is to unite or increase, They *synthesize.* Subtraction and division are operations that split up and reduce. They *analyze*; i.e., they separate a numerical quantity into parts.

The terms of addition and multiplication (the addends of an addition process, and the factors in multiplication) are interchangeable. $3 + 4 + 2 = 9$; $3 + 2 + 4 = 9$; $4 + 2 + 3 = 9$.* *The order of the addends*

* Help pupils discover these generalizations.

[6] Robert L. Swain, *op. cit.*, p. 44.

*does not affect the sum.* In multiplication $3 \times 4 \times 2 = 24$; $4 \times 3 \times 2 = 24$; $2 \times 4 \times 3 = 24$. *The order of the factors does not affect the product.* Since these statements are true of all addition and all multiplication, they constitute accepted generalizations known as the **commutative law of addition** and the **commutative law of multiplication.** By similar manipulation we formulate the **associative law of addition:** to add 2, 3, and 4, for example, we may say that $2 + 3 = 5$, and $5 + 4 = 9$. Hence $2 + 3 + 4 = (2 + 3) + 4 = 9$. We could as well have said $4 + 3 = 7$ and $7 + 2 = 9$. Therefore, whether we "associate" the 3 with the 2 or with the 4 in adding 2, 3, and 4, the result is the same, 9.

Likewise in multiplying $2 \times 3 \times 4$, we may first associate the 3 with 2, or $2 \times 3 = 6$, and continue with $6 \times 4 = 24$, or we may associate the 3 with 4, or $3 \times 4 = 12$, and continue with $2 \times 12 = 24$. This illustrates the **associative law of multiplication,** which says that the factors of a product may be grouped in any way.

The **distributive law** links multiplication and addition and should really be called the distributive law of multiplication with respect to addition. In $2(3 + 4) = 6 + 8 = 14$ the multiplication of 2 is distributed over both 3 and 4, instead of over 7.

Operations involving synthesis (addition and multiplication) obey the commutative laws. These laws can never be applied to analytical operations (subtraction and division).

Such generalizations as the commutative laws, with all the long names involved, are suitable not for the slow pupil but for the teacher and for the enrichment program of the bright pupils. But there are initial concepts of a generalization type with which even primary children should become acquainted; for example, $\begin{array}{r} 2 \\ +3 \\ \hline \end{array}$ gives the same result as $\begin{array}{r} 3 \\ +2 \\ \hline \end{array}$, and $2 + 3$ the same as $3 + 2$.*

## 6. Number Bases as a Basic Concept

Among the understandings that teachers should acquire and that may be of interest to many bright pupils is the concept of number bases other than 10. In dealing with number systems certain principles apply, whether the base is 10 or some other number that is sometimes used, like 2, 6, or 12.

* Help primary children discover this.

The **base** of a number system is the number of units of a group that make one unit of the next higher group (or order). Or we may say that it is the number of units in the first collection. In our system on a base of 10, the digits 1, 2, 3, 4, 5, 6, 7, 8, and 9 indicate a counting series. But 10 is our first collection; therefore, on accumulating that many, we collect it into *one* 10 and begin using the same digits over again, placing the 1, which now means one 10, one place farther to the left and using a 0 to keep it there (10).

If the base were 12, eleven symbols would be needed to count the first collection (12)—perhaps 1, 2, 3, 4, 5, 6, 7, 8, 9, X, and E, for one-figure symbols would have to be devised for 10 and 11. On a base of 12, 10 would be equivalent to one 12 (that is, 1 of the first collection). And 11 would mean one 12 + one unit; therefore, $11 on a base-12 system would equal $13 on a base-10 system.

In order to use the valuable place-value principle, this base-12 system would increase by powers of 12 instead of by powers of 10 as our system does, and the names of our orders—tens, hundreds, etc.—would not apply to the values in this system.*

| $12^4$ | $12^3$ | $12^2$ | $12^1$ | $12^0$ |
|---|---|---|---|---|
| 20,736 | 1728 | 144 | 12 | 1 |
| 1 | 5 | 4 | 2 | 9 |

The number 15,429 on a base of 10 means:

| | | | |
|---|---|---|---|
| 1 ten thousand | = | 10,000 | ($10^4$) |
| 5 thousands ($5 \times 1000$) | = | 5,000 | ($10^3$) |
| 4 hundreds ($4 \times 100$) | = | 400 | ($10^2$) |
| 2 tens ($2 \times 10$) | = | 20 | ($10^1$) |
| 9 units ($9 \times 1$) | = | 9 | ($10^0$) |
| | | 15,429 | |

The number 15,429 on a base of 12 means:

| | | | |
|---|---|---|---|
| $1 \times 20{,}736$ | = | 20,736 | ($12^4$) |
| $5 \times 1728$ | = | 8640 | ($12^3$) |
| $4 \times 144$ | = | 576 | ($12^2$) |
| $2 \times 12$ | = | 24 | ($12^1$) |
| $9 \times 1$ | = | 9 | ($12^0$) |
| | | 29,985 | |

* Help pupils build up base-12 values the way they learned to build them up for a base of 10.

Since the zero power of any number is equal to 1 regardless of the size of the base, the first two-figure number is always written 10 if the system includes a zero. Thus $15,429 on a base of 12 represents the amount written as $29,985 on a base of 10.

Some advantages are claimed for using 12 as a base for our number system. We measure many articles by the dozen—though probably fewer than in the past, since bananas, oranges, and many other articles that formerly were sold by the dozen are now sold by the pound. Likewise, pencils and many other small articles are sold by the gross (12 × 12). One of the chief arguments advanced for this base is that 12 has more factors than 10 for use in reductions. The Duodecimal Society of America has for some time been advocating the adopting of a base of 12 for our number system.

The binary system, with a base of 2, is impractical for use in general computations because of the length of written numbers; e.g., 89 on a base of 10 would be written 1,011,001 in order to have the same value on a base of 2.) With a base of 2, only one digit besides zero would be used, and it would be 1, for as soon as the first collection (2) was counted, it would become 1 of the collection and written one place farther to the left—that is, 10—meaning one 2 and 0 units. If place value is used, these numbers will increase toward the left in powers of 2:*

| $2^4$ | $2^3$ | $2^2$ | $2^1$ | $2^0$ |
|---|---|---|---|---|
| 16 | 8 | 4 | 2 | 1 |
| 1 | 0 | 1 | 0 | 1 |

Again new names for the orders would have to be devised, for tens, hundreds, thousands, and so on, would not apply to the values. With a base of 2, the number 10,101 would be equivalent to 21 only in a base-10 system:

$$\begin{array}{lcr} 1 \times 16 & = & 16 \\ 0 \times 8 & = & 0 \\ 1 \times 4 & = & 4 \\ 0 \times 2 & = & 0 \\ 1 \times 1 & = & 1 \\ \hline & & 21 \end{array}$$

In spite of the great length of high-value numbers on a base-2 system, the binary system has made a great impact today because it makes

* Have pupils build up base-2 values.

possible modern digital computing by machines. These machines count on electrical relays "off" and "on" and therefore only two digits are needed.

It seems obvious that modern man should have some comprehension of, or at least a realization of, the existence of number systems based on numbers other than 10. A teacher who adequately comprehends the broader areas of arithmetic and is interested in them himself is in an extremely favorable position to arouse the interest of his pupils.

## COMPETENCE CHECK

**1.** In speaking of number symbols can the words "figures" and "numerals" be used interchangeably?
**2.** How does the number of the set of all students in tax-supported colleges in the United States compare with the set of all instructors in those colleges?
**3.** Name five subsets of all the students in tax-supported colleges in this country.
**4.** What number would be used to label the set of the ears of six people?
**5.** Name something that would be a matching set for those ears.
**6.** Draw a line 6 inches long and scale it from $-3$ to $+3$.
**7.** On the line locate approximately $-2.75$; $+\frac{4}{5}$; $-1\frac{1}{2}$; $+2.99$.
**8.** How far is it in inches from 2.75 to $+2.99$ on your line? From $-2.75$ to 0? From $-1\frac{1}{2}$ to $+\frac{4}{5}$? From $-2.75$ to $-1\frac{1}{2}$?
**9.** How might signed numbers be used in relation to a football game? A family budget? Topography? An automobile battery?
**10.** What will 10 mean if it is known to be on the decimal number system? On the duodecimal system? On the binary system? On a system with a base of 8?
**11.** Using the number 9 explain its series meaning; its collection meaning; its ratio meaning; its relational meaning.
**12.** A concept of number involves separating a group into distinct things (such as 3 apples), and then thinking the 3 separates into a 3 group (a whole). Explain this statement.
**13.** How are analysis and synthesis involved in the thought processes used in the preceding question?
**14.** Define and illustrate each of the following:

1. Rote counting
2. Rational counting
3. Cardinal use of a number
4. Ordinal use of a number
5. Enumeration
6. Abstract number

7. Concrete number
8. Measuring
9. Integer
10. Common fraction
11. Decimal fraction
12. Signed numbers
13. Sets
14. Matching sets
15. Empty sets
16. Subsets
17. Rationale
18. Generalizations
19. A base of 10
20. Binary number system
21. Duodecimal number system
22. Successive powers of 10

**15.** Which of the four fundamental processes analyze and which synthesize? Explain.

## OPTIONAL ASSIGNMENTS

**1.** What would each of the following be on the duodecimal scale: 20; 42; 100?
**2.** How many beads should be on the lines of an abacus for that system?
**3.** Convert the following binary numbers to their equivalent values on a base of 10: 11; 101; 1111.
**4.** Could 43 represent an even number in some scale? Could 12 represent an odd number in any scale?
**5.** Give a special report on numerology.
**6.** Explain the five commutative laws of arithmetic and give illustrations of them.
**7.** To which of the four fundamental processes do these laws apply?
**8.** Express each of the following in terms of powers of 10 in a base-10 system: 169; 7241; 908; 25,000.

## REFERENCES

Calandra, Alexander, "Teaching Signed Numbers in Grade 8," *Arithmetic Teacher*, November, 1958, pp. 259–260.
Lerner, Norbert, and Sobel, Max A., "'Sets' and Elementary School Mathematics," *Arithmetic Teacher*, November, 1958, pp. 239–246.

chapter 10

# First Steps in Arithmetic Learning

## I. Variance in Theory of Beginning Arithmetic Instruction

There is no universally accepted program of beginning arithmetic instruction in our elementary schools. In some schools it is begun in kindergarten; in others, formal arithmetic teaching is deferred to the second or third grade, and in some cases even later. For all these practices there is some supporting experimental evidence. Brueckner and Grossnickle's[1] comprehensive summary of the place of arithmetic in the primary grades indicates that this is a question on which there has never been general agreement in thought or practice. According to reported surveys, the chief reason for deferring arithmetic instruction is a wish to lighten the load for beginning pupils. This, its proponents say, is desirable because (1) the child thus has more time for reading, and (2) the arithmetic as taught is too difficult for beginning pupils, as evidenced by the fact that more children repeated grades after the second because of inability to do arithmetic than for any other reason—a situation which apparently was not improved by giving additional time to arithmetic in the daily schedule.

Influential in the movement to defer arithmetic was the report of the Committee of Seven.[2] As a result of its studies, the committee found that easy addition and subtraction facts *could* be learned at the mental ages of 6 to 7 years and the more difficult facts at the mental ages of 7

[1] L. J. Brueckner and Foster E. Grossnickle, *How to Make Arithmetic Meaningful*, Holt, Rinehart & Winston, New York, 1947, chap. 5.

[2] C. W. Washburne, "The Work of the Committee of Seven on Grade Placement in Arithmetic," National Society for the Study of Education, *Thirty-Eighth Yearbook, Part I*, 1939.

to 8 years; however, it recommended that the teaching of these combinations be delayed until the mental ages of 8 to 9 years in the interest of better learning. Such reasons for deferment were valid when the generally accepted objectives for beginning work in arithmetic were to acquaint children with the basic addition and subtraction facts, and by continued drill attempt to make the responses automatic.

From this traditional drill theory to the incidental theory is a long distance. But some of the so-called progressive group would make the number program entirely, or almost entirely, incidental, giving numbers attention only as they occur in connection with other experiences in the classroom.

A point of view that is widely accepted at the present time holds that children enter school with some already established number concepts which should be recognized and developed further. Moreover, some studies have shown that a primary child has an inherent interest in numbers when an informal situation encourages this interest. These premises are accepted by the advocates of a planned, systematic, and sequentially developed program of arithmetic, involving both its social applications and the mathematical meaning of number. It is to such a theory that this book subscribes.

## 2. Number Ability on Entering School

A significant number of research studies have shown that when children enter school they have varying degrees of number comprehension. A typical study by Brownell[3] is summarized by Brueckner and Grossnickle as follows: "He found that most pupils entering the first grade can do rote counting through at least 20, identify numbers of objects through at least 10, and make comparisons of amounts through 7. They are able to answer problems based on number combinations having sums up to 10. These results show conclusively that most pupils enter the first grade with a considerable variety of number concepts. But there are also many who have little knowledge of number."[4]

The teacher's problem thus becomes one of holding the interest of all the children and providing diversified experiences to avoid boring the more advanced pupils and at the same time keep the others from being frustrated.

[3] W. A. Brownell, *Arithmetic in Grades I and II*, Duke Univ. Press, Durham, 1941.
[4] L. J. Brueckner and Foster E. Grossnickle, *op. cit.*, p. 159.

### 3. Arithmetic Readiness

Readiness, as applied to the child's ability to undertake new subject-matter learning, is a frequently used but commonly misinterpreted term. To say that a child is ready for first-grade arithmetic is a very broad and general statement, but hardly verifiable. Much depends upon the type of material that is presented and the type of procedures used. Some of the indefiniteness as to readiness might be avoided if, in trying to determine what number experiences to give a child and when to give them, teachers proceeded in terms of the child's background for specific new learnings. Accomplishing this effectively, however, involves individual work with pupils, for readiness is an individual matter and should deal with specific areas.

Furthermore, readiness involves not only preparedness but also willingness, and willingness is enhanced by success. Whether the child is so prepared that he can succeed in a step in arithmetic learning is of paramount importance for the teacher.

A number of commercial arithmetic readiness tests are available. However, teachers can construct their own with little difficulty or devise an inventory check sheet with such items as:

1. Can count by rote to ______ .
2. Can do rational counting to ______ .
3. Names number symbols to ______ .
4. Writes number symbols to ______ .
5. Readily recognizes groups to ______ .
6. Can tell time on the hour ______ .
   on the half-hour ______ .
   at lesser intervals ______ .
7. Recognizes and names coins______ ______ ______ ______ .
8. Recognizes square ______ ; circle ______ .
9. Recognizes and names $\frac{1}{2}$ an object.
10. Can construct groups to ______ .

In addition, the teacher may recognize evidences of number precocity in certain children and of extreme immaturity in the number comprehension of others, and record this information in his anecdotal records for individual attention later.

Since a teaching program must take into consideration the widely differing abilities, needs, and interests of beginning pupils, the alert teacher will have ready some enrichment materials for the very bright, and some special group and individual work for the slow.

## 4. Concepts of Sequential Development

Sequential development is so important in arithmetic learning that it is essential that children acquire the preliminary concepts upon which later ones are based. A child needs to see each new idea as a clear and orderly extension of what he already knows and understands. Therefore, systematic number instruction has a definite purpose when arithmetic is first taught. However, there is much overlapping in the development of these concepts. For example, a child does not complete his learning about counting before he learns some computational processes. Earlier concepts are expanded and extended beside and in relation to additional concepts developed later.

As was stated earlier, almost every child enters first grade with some ability to do rote counting—perhaps to 10, perhaps considerably farther. Although there has been some difference of opinion as to the value of rote counting as a prerequisite to rational counting, it seems logical to assume that a child who has learned by rote the names of the numbers in the proper order can more readily accomplish the number identification of objects (a one-to-one correspondence) because he can concentrate his thinking largely on the matching process, since the names come more or less automatically. Thus he realizes he has use for the number names he learned previously.

The present-day teaching of arithmetic places much emphasis on the generalization that all four of the fundamental processes are basically processes of regrouping, and all are actually extensions of counting. To help children see these relationships, frequent experiences in counting should be provided to prove the results obtained by the various processes. Thus the child realizes that the fundamental processes are really timesavers—short cuts—that he can use instead of counting.

## 5. Meaning in Mathematical Aspects of Arithmetic

Though a child entering school may have some ability to count or even be able to do some rational counting, he rarely has much understanding of number meanings and relationships. The teacher must see that he acquires this, for it is basic to understanding arithmetic.

Arithmetic symbols, like language symbols, are a means of communication. As with language symbols, unless a pupil has a meaningful concept for the number the symbol stands for, the symbol can have no meaning for him. For example, unless he has some concept for the spoken word "elephant," he can have no understanding of what is represented by the printed or written symbol "elephant." Likewise, unless the spoken word "seven" brings to mind the concept of a number that is more than six and less than eight, and that can be taken apart into four and three, five and two, and so on, seven has no meaning for him and he is not ready to use the symbol 7 in any combination or process. These concepts we may refer to as the *language* of arithmetic; it is quite apart from the *processes* of arithmetic, but is prerequisite to the process concepts.

Thus one of the teacher's reponsibilities is to see that each pupil acquires meaning for the number he so glibly recites in counting. This he can do by constantly emphasizing the number aspects of the child's firsthand experiences. Hickerson calls this procedure the "experience-language approach to numbers."[5]

Pupils progress from *things* to *symbols.* Symbols should be used only after meanings and understandings are established. At first the pupil feels and sees and thinks with sticks or checkers that he can group or separate. Eventually he discovers that symbols facilitate his thinking and enable him to record the results; then he is ready to use them.

Since the numbers we use are part of a number system, beginning pupils should be helped to become acquainted with this system. A basic need here is to acquire meanings for the numbers from 1 to 9. Then when 10 is needed, the teacher can show that for convenience the 10 sticks are tied into a bunch and called a *ten*; this leads gradually into place value and helps pupils see the great advantage of working with 4 tens and 2 ones rather than with 42 loose sticks. Hickerson, however, opposes teaching the science of numbers at this level: "A systematic study of arithmetic as a number system should be made . . . in the secondary school and college, not in the elementary school."[6]

Many kinds of charts are used to show the orderly and systematic arrangement for writing numbers up to and beyond 100; the accompanying two are illustrative. A teacher must decide what pattern to use for the hundred square, and use it consistently.

[5] J. Allen Hickerson, *Guiding Children's Arithmetic Experiences*, Prentice-Hall, New York, 1952.

[6] *Ibid.*, pp. 36–37

| | | | | | | | | | |
|---|---|---|---|---|---|---|---|---|---|
| | 1 | 2 | 3 | 4 | 5 | 6 | 7 | 8 | 9 |
| 10 | 11 | 12 | 13 | 14 | 15 | 16 | 17 | 18 | 19 |
| 20 | 21 | 22 | 23 | 24 | 25 | 26 | 27 | 28 | 29 |
| 30 | 31 | 32 | 33 | 34 | 35 | 36 | 37 | 38 | 39 |
| 40 | 41 | 42 | 43 | 44 | 45 | 46 | 47 | 48 | 49 |
| 50 | 51 | 52 | 53 | 54 | 55 | 56 | 57 | 58 | 59 |
| 60 | 61 | 62 | 63 | 64 | 65 | 66 | 67 | 68 | 69 |
| 70 | 71 | 72 | 73 | 74 | 75 | 76 | 77 | 78 | 79 |
| 80 | 81 | 82 | 83 | 84 | 85 | 86 | 87 | 88 | 89 |
| 90 | 91 | 92 | 93 | 94 | 95 | 96 | 97 | 98 | 99 |
| 100 | | | | | | | | | |

| | | | | | | | | | |
|---|---|---|---|---|---|---|---|---|---|
| 1 | 11 | 21 | 31 | 41 | 51 | 61 | 71 | 81 | 91 |
| 2 | 12 | 22 | 32 | 42 | 52 | 62 | 72 | 82 | 92 |
| 3 | 13 | 23 | 33 | 43 | 53 | 63 | 73 | 83 | 93 |
| 4 | 14 | 24 | 34 | 44 | 54 | 64 | 74 | 84 | 94 |
| 5 | 15 | 25 | 35 | 45 | 55 | 65 | 75 | 85 | 95 |
| 6 | 16 | 26 | 36 | 46 | 56 | 66 | 76 | 86 | 96 |
| 7 | 17 | 27 | 37 | 47 | 57 | 67 | 77 | 87 | 97 |
| 8 | 18 | 28 | 38 | 48 | 58 | 68 | 78 | 88 | 98 |
| 9 | 19 | 29 | 39 | 49 | 59 | 69 | 79 | 89 | 99 |
| 10 | 20 | 30 | 40 | 50 | 60 | 70 | 80 | 90 | 100 |

Most of the new elementary-arithmetic textbooks also use the number line. This is merely a scale with numbered intervals as in the following:

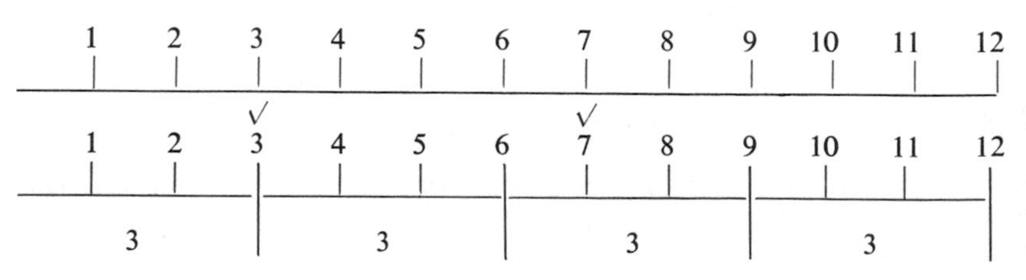

The first line shows how a number line can be used in addition. In adding 3 and 4, the pupil counts 3 spaces and then 4 spaces; thus he knows that 7 is the right answer for 3 and 4 more. The second line shows the use of a number line in multiplication. In multiplying 4 and 3, the pupil counts off 3 spaces and marks them, and then 3 more, and so on, until he has fours 3's; thus he sees that the answer for four 3's is 12. Number lines can also be used to check answers to combinations that are written from memory without computing. There are innumerable possibilities for their use in subtraction, division, fractional equivalents, and decimals, and they can be adapted to every grade level.[7]

## 6. Four Stages of the Development of Group Concepts

A child achieves understanding of the number processes gradually, and an efficient teacher helps him to achieve that understanding by stages—usually the following four: (1) the *concrete*, or objective stage; (2) the *pictorial*, or picture stage; (3) the *semiconcrete*, or representative-marks stage; and (4) the *abstract*, or symbolic stage. Certain materials are associated with these four stages. For the concrete stage real objects are used—manipulative materials that children can feel, touch, handle, and move, be they classroom chairs, counter sticks, checkers, or even boys and girls. Pictorial aids are commonly provided by textbooks and workbooks—a picture of six birds, four balls, and so on. Semiconcrete aids are frequently devised by the teacher—five circles to represent five apples or five pennies.

The aids in these three consecutive stages require successively greater use of the imagination and less reliance on physical manipulation. The abstract or symbolic stage requires the child to think through the manipulative processes purely by using his imagination. This is the stage that too often a child fails to utilize; instead he tries to manipulate *figures* in a sort of trial-and-error procedure, a frequent cause of mathematical inefficiency. Thinking through manipulative processes involves interpreting mathematical symbols in place of descriptive words associated with real objects.

At the concrete stage a child might be asked to answer the following question (four chairs having been placed in one group and four chairs

[7] Commercially made number lines are available; see *Arithmetic Teacher*, October, 1958, p. 192.

in another group): "There are four chairs in this group and four chairs in this other group; when we put them all together, how many chairs are there in the big group?" He puts the chairs together and if necessary touches each one as he counts them.

At the pictorial stage, a page of his workbook might have a picture of four brown chairs and four green chairs; then the question might be: "If the green chairs are placed in the square with the brown chairs, how many chairs will there be inside the square?" In this case no manipulation is possible, but in his imagination he *thinks* the four green chairs into the square with the brown ones, and if necessary he can point to each of the chairs as he counts them.

At the semiconcrete stage there would be no real chairs and no pictures of chairs. But if a pupil hesitates, when asked the question: "How many chairs are four chairs and four more chairs?" the teacher may indicate the number by putting four $x$'s and four more $x$'s on the chalkboard to enable the child to visualize the entire group and if necessary count to obtain the answer.

A child at the abstract stage has only "4 chairs + 4 chairs = ______ chairs." From this he must interpret the value of the numerical symbols and the process indicated by "+." There is also the strange new symbol "=" for which he must acquire meaning. Teachers who use beginning number books must realize that these materials are only for pupils who have reached the abstract stage.

Grouping is basic to number processes. Before a child can be expected to put groups together and take them apart, he must have become acquainted with groups to the extent that he readily recognizes a collection of marks or objects as associated with the appropriate number symbols. He progresses by counting objects in groups until he can recognize a "set" of three or four or six, and so on, without counting by ones to get their cardinal. He must learn not only to recognize and identify such groups but also to form groups—to set out four blocks or put six chairs in a row, and form other such groups. Next somewhat larger numbers are arranged as combinations of smaller groups. It is much easier to recognize the number in this group: || || || ||, than the same number in this group: ||||||||.

The human eye is capable of what is called accommodation. This ability enables it to change focus readily from the page of a book, for example, to a doorway through which someone is coming, and obtain a clear image of that person. Some comparable adjustment process is needed to enable a child to use analysis and synthesis almost simultaneously when he sees such a group as

x x
x
x x

. He must see the group as a whole identified as a 5 group (synthesis), and at the same time he must learn to recognize it as composed of 5 separate entities (analysis), or as 4 and 1 more, or 2 and 2 and 1, and so on, as he looks at it at different "focuses." When he reaches this stage in comprehending groups, he is ready to deal with combinations, and shortly thereafter he should become acquainted with equations.

### 7. Acquiring the Equation Concept

An alert primary child can be shown that an equation is like a teeter board—it has to be in balance. Soon he will rise to the challenge of the new word (used quite incidentally) and say, "See, I made an equation." In $2 + 3 = 5$, as in all equations, the "=" is the fulcrum. The equation will not be in balance if the two sides are not equal. Two small children (or two small groups of checkers) can be balanced by having one child (or checker) that is as big as both children (or groups of checkers) on the other side.

This procedure should begin with concrete materials—a balance, for example, with equations arranged with checkers or any objects that are of equal weight; the equations should be recorded in figures. Some equations can be written and then proved to be equal by means of balanced weights. Such manipulations take the drudgery out of practice, and at the same time fix in the child's mind the principle on which equations are based. Commercial toys that are available serve this purpose very well.

With guidance and practice, children can learn to find the missing number in such an equation as $4 + ? = 6$. Then they apply the equation to subtraction; for example, $5 - ? = 3$. With 5 on one side and 3 on the other, how many must be taken from the heavy side to balance, or how many added to 3 to balance 5? Primary children for whom combinations have reality and meaning through such experiences will not find the next step difficult; they will be able to *think* the manipulative operations and use symbols and equations with meaning and understanding.

When larger numbers are involved, various materials are desirable.

Ten wires with 10 beads each, perhaps with the 5's in different colors, help children compute 20 + 4 = ? and 15 − 4 = ? and so on. Also useful are 100 spools or 100 clothespins on a string, with every fifth one colored. The 100 counting board, the tens square, and the 100-dot chart are likewise helpful. All these types of concrete aids enable a child to visualize a process as he records it.

## 8. Comprehending the Relationship of the Four Processes

In arithmetic teaching some years ago a child learned addition combinations first, then subtraction, then multiplication, then division. As a result, he thought of the four fundamental processes as four unrelated areas of arithmetic. But with modern theories of teaching arithmetic emphasizing relationship and system in numbers, the child is introduced very early to all four processes, though the symbols for multiplication and division are not used at that time. Hence a first-grade child may see xx xx and say it is two and two, or he may quite as easily see that it is 2 twos. Then he will learn that xx xx xx may be two and two and two, or be called, more quickly, 3 twos.

With these adding and multiplying procedures (though it is not yet time to use the word multiplying), the child has been putting groups together. Then he sees that by manipulating the same objects he can take the groups apart. He put two and two together to make four; now he removes xx from xxxx and has xx left. When he put xx and xx and xx together, he had xxxxxx and he saw that he had made six from 3 twos. Now he has xxxxxx and by setting them off by twos he sees again that there are 3 twos in six. All of this is valuable foundation work.

These manipulations should be done with real objects in real-life situations; for example, "We have four boys and six girls in our class; how many books do we need?" And by no means should the teacher tell all the number stories. Children should learn to make up number stories to fit the combinations they are ready to work with. This creative phase of arithmetic is a long-neglected area for pupils. By creating number situations themselves, children will learn *when* to add and *why* they add, as well as *how* to add—accomplishments far from well attained in arithmetic teaching in the past, even in higher grades. A thorough understanding of a number situation is requisite to, and perhaps more important than, the number process itself. There is little doubt that some experience in creating and stating number situations makes more understandable the situations set up by others.

### 9. Social Aspects of Arithmetic

The preceding section has set forth some mathematical aspects of arithmetic with which the beginner should become acquainted, but all these concepts can and should be given a social setting and tied in with the child's everyday experiences. To this end a teacher will provide many incidental uses of numbers: How many books are needed? On what page is our story (the pupils having found it in the table of contents)? How many children in each row are taking milk today? How many in all? How many are absent today? What day of the week and month is it? For this game we need four children in each group; Lois may choose four for her group. The teacher may make a chart containing number information on which the numbers can be changed from day to day.

> There are 26 children in our room.
> There are 50 stars in our flag.
> There are 6 windows in our room.
> Miss Davis ordered 20 cartons of milk today.

Such a chart becomes an experience reading chart; other statements can be added from time to time.

In the "Show and Tell" time the teacher should commend children who use numbers in their reports and should call attention to their use. If Tommy says, "My grandma came to visit us; she can stay two weeks." The other pupils may count the time on the calendar and discuss it. The teacher might say, "Let's mark this day on our calendar and see if it is the day Tommy's grandma leaves, and whether we are right." Or when a child reports, "Our cat has some kittens; there are four, and only one of them is white; all the rest are gray," This provides opportunity for combination practice with 4 and 1 and 5, using semiconcrete materials and then abstract symbols.

Since grouping things—putting them together and taking them apart—always entails action, symbols for the four processes should be thought of as signs that tell what action is indicated; for example, "+" tells us to put two or more groups together. For this reason $2 + 2 + 2$ should be introduced before $\begin{array}{r}2\\2\\+2\\\hline\end{array}$, and $5 - 2$ before $\begin{array}{r}5\\-2\\\hline\end{array}$.

However, children should early be given number experience in which they learn to analyze the situation and decide what action is called for. If they find that 2 pupils are absent in the first row, 1 in the second, and 1 in the fourth, they must put all these together $(2 + 1 + 1)$ to find how many in the class are absent. Later they learn that when putting several groups of the same size together, instead of $2 + 2 + 2$ they can say three 2's, and eventually $3 \times 2$.

Since computing with any of the four processes involves action, some form of manipulation, or even dramatization, is a real learning experience. Drawing pictures aids in identifying and forming groups, but is of doubtful value in illustrating the processes. "Five birds were sitting on a fence; two flew away. Make a picture to tell the story," is not a good assignment. Obviously it would take more than one picture to tell that story. Children should not be encouraged to formulate half-truths. Neither should they be asked to delineate something which will take them several minutes but which actually is worth only one minute as far as number value is concerned.

Schatz[8] has reported on a recent study that tested "the hypothesis that computation with numerals should wait until analogous operations with physical counterparts had been thoroughly understood and mastered and, even then, not until the symbol as a means of recording numbers had been used extensively." She says, "To the child who had developed some sensitivity about numbers and number relationships, the elementary classroom was full of things that suggested groupings and natural divisions and invited estimation, measurement, and computation." The calendar, the clock, the thermometer, and many other articles of regular classroom equipment have mathematical potential. One of the conclusions of her report is that "a gradual introduction to symbolism tends to avoid many of the complications that occur when children are confused by too much symbolism and too little attention to meanings."

The social aspects of arithmetic include the use of stories and songs in which numbers are an important element. These should not be overlooked. Representative of them are the songs, "Five Little Chickadees" and "The Twelve Days of Christmas," and the rhyme, "One, Two, Buckle My Shoe." Such material is plentiful. Much of it will be found in kindergarten and primary books of music and poetry. There

[8] Esther Schatz, "Arithmetic," *Childhood Education,* November, 1957, pp. 127 ff.

are also a number of good counting story books—for example, Karla Kuskin's *James and the Rain* (Harper, 1957) and John Langstaff's *Over in the Meadow* (Harcourt, Brace & World, 1957).

An efficient primary teacher can provide many number experiences of a social nature for his pupils during the entire school day, and gradually include more and more of the mathematical aspects of their social situations.

## 10. Opportunities for Discovery

Most children like to figure things out for themselves and to feel independent, provided the "problem" is within their ability and understanding so that success is possible.

Both Spitzer and Eads advocate the discovery method, in which children are confronted with a new problem situation and try to figure out the solution. "Bill has 6 marbles and Craig has 5 more than Bill; how many marbles has Craig?" If given this problem at a suitable stage in their learning, the combination $6 + 5$ being new to them, various procedures will be used by the different children to arrive at the solution. One may say, "Well, if Craig had 6 more than Bill, he'd have 12, but he's 1 short of that, so he has 11." Another might say, "6 and 3 are 9, and then 2 more make 11." In each case the pupil apparently has an understanding of number relationships. All correct solutions will be accepted, but eventually the less efficient ones will be discarded.

According to Eads,[9] more time should be allotted in arithmetic for children to make discoveries and express their thinking. She maintains that "listening to children think" is an essential part of teaching meaningful arithmetic, but that teachers talk rather than listen, and children use their energies not in thinking but in listening for clues to the set answer the teacher wants—often the only one he will accept—which results in verbalism.

Many others, among them Brownell,[10] maintain that effective instruction is contingent upon understanding the mental processes of the pupils.

[9] Laura K. Eads, "Let's Think About Arithmetic," *Grade Teacher*, March, 1958, p. 55.

[10] W. A. Brownell, "Development of Children's Number Ideas," reported by C. W. Hunnicutt and William J. Iverson, *Research in the Three R's*, Harper, New York, 1958, pp. 376–379.

## COMPETENCE CHECK

1. What is meant by the incidental method of teaching arithmetic? List some arguments for and against it.
2. Define sequential development of arithmetic. Give illustrations.
3. What is a generalization?
4. What is meant by the mathematical aspects of arithmetic?
5. To what extent do you agree or disagree with the present author regarding the mathematical aspects that beginning pupils can comprehend? Cite illustrations.
6. Compare arithmetic with the language arts as far as acquiring concepts for abstract symbols is concerned. (Hickerson is helpful here.)
7. Construct an aid for counting and computing, either one of those suggested or some other type, and explain its use and value.
8. Explain the terms *analysis* and *synthesis* as they pertain to a number group at the primary level.
9. Devise a manipulative procedure to help acquaint the child with equations.
10. In introducing equations which do you think is the most readily understood—a question mark (?), a blank (_), or the letter n (for number to be found)?

$$4 + ? = 9$$
$$4 + \_ = 9$$
$$4 + n = 9$$

    Give reasons for your answer.
11. Devise several arithmetic situations in whose solutions drawings would be helpful.

## OPTIONAL ASSIGNMENTS

1. Prepare a bibliography of stories, rhymes, and songs that would be suitable for correlation with primary number work.
2. Construct a fairly complete inventory check sheet for first-grade arithmetic based on any course of study you choose.
3. Does this check sheet take into account the range of ability usually found among first-grade children? Justify your answer.

## REFERENCES


Eads, Laura K., "Teaching Mathematics in Grade One," *Grade Teacher*, November, 1958, p. 52.

Eads, Laura K., "Teaching Mathematics in the Kindergarten," *Grade Teacher*, October, 1958, p. 55.

Grossnickle, Foster E., "Exploratory Materials for Teaching Arithmetic," *Education*, January, 1959, pp. 267–271.

Swenson, Esther J., "Arithmetic for Preschool and Primary-Grade Children," National Society for the Study of Education, *Fiftieth Yearbook*, *Part II*, 1951, pp. 53–75.

chapter 11

# Addition and Its Applications

## 1. Need for Proficiency in Daily Uses of Arithmetic

Proficiency as the term is used here does not mean rapid-fire computation of a long list of figures. Rather it means the ability to add a few figures with reasonable speed and near 100 per cent accuracy, with confidence that the result is correct.

It is true that machines ranging from very simple to highly complex do the computing in banking and accounting offices, in supermarkets, and even in modern public school offices, but there are innumerable small computations for which machines are neither available nor feasible. Did the waitress add my dinner check correctly? Did my bank deposit slip show the correct total? Is the balance in my checkbook correct? Is the number of miles I estimated with the road map correct? Such questions arise almost daily. The ability to compute accurately and eventually become proficient is an important goal in arithmetic, and its foundations should be laid in the primary grades.

## 2. Need for Understanding in the Primary Grades

As was pointed out in the preceding chapter, giving meaning to numbers and to the mathematical aspects of arithmetic is part of the foundation work in arithmetic. Some procedures for doing this in the primary grades have already been indicated. Drill in addition should follow understanding of groups and the putting together and taking apart of those groups. The process of addition is essentially the rearranging of groups, usually for simplification; for example, in thinking and saying and writing, "I have 23 pupils" is preferable to "I have 16 and 3 and 4 pupils." Effective practice provides the needed fixations for accuracy and results in gradually increasing speed. As we saw in Chapter 10, in his early number experiences a child puts groups (in concrete form) together and determines the total value by counting. He soon learns that he saves time if he memorizes the combinations for addition.

### 3. Need for Mastery of Facts

The most frequent cause of errors in addition, as well as lack of speed, is failure to master the addition facts. If number relationships are understood and the ability to use figures and symbols without relying on manipulative devices is attained, speed should come with practice, particularly on the third- and fourth-grade levels. The form in which algorisms for combinations involving addition facts are presented, whether horizontal ($6 + 7 = ?$) or vertical $\left(\begin{array}{r} 6 \\ +7 \\ \hline \end{array}\right)$ should not affect the speed or accuracy at this stage; the fact is the same.

### 4. Need for Terminology

**Addition** may be defined as the process of determining, without counting, a single number equal in value to the combined value of two or more other numbers. The words *add* and *addition* are derived from the Latin verb *addere*, meaning "to give to." Thus in adding 2 and 4 we give 4 to 2, or vice versa. **Addends** is the term used for the numbers added, and **sum** for the number resulting from the adding process.

The **primary addition combinations,** often referred to as **number facts,** are all the combinations of single-digit numbers; e.g., $4 + 5 = 9$. When the *reverse* of every combination ($5 + 4 = 9$, as well as $4 + 5 = 9$) and all the zero combinations ($1 + 0 = 1$, etc.) are included, there are 100 addition facts (and a corresponding number of subtraction facts).

A **decade combination** involves the addition of a one-digit number and a two-digit number; e.g., $21 + 6 = 27$. **Adding by endings** is a process in which a primary combination is used as the right-hand figure and the correct decade number is attached; e.g., $\begin{array}{r} 24 \\ +5 \\ \hline \end{array}$ $\begin{array}{r} 34 \\ +5 \\ \hline \end{array}$ $\begin{array}{r} 54. \\ +5 \\ \hline \end{array}$ However, when the sum of the primary combinations in the units column is larger than 9 (thus involving a two-digit number) the process is called **higher**

**decade addition** and involves bridging; e.g., $\begin{array}{r} 25 \\ +8 \\ \hline \end{array}$ puts the sum in the decade of the thirties instead of the twenties.

**Column addition without carrying** is such a computation as $\begin{array}{r} 4 \\ 3 \\ +2 \\ \hline \end{array}$ or $\begin{array}{r} 216 \\ +123 \\ \hline \end{array}$; the total of no column is more than a one-digit figure. **Column addition with carrying** is preferably called **column addition with reduction.** Carrying, a long-used term, is a familiar process that is too often done in routine fashion with no meaning attached. For example, in $\begin{array}{r} 46 \\ +29 \\ \hline \end{array}$ the pupil says, "6 and 9 are 15; put down the 5 and carry the 1; 4 and 1 are 5 and 2 are 7." The term reduction is used in many cases in arithmetic; it always indicates a change in form but not in value. With the reduction concept in mind, we would state $\begin{array}{r} 46 \\ +29 \\ \hline \end{array}$ thus: "6 units and 9 units are 15 units. That is really 1 ten and 5 units, so we write the 5 units in the units place in the answer and the 1 ten in the tens column to add with the 4 tens and 2 tens, making the answer 75." Here we have reduced 15 units to 1 ten and 5 units for convenience, instead of merely carrying 1.

## 5. Need to Understand Fundamental Generalizations

"The modern method of addition is a complex process, and children must spend some years in mastering the various skills which it demands."[1] Part of the complex process of becoming proficient in addition involves *understanding* a few fundamental generalizations, and *knowing* a large number of number facts acquired by memorization. The following generalizations* are basic:

1. *Only like numbers can be added.* Hence 3 pennies and 4 pennies can be added, but 3 pennies and 4 dimes cannot be added without reduction so that all will be cents. Likewise 2 feet and 5 inches can be added—combined into one number—only when the feet are reduced to inches, or the inches to a fraction of a foot; $\frac{2}{3}$ and $\frac{3}{5}$ can be added only when they are reduced to like parts (fifteenths). Since reduction is so

* Pupils can help develop them.

[1] Harold D. Larsen, *Arithmetic for Colleges*, Macmillan, New York, 1954, p. 55.

often involved in finding like numbers, the term can readily be applied, as was mentioned above, to adding numbers with two or more digits.

2. *The order of the addends does not affect the sum.* The sum is the same for $3 + 4 + 2$ as for $2 + 3 + 4$. This is the commutative law of addition referred to in Chapter 9. If this generalization is understood, the practice of teaching a combination and its reverse form simultaneously should not cause confusion. They are commonly so taught ($4 + 2$ and $2 + 4$), though some people oppose this procedure.

3. *Grouping the addends does not affect the sum.* The result is the same for $(3 + 4) + 2$ as for $3 + (4 + 2)$. It does not matter whether the 4 is associated with the 3 or with the 2 as a first step in adding the three numbers. This, the associative law of addition, is correlative to the commutative law and was also referred to in Chapter 9.

4. *The sum of two addends is unchanged if one is reduced and the other increased by the same number.* Thus in $\begin{array}{r}4\\+3\\\hline 7\end{array}$ when 2 is added to 4 and subtracted from 3 the problem becomes $\begin{array}{r}6\\+1\\\hline 7\end{array}$ and the result is 7 in both cases. This is called the **principle of compensation;** it is illustrated when consecutive addition facts are compared, as in $\begin{array}{r}4\\+1\\\hline 5\end{array}$ $\begin{array}{r}3\\+2\\\hline 5\end{array}$ $\begin{array}{r}2\\+3\\\hline 5\end{array}$ $\begin{array}{r}1\\+4\\\hline 5\end{array}$.

## 6. Varied Opinions on Using Zero Facts

Authorities differ regarding drilling on the zero facts. Zero does not represent a number in the sense that the other digits do; furthermore, a pupil learns his combinations first with concrete counters of some sort and it is difficult, if not impossible, to show $3 + 0$ with counters. Therefore it would seem that these combinations might well be omitted. Eventually, however, a pupil must know what to do with such a computation as this: $\begin{array}{r}168\\+201\\\hline\end{array}$. Wheat[2] is most insistent that the zero combinations not be taught; he maintains that zero is merely a place holder,

[2] H. G. Wheat, *How to Teach Arithmetic*, Row, Peterson, Evanston, 1951, pp. 319, 416.

and in such a problem as this indicates only that there are no tens to be added to the 6 tens of the first addend. Brueckner and Grossnickle[3] include the zero combinations, and Taylor and Mills[4] advocate teaching them. According to Swenson, "The so-called 'zero combinations' in addition and subtraction are usually not needed until they are introduced in connection with the addition and subtraction of two-place numbers."[5]

## 7. Checking Computations

As soon as addition has been extended beyond the primary number facts, pupils should be taught to check every computation, and to consider none complete until it has been checked. The most elementary and the most commonly used method of checking addition is to add *up* a column which previously was added *down*, or vice versa, to see if the same result is obtained.

Another method, useful because it changes the combination of digits, is to omit the top number, add all the rest, and then add the omitted number to the sum of all the others. However, this process is not recommended for grades lower than the fourth.

For longer columns and larger numbers older children will be interested in checking by casting out 9's. The rule for this sounds very complex: The excess of 9's in a sum is equal to the excess in the sum of the excesses in the addends. But the process resolves itself into very simple computation. In this check, each of the addends is divided by 9 and the excess (the remainder) is recorded in each case, thus:

| | | Quotient | Remainder | (excesses) | |
|---|---|---|---|---|---|
| 3698 | (÷9) | 410 | 8 | | |
| 2417 | (÷9) | 268 | 5 | | |
| +6210 | (÷9) | 690 | 0 | 13 (sum of excesses) | 4 |
| 12325 | (÷9) | 1369 | 4 | | 4 |

The sum of the excesses of 9's in the addends is 13 which has a 9 and an excess of 4. Dividing the original sum (12,325) by 9 gives an excess of 4. Therefore, the addition is presumably correct.

[3] L. J. Brueckner and Foster E. Grossnickle, *How to Make Arithmetic Meaningful*, Holt, Rinehart & Winston, New York, 1947.

[4] E. H. Taylor and C. N. Mills, *Arithmetic for Teacher Training Classes*, Holt, Rinehart & Winston, New York, 4th ed., 1955.

[5] Esther J. Swenson, "Arithmetic for Preschool and Primary Grade Children," National Society for the Study of Education, *Fiftieth Yearbook, Part II*, 1951, p. 63.

Dividing each of the numbers by 9 can easily involve errors and necessitate repetition of the work. A simpler procedure is to add the digits in each of the addends, and continue to add digits until all are reduced to one-digit numbers, then add these one-digit numbers and find the excess of that number over 9; this should correspond to the excess in the original sum. In the following example the excess in both cases is 4.

| | | | | |
|---|---|---|---|---|
| 3698 | 26 | 8 | | |
| 2417 | 14 | 5 | | |
| +6210 | 9 | 9 | 22 | 4 |
| 12325 | 13 | 4 | | 4 |

A procedure involving still less computation and possibility of error is to remove every 9 or combination of digits that makes 9 from each addend and also from the sum, thus:

| | | | | | |
|---|---|---|---|---|---|
| 3698 | Take out 3 and 6 and also 9. | Excess | 8 | | |
| 2417 | Take out 7 and 2. | Excess | 5 | | |
| +6210 | Take out 6 and 2 and 1. | Excess | 0 | 13 | 4 |
| 12325 | Take out 1 and 3 and 5. | Excess | 4 | | 4 |

Remember, however, when checking computations by casting out 9's that if your answer is wrong by an amount equal to 9 or to any multiple of 9, or if figures in the answer are transposed, the sum will appear to be correct. For example, adding digits we have:

| | | | | | | | | | | |
|---|---|---|---|---|---|---|---|---|---|---|
| 326 | 11 | 2 | | | 326 | 11 | 2 | | |
| 431 | 8 | 8 | | | 431 | 8 | 8 | | |
| +125 | 8 | 8 | 18 | 0 | +125 | 8 | 8 | 18 | 0 |
| 882 | 18 | | | 0 | 828 | 18 | | | 0 |
| 891 | 18 | | | 0 | | | | | |

Though 891 would be an incorrect answer, its digits give the same sum as that of 882. The error is an amount equal to 9. Because of a transposed figure, the answer 828 is in error by 54 (a multiple of 9), but at the same time appears to be correct, when this method of checking is used.

A checking can also be made by casting out 11's but the procedure is more difficult and therefore less practical.

Though checking is considered essential to insure the accuracy of answers, the ability to estimate answers and to recognize gross errors by insight should receive attention in all arithmetic computations. The pupil who adds 24, 21, 16, and 25 and gets 124 should realize that his answer is too large, because these numbers are all less than 30 and four 30's is only 120. Estimating the reasonableness of answers should be encouraged at every step of arithmetic practice.

## 8. Stages of Difficulty in Addition

In general, elementary textbooks in arithmetic are scientifically developed and addition problems carefully graded. However, teachers should be aware of the levels of difficulty and present the problems accordingly. For our purpose addition problems are classified on the basis of six levels of difficulty.

*First Level.* The basic addition facts constitute the first level. Though there has been much research aimed at grouping them in order of difficulty, no general agreement has been reached on such a classification. Some authorities[6] maintain that an understanding of number relationships affects learning the combinations more than their intrinsic difficulty does. Taylor and Mills,[7] on the other hand, group the facts into 20 very hard, 11 hard, 20 average, and 12 easy sets, based on study of 5000 papers from pupils in the first five grades. Teaching addition on this level was discussed in Chapter 10.

*Second Level.* Probably correctly placed on this level are two-place numbers involving only exact tens, such as $\begin{array}{r}40\\ +20\\ \hline\end{array}$. Using the hundred square so the child is satisfied by counting that four 10's *is* 40, and knows why it is so written, is preparatory for this level. Furthermore, the computation should be presented on the concrete basis by using sticks tied into tens. The child sees that 4 tens and 2 tens *are* 6 tens and that there are no loose units to be counted in this problem. He may write the sum as 60 and untie the bundles of sticks and count to verify that the total is 60.

*Third Level.* This level includes addition of two-place numbers involving both tens and units. For this, bundled counters and single sticks are used until the process is well understood.

$$\begin{array}{r}42\\ +36\\ \hline\end{array} \qquad \begin{array}{rr}4\text{ tens} & 2\text{ units}\\ +3\text{ tens} & 6\text{ units}\\ \hline 7\text{ tens} & 8\text{ units}\end{array} \qquad \text{or } 78; \qquad \text{checked by counting}$$

[6] L. J. Brueckner and Foster E. Grossnickle, *op. cit.*, p. 207; and Brownell as quoted by them, p. 206.

[7] E. H. Taylor and C. N. Mills, *op. cit.*, p. 41.

*Fourth Level.* Addition involving reduction is on the fourth level.

| | | |
|---|---|---|
| 35<br>+16 | 3 tens 5 units<br>+1 ten 6 units<br>———————<br>4 tens 11 units | Eleven units is enough to make another ten, so 11 units are reduced to 1 ten and 1 unit. |

4 tens
+1 ten 1 unit
———————
5 tens 1 unit or 51

For this computation 10 of the 11 loose sticks are tied into a ten-bunch and are placed with the other 4 tens.

In the writer's opinion, there are no more effective manipulative materials for combining groups and taking groups apart in learning place value than bundled sticks—even toothpicks. Some variety is desirable, however, and there are various possibilities—the abacus, the the tens block, the tens square.[8] In teaching the position of units, tens, and hundreds, such devices as pockets, with a strip of paper in the tens pocket being worth ten times as much as a strip in the units pocket, are far less convincing to a child than using a bunch of ten units for a ten to the left of units, and a banded collection of 10 ten-bunches for a hundred in the place to the left of tens.

After children know the relationships and values of the places, they can understand that a ticket in the third place from the right stands for one *hundred* and that a ticket in the pocket to its right is only one *ten.* But this is little different from figures in a three-place numeral, e.g., 111, in which the 1's have different values, and this is hardly a beginning step.

Some textbooks introduce place value by means of coins and coin values: 10 pennies = 1 dime, 10 dimes = 1 dollar. This device has a number of disadvantages. (1) The child is told that 10 pennies equal a dime in value, but he has no visible evidence of it, nor of the assertion that 10 dimes are the same as a dollar. (2) Only certain coins are selected; the nickel and the quarter, both familiar to him, are ignored. A child who has 35 cents does not necessarily have three dimes and five pennies.

Hickerson[9] presents several reasons for believing that using our monetary system to teach the decimal nature of our number system is

[8] Herbert F. Spitzer, *The Teaching of Arithmetic*, Houghton Mifflin, Boston, 2nd ed., 1954, pp. 48, 75.

[9] J. Allen Hickerson, *Guiding Children's Arithmetic Experiences*, Prentice-Hall, New York, 1953, p. 35.

not altogether desirable, and Sanderlin[10] expresses similar doubt. Taylor and Mills,[11] however, advocate its use; and Marks, Purdy, and Kinney[12] suggest its use when place value is introduced.

Stone's statement reflects an adherence to the drill theory of teaching arithmetic, which paid little attention to meaning, that was prevalent about forty years ago: "It is of vital importance that a pupil know the meaning of addition such as 'five and four are nine,' etc., but it makes little if any difference whether or not he knows why we 'carry.' The important thing is that he has the proper *habit* of carrying."[13]

*Fifth Level.* On the next level of difficulty is higher decade addition involving bridging, e.g., $\begin{array}{r} 24 \\ +7 \\ \hline \end{array}$. This may at first appear to be a practice type of computation on the addition-involving-reduction level. But a higher-level designation seems warranted because the purpose of this step is to have pupils make one mental response to $\begin{array}{r} 27 \\ +4 \\ \hline \end{array}$ as 31 rather than two mental responses (11 and 3) before giving the sum as 31. This purpose is better served in drill work if the example is written in horizontal form (27 + 4) rather than in the vertical form, but both forms should be used in practice. This type of addition is often called addition by endings and a series like the following is used for quick review:

$$\begin{array}{r} 14 \\ +7 \\ \hline \end{array} \qquad \begin{array}{r} 24 \\ +7 \\ \hline \end{array} \qquad \begin{array}{r} 34 \\ +7 \\ \hline \end{array} \qquad \begin{array}{r} 44 \\ +7 \\ \hline \end{array} \qquad \begin{array}{r} 54 \\ +7 \\ \hline \end{array}$$

*Sixth Level.* Faster pupils can quickly acquire another procedure in the bridging process to increase speed. For example, in $\begin{array}{r} 27 \\ +5 \\ \hline \end{array}$ take enough from the smaller number to raise 27 to the next decade (30); 3 is needed; then add the 2 left in the small number and you have 32. Practice of this sort is profitable for many of the capable pupils. The most advanced might well apply this technique to higher numbers;

[10] M. T. Sanderlin, "Teaching Carrying in Arithmetic," *The Instructor*, May, 1947, p. 15.

[11] E. H. Taylor and C. N. Mills, *op. cit.*, p. 49.

[12] John L. Marks, C. Richard Purdy, and Lucien B. Kinney, *Teaching Arithmetic for Understanding*, McGraw-Hill, New York, 1958, pp. 128–130.

[13] John C. Stone, *The Teaching of Arithmetic*, L. W. Singer, Syracuse, 1922, p. 5.

e.g., in 29 add to the first number the tens in the second number

```
  29
  32
 +46
```

(29 + 30), getting 59; then add the 2 and get 61; so also to get 101, 107. Practicing this procedure will markedly accelerate mental addition.

Pupils are sometimes encouraged to group digits in adding, especially to find pairs or groups that make 10.

```
  6⎫
  3⎬ 10
  1⎭
  2╲
  9 >10
 +8╱
 ---
 29
```

This technique may help some pupils to attain more speed, but it can easily lead to errors because of omission and hence is not generally recommended except for older pupils.

Whatever the level or the process used, pupils should early acquire the habit of stating only sums, not naming the addends. Whether the following is done silently or orally:

```
  26
  14
  62
  17
 +15
 ---
 134
```

the pupil should say 10, 12, 19, 24; and then 4, 5, 11, 13.

## 9. Tests of Proficiency

Spitzer suggests that pupils use a tapping test to determine how well they know the addition combinations. He gives the following instructions: "Tap or touch your desk with your finger as you think or say the sum to each combination. If your tapping is regular and reasonably fast, you know the facts well enough. Mark any combinations you do not know well."[14]

[14] Herbert F. Spitzer, *op. cit.*, p. 122.

Brueckner and Grossnickle[15] believe that a pupil has mastered a basic fact in addition when he has the following knowledge and abilities:

1. He can represent the fact with concrete objects.
2. He knows that addition means putting numbers together.
3. He can reproduce the fact promptly and confidently by dramatization, by markers, or on an abacus.
4. He discovers that interchanging the position of numbers does not change the sum.
5. He knows how to write the fact in both vertical and horizontal forms.
6. He can verify the result by using other known facts.
7. He can use the fact in a problem.
8. He can give the sum quickly and confidently.

In the writer's opinion, pupils who do well on the two informal evaluation procedures described above may be said to have attained proficiency in adding whole numbers.

## COMPETENCE CHECK

**1.** Explain and illustrate Swain's statement: "Addition procedures involve: (1) the separate summing of the digits representing units, tens, hundreds, etc.; (2) the rearrangement of the results in standard numeral form."

**2.** State the commutative law of addition, the associative law of addition, and the principle of compensation. Give illustrations of each one.

**3.** What is one other principle or generalization on which addition is based? Illustrate it.

**4.** Check each of the following addition computations by three methods:

| | | |
|---:|---:|---:|
| 1645 | 621 | 4316 |
| 2098 | 136 | 19 |
| 4612 | 996 | 208 |
| 8211 | 428 | 1961 |
| 7586 | 734 | 4 |
| +2945 | 296 | 36 |
| | +416 | +1000 |

**5.** Make a table of the basic addition facts (45 primary facts with sums not greater than 10).

**6.** Make a table of the rest of the addition facts that have no addends greater than 9.

**7.** Tabulate the zero facts in addition.

[15] L. J. Brueckner and Foster E. Grossnickle, *op. cit.*, p. 213.

8. Illustrate decade addition, and decade addition that involves bridging.
9. State a general principle for cases in which bridging is needed.
10. Do you disagree with the six levels of difficulty proposed in this chapter? If so, where, and why?

## OPTIONAL ASSIGNMENTS

1. State Hickerson's four reasons for believing that "using our monetary system to teach the nature of the number system is not altogether desirable."
2. List several points of difference between Hickerson's theory of learning to add whole numbers and the theories expressed in this or other texts you have consulted.
3. Write a brief pro and con discussion on any procedure or subject-matter content mentioned in the chapter on which textbook writers are not in agreement.

## REFERENCES

Hickerson, J. Allen, *Guiding Children's Arithmetic Experiences*, Prentice-Hall, New York, 1952, chap. 6.

Swain, Robert L., *Understanding Arithmetic*, Holt, Rinehart & Winston, New York, 1957.

chapter 12

# Subtraction and Its Applications

## 1. Addition and Subtraction Correlative

The fact that subtraction is discussed in a separate chapter from addition does not mean that it constitutes an entirely separate area of arithmetic computation. As was said in an earlier chapter, of the four fundamental operations, addition and multiplication involve putting together (combining) groups, whereas subtraction and division involve separating a larger group into smaller groups. Subtraction is very closely related to addition and should be taught with it.

If addition is merely a process of rearranging quantities—2 books here and 3 books there put into one group of 5 books instead of two separate groups—subtraction involves separating the 5 books into the desired groups—perhaps 1 book in a group that is given away, and 4 books in the group that remains. There are two groups now instead of one, but the total number of books is the same.

## 2. The Minus Sign as a Sign of Separation

As we said earlier, "+" and "−" are action signs; "+" means we are to rearrange two or more groups into one large group; "−" means we are to rearrange by separating a large group into two smaller ones. Thus in 6 − 5, 6 followed by "−" indicates that something is to be separated from the 6; this obviously involves rearranging the 6 objects into two groups of which 5 is one. In this situation the usual question is, "How many are in the other group?" Using manipulation we remove the 5 from the 6 group and see how many remain in the other group.

## 3. From Objects to Words to Symbols

In a child's first experience with subtraction he removes some objects from a group and then expresses the process in words: "I took two pencils away from five pencils and three are left." Then he writes the number story (somewhat abbreviated) as: "From 5 pencils take 2 pencils and that leaves 3 pencils." He makes up other similar problems, and he reads and interprets and finds answers to some made by the teacher, and then some from the workbook. By this time he understands the still more abbreviated form: 5 pencils − 2 pencils = 3 pencils as he learns the meaning of the symbol "−" for "take away" and again sees the "=" which he has learned to call "are" in adding.

Then as he writes 5 − 2 = 3, he reads it "Five take away two are three." This procedure fits into the first subtraction concept, finding the remainder (discussed below), and the symbols are read from left to right as he is accustomed to do in reading sentences and in horizontal addition problems. Incidentally this keeps the visual image of the arithmetic equation before him. He will be taught, too, that 5 − 2 = 3 may also be written as $\begin{array}{r} 5 \\ -2 \\ \hline 3 \end{array}$, just as is true in addition.

## 4. Acquaintance with Triads

In subtraction we must account for both the groups that have been made from the original larger group; for example, if John had 6 pennies and lost 2 of them, those 2 are one group and the 4 he still has are the other. With this idea in mind much combined addition and subtraction can be done by paying attention to familiar triads.* In the 6 family, for example, 5 + 1 = 6; 4 + 2 = 6; 3 + 3 = 6; 2 + 4 = 6; 1 + 5 = 6. In such problems manipulation of course precedes memorization; and when the child has become very familiar with the 5 and 1 combination for 6, he remembers that in 5 + ? = 6 the 1 goes there. Then having become accustomed to the equation form, when it is written 6 − 5 = ? and 6 − 1 = ? he associates 1 and 5 as a combination that makes 6.

---

* Pupils should have opportunity to make many equations representing triads.

This concept of subtraction is in reality the additive method, but it is very effective in showing the close relationship between addition and subtraction. It does not necessarily follow that the additive method should be used in compound subtraction, particularly when reduction is involved, e.g., $\begin{array}{r} 65 \\ -47 \\ \hline \end{array}$. However, much work of this sort can be done with the basic combinations, first in addition and then in subtraction, as will be seen from the following table of combinations:*

| Objects | Combinations | Number of Groups |
|---|---|---|
| 2 | 1 +1 | 1 |
| 3 | 1 +2; 2 +1 | 2 |
| 4 | 1 +3; 3 +1; 2 +2 | 3 |
| 5 | 1 +4; 4 +1; 2 +3; 3 +2 | 4 |
| 6 | 1 +5; 5 +1; 2 +4; 4 +2; 3 +3 | 5 |
| 7 | 1 +6; 6 +1; 2 +5; 5 +2; 3 +4; 4 +3 | 6 |
| 8 | 1 +7; 7 +1; 2 +6; 6 +2; 3 +5; 5 +3; 4 +4 | 7 |
| 9 | 1 +8; 8 +1; 2 +7; 7 +2; 3 +6; 6 +3; 4 +5; 5 +4 | 8 |

After the children have studied each "family," e.g., 5, with manipulative aids for addition ($4 + 1 = ?$; $1 + 4 = ?$; $2 + 3 = ?$; $3 + 2 = ?$) they will do corresponding subtraction with the aids ($5 - 1 = ?$; $5 - 4 = ?$; $5 - 3 = ?$; $5 - 2 = ?$). When these aids are dispensed with, frequent practice with games or other motivating incentives will enable some of the children to become proficient. Not until they are reasonably proficient in the basic combinations will they be ready for the higher levels of subtraction.

* Give the pupils an opportunity to discover this pattern of combinations.

## 5. Three Subtraction Concepts

Too often overlooked by primary teachers is the need to clarify three concepts in subtraction. This can and should be done before a pupil goes beyond the basic subtraction combinations.

In some textbooks all three concepts are interspersed in groups of verbal subtraction questions, no attention being given to any differentiation of types. If real understanding is to be established, each concept must be dealt with separately. There is probably general agreement that the take-away concept is the most readily comprehended. "John had 6 pennies and spent 4 of them. How many did he have left?" By manipulation of disks or other counters, we take the 4 away and see that he has 2 left. We record the process with figures: $6 - 4 = 2$. A child should be introduced to the use of subtraction in problem situations of this type, and he should make up many such problem situations to be solved with figures. This concept we will call **finding the remainder.**

A second concept, which involves a quite different thought process, we shall call **finding the difference.** "We have 6 red books and 2 blue books. How many more red books than blue books are there?" The thoughtless teacher will say, "Well, you know how to find the difference between 6 and 2." The pupil says, "Subtract?" The teacher answers, "Yes, of course." The child tries to remember that when we compare two numbers we *subtract* to find the difference, but he probably does not know *why* we subtract.

When the teacher is ready to introduce this concept, he should have the child begin by using manipulative procedures with a one-to-one correspondence; thus the child takes away as many red books as correspond to the number of blue ones and sees for himself that there are 4 more red ones. Much of this type of experience, in which he applies the process by means of symbols and makes up a number of similar problem situations and finds their solutions, gives the child such confidence that he will not have to ask, "Subtract?" The teacher should also provide groups of exercises that include both finding the remainder and finding the difference.

When these two concepts are well established, it is time to introduce the third concept, **finding what must be added.** "Jane needs 8 cents for a candy bar. She has 5 cents; how much more does she need?" Using counters, the child can lay down the 8 cents it takes and count off the 5

Jane has. Thus he sees that subtracting what Jane has from what she needs shows what must be added to 5 to make 8. This ability is recognized as one of the values gained from using the additive method of subtraction discussed earlier in this chapter.

With attention thus given to the three subtraction concepts, meaning will be attached to subtraction, and there will be more motivation for memorizing the combinations for quick use. When pupils have become proficient at this level, they are ready to proceed to the higher levels of subtraction.

## 6. Higher Levels of Subtraction*

If understanding and use of the basic combinations have been well established, the children will have less difficulty with decade subtraction and the so-called compound subtraction: (1) $\begin{array}{r}50\\-30\\\hline\end{array}$ $\begin{array}{r}70\\-20\\\hline\end{array}$; (2) $\begin{array}{r}26\\-\ 5\\\hline\end{array}$ $\begin{array}{r}36\\-\ 5\\\hline\end{array}$; (3) $\begin{array}{r}38\\-16\\\hline\end{array}$ $\begin{array}{r}27\\-12\\\hline\end{array}$. These, too, should be presented in problem situations that are within the pupils' comprehension and experience.

The one best sequence for levels of either addition or subtraction problems has never been determined. Textbooks differ somewhat on the order of their introduction. The order presented here is widely accepted and is based on logical reasoning. However, the order followed in a particular classroom is usually that used in the basic text.

When subtraction involving reduction is introduced, e.g., $\begin{array}{r}26\\-19\\\hline\end{array}$, the procedure should be done first with bundled sticks. One of the tens should be broken up so that there will be enough units (loose sticks) from which to take 9; and when one of the 2 tens has been used and the other one taken away by subtraction, no ten should be left. Such procedures can be checked by beginning with 26 loose sticks and removing 19 of them to see that 7 *are* left, and then putting 19 and 7 together to see that there are 26. Again the teacher should provide the series of experiences—manipulative procedure, computation, and application in many problem situations.

* Able pupils should be encouraged to do some exploring here.

## 7. Special Zero Difficulties

In the subtraction indicated by $\begin{array}{r} 70 \\ -20 \\ \hline \end{array}$, zero will give little difficulty because it is simply a place holder and indicates that no units are involved. Just as in adding $\begin{array}{r} 20 \\ +30 \\ \hline \end{array}$, we merely place 0 in the answer. But when zero is involved in subtraction with reduction, it is important for the child to *understand* what is being done. In $\begin{array}{r} 20 \\ -\ 6 \\ \hline \end{array}$, using bunched sticks first, he sees 2 tens (20) and wants to remove 6 sticks. He must untie 1 ten so as to have 10 loose sticks. Now it is easy to remove 6 sticks and see that he has 1 ten-bunch and 4 units (single sticks) left. He then records his procedure as $\begin{array}{r} 20 \\ -\ 6 \\ \hline 14 \end{array}$. He can check his answer by counting and have confidence in it.

Later the procedure will involve three or more digits. The child will see that it is safer—and more likely to give a correct answer—if he reduces step by step: 1 of the hundreds reduced (retied) to tens, and then 1 ten reduced (untied) to units. In $\begin{array}{r} 300 \\ -125 \\ \hline \end{array}$ he may indicate his reduction as $\begin{array}{r} 2\ 9\ \ \ \\ \not{3}^1\not{0}^1 0 \\ -1\ 2\ 5 \\ \hline \end{array}$, provided he is able to interpret all the figures. With continued practice and encouragement the pupil will eventually acquire the ability to do the reduction and subtraction mentally. A few bright pupils will quickly discontinue using the "crutch."

## 8. Terms and Principles Involved in Subtraction

The terminology of subtraction is not necessary until pupils are in grades above the primary. However, the following definitions should be part of the arithmetic learning of middle- and upper-grade pupils, and certainly of the teacher.

**Subtraction** is the process of finding the remainder when one number is taken from another. The **minuend** is the number representing the whole from which a given number, called the **subtrahend,** is taken. The **remainder** or **difference** is the number remaining after the subtraction has been performed:

```
  29 minuend
 −16 subtrahend
 ---
  13 remainder or difference
```

The **basic** or **primary subtraction facts** are those whose minuend is less than 10. **Subtraction with reduction** is subtraction in which the figures in the subtrahend are larger than those of their corresponding orders in the minuend; this makes it necessary to reduce one of the next order to the left to 10 of the value to its right, so that there will be enough in that order to subtract the figure in the corresponding order in the subtrahend. For example, in $\begin{array}{r} 26 \\ -18 \\ \hline \end{array}$, 8 is larger than 6 in the corresponding order; therefore, 1 ten is reduced to units which with the 6 units makes 16 units; from this it is possible to subtract the 8 units.

**Principle 1.*** *Only like numbers can be subtracted.*

**Principle 2.** *When the sum of two addends and one of the addends are known, the second addend can be found by subtraction.*

**Principle 3.** *If the same number is added to the minuend and the subtrahend, the difference is not changed.* (As in addition, this may be called the principle of compensation.)

**Principle 4.** *The sum of the difference and the subtrahend is equal to the minuend.*

## 9. Importance of Meaning and Use

As was true in addition, when early experience in subtraction is accompanied by meaning and understanding, use of the subtraction combinations will be attained gradually and the need for mastering them will be motivation for memorizing them. Practice at this stage, if made interesting, aids in memorization.

As was said in Chapter 10, children should see a use for the combinations in number situations, and should be able to make up many number stories. The combinations, subtraction as well as addition, should tie in with their school and environmental experiences and thus have *real* meaning.

* Pupils should help develop these principles.

The various techniques for promoting relational thinking and understanding have their place; but they should not be employed to the extent that they become a hindrance and deter the rapid answering that should result from memorization. For example, such combinations as $7 + 8 = 15$ may be comprehended as 1 more than $7 + 7$, an easy double; $11 + 6$ as 1 more than $10 + 6$; and $8 + 6$ as 2 more than $6 + 6$. However, overemphasis on these concepts is comparable to overemphasis on phonetic structure in reading; it detracts from the over-all grasp. These techniques are valuable in discovering answers by relationships—for example, when building up tables of combinations—but are not conducive to the rapid responses eventually desired.

## 10. Two Methods of Subtraction

Although no teacher expects to teach more than one method of subtraction to a given class, every teacher should understand both methods and be able to teach them. Many studies have been made to determine which of these methods is better, but there has as yet been no conclusive evidence that either is definitely superior to the other.

These two methods stem from two methods of thinking regarding the process of subtraction: the **take-away concept** and the **additive concept**. In doing

$$\begin{array}{r} 249 \\ -123 \\ \hline 126 \end{array}$$

by the take-away method we say 3 from 9 = 6, 2 from 4 = 2, and 1 from 2 = 1. When doing the computation by the additive method we say 3 and ? = 9 ($3 + 6 = 9$), 2 and ? = 4 ($2 + 2 = 4$), 1 and ? = 2 ($1 + 1 = 2$), and place the digits of the second addend (the remainder) in order. Both of these methods were discussed earlier in this chapter.

However, when a digit in the subtrahend is more than the corresponding figure in the minuend, some method of reduction is necessary. It may be done by either of two processes commonly referred to as the **decomposition** and the **equal-additions methods.**

The decomposition method is the one adhered to in discussing higher levels of subtraction in this chapter. **Decomposition** is a term widely used for "breaking down"—e.g., breaking down ten to provide additional units; the term **reduction** is used for this process in this text. Whichever term is used, the process is the same as that for which the term "borrowing" has long been used. Borrowing hardly seems appropriate, since the number taken from the order to the left is taken for keeps.

The equal-additions method applies the principle of compensation referred to earlier: If the same quantity is added to both the minuend and the subtrahend, the difference is not changed. In $\begin{array}{r} 432 \\ -178 \\ \hline 254 \end{array}$, we say that 8 units cannot be taken from 2 units. We can add 10 units to the minuend and thus have 12 units; from this take 8 and 4 is left. Since we added 10 units to the minuend, we must add 10 units to the subtrahend, but in this case we choose to call these units 1 ten and add it to the 7 tens. But again the 8 tens in the subtrahend is too large to subtract from 3 tens in the minuend. Hence we add 1 hundred (10 tens) to the minuend, which with the 3 tens make 13 tens; from this we subtract 8 tens, leaving 5 tens. Since we added 1 hundred (10 tens) to the minuend, we must add 1 hundred to the subtrahend, and we then have 2 hundreds to subtract from 4 hundreds for a remainder of 2.

Although this process, frequently called the Austrian method, sounds complex in its rationalization, practice with it produces rapid computation. Some arithmetic authorities advocate teaching it to older children; there is some research evidence indicating that pupils thereby attain speed in subtraction.

## 11. Checking for Accuracy in Subtraction

As was said previously, every pupil should acquire the habit of checking all his computations for accuracy from the time he learns column addition and compound subtraction.

Subtraction is usually checked by adding the subtrahend and the remainder; if the result is the same number as the minuend, the subtraction is correct. A good form to use in the beginning is to keep the subtrahend and the remainder in the same positions they have in the subtraction; e.g.,

$$\begin{array}{r} 29 \\ -16 \\ \hline 13 \end{array} \qquad \begin{array}{r} \\ 16 \\ +13 \\ \hline 29 \end{array}$$

As soon as the pupil can dispense with the actual figures and mentally add the subtrahend and the remainder when he completes his problem, he should be permitted to do so, but the teacher has no assurance that he has checked his answer. Having him write the word "checked" will remind him to check his answer and will assure the teacher that he has.

Subtraction computations can also be checked by casting out 9's, but except for practicing this procedure or securing variety, it is not generally practicable from the standpoint of time, for the other procedure is much faster.

Whatever the technique of checking, the matter of considering whether the answer is reasonable should never be overlooked. Pupils should be trained early to estimate answers and not accept just any number for the answer. For example, in such a problem as

$$\begin{array}{r} 504 \\ -498 \\ \hline 116 \end{array}$$

a moment's look should tell a child that he has made an error. Since 498 is practically 500, very few will be left when it is subtracted from 504; obviously 116 is not right. At a lower level, "John had 14 marbles and lost 8 of them. How many did he have left?" A careful look at his solution,

$$\begin{array}{r} 14, \\ -\ 8 \\ \hline 16 \end{array}$$

should tell the pupil that John had only 14 marbles to start with and so could not possibly have more left after he had lost some.

In all arithmetic work, estimation of the answer and consideration of whether it is reasonable will greatly increase accuracy.

If attention is given to the steps and processes discussed in this chapter, and to the trouble spots to insure understanding, in the writer's opinion subtraction will be taught much more effectively in the elementary grades than it has been in the past.

## COMPETENCE CHECK

1. What are triads? What part may they play in subtraction?
2. What reasons are there for teaching some addition facts before attempting any subtraction?
3. List the basic addition and subtraction facts for which 8 is the total.
4. Which of the following are basic subtraction combinations: 9 − 3; 4 − 2; 11 − 6; 8 − 7; 10 − 2?
5. Under what circumstances and to what extent do you approve of using flash cards?

6. When making flash cards why is one corner sometimes clipped off, as here: ?
7. Make a table of subtraction combinations with sums not greater than 10. Did you include the zero facts? Explain why you did or did not.
8. Name three types of questions about the relationship of numbers that subtraction answers.
9. Write two problems that illustrate each type.
10. What are some of the discoveries you might help pupils make about subtraction?
11. List the following computations according to difficulty and give reasons to support your arrangement:

| (1) | (2) | (3) | (4) | (5) | (6) | (7) |
|---|---|---|---|---|---|---|
| 6 | 3000 | 67 | 25 | 301 | 400 | 60 |
| −2 | − 149 | −21 | − 6 | − 27 | −399 | −40 |

12. Explain the concept of "+" and "−" as action signs.
13. Explain and illustrate the principle of compensation.
14. What step constitutes teaching the subtraction algorism?
15. Compute 5000 − 269 and write every step of the computation.

## OPTIONAL ASSIGNMENTS

1. Explain Larsen's statement that four methods of subtraction are taught in our schools.
2. Write a discussion of Chambers' plan for developing readiness in subtraction.
3. Consult the following references and compare the research findings reported by Rheims and Rheims, Brownell, and Cosgrove on the relative merits of the decomposition and equal-additions methods.

## REFERENCES


Brownell, W. A., "An Experiment on 'Borrowing' in Third Grade Arithmetic," *Journal of Educational Research*, November, 1947, pp. 161–171.

Chambers, M. B., "My Plan for Developing Readiness in Subtraction," *The Instructor*, November, 1952, p. 52.

Cosgrove, Gail E., "How Do You Subtract?" *Journal of Education*, February, 1954, p. 141.

Larsen, Harold D., *Arithmetic for Colleges*, Macmillan, New York, 1954, chap. 4.

Rheims, G. B., and Rheims, J. J., "A Comparison of Two Methods of Compound Subtraction: The Decomposition Method and the Equal-Additions Method," *Arithmetic Teacher*, October, 1955, pp. 63–69.

chapter 13

# Multiplication and Its Applications

## 1. Meaning of Multiplication

Just as the child has learned that adding is faster than counting for determining the total number in several groups, so, when introduced to multiplication, he will discover that in many situations multiplication is even faster than adding. He has learned that by addition $3 + 4 + 5 = 12$. As in this case, addends may represent groups of various sizes; but multiplication cannot be used in this situation. However, when a number of groups of like size are to be combined—e.g., $3 + 3 + 3 + 3$—multiplication is a short cut to the answer, that is, when multiplication combinations are memorized. This fact provides incentive and motivation for memorizing the tables.

This concept—that multiplication consists of combining a number of equal groups or equal amounts—is adequate for the early elementary grades. However, the teacher should not emphasize the idea that multiplication always produces a larger number, for when fractions are involved, the product may be smaller than the multiplicand, as in $\frac{1}{3} \times 12 = 4$. If such a generalization is made, the teacher should make very clear the fact that the literal meaning of "multiply" (to increase many times) applies only when both the multiplicand and the multiplier are whole numbers.

## 2. Steps in Multiplication

The *simplest step* involves finding the product of two single-digit numbers; e.g., $4 \times 5 = 20$. As in all fundamental processes, much work should be done with counters to make the meaning clear, and problem applications should accompany the computation process. With such a problem as this: "Each of the 4 boys has 5 cents. How many cents will there be if they put their money together?" we find that they will have 5 + 5 + 5 + 5 or 20 cents, or four 5's altogether. If enough exercises involving these primary multiplication combinations are provided, it will become obvious to the pupil that he can save much time by memorizing them. Furthermore, there can be little progress with the further steps in multiplication unless these basic combinations *are* learned.

The *second step* in order of difficulty involves multiplying any whole number by a single-digit multiplier without reduction; e.g., $\begin{array}{r} 123 \\ \times\ 3 \\ \hline 369 \end{array}$. Here the distributive law of multiplication is applied: 3 × 123 = (3 × 1 hundred) + (3 × 2 tens) + (3 × 3 units), or (3 × 100) + (3 × 20) + 9, or 300 + 60 + 9 = 369. This is comparable to adding $\begin{array}{r} 123 \\ 123 \\ +123 \\ \hline 369 \end{array}$, with the resultant 3 hundreds, 6 tens, and 9 units, or 300 + 60 + 9 = 369; but multiplication provides a short cut.

The *third step* involves multiplying any whole number by a single-digit number, requiring reduction. For $\begin{array}{r} 724 \\ \times\ 5 \\ \hline \end{array}$ we may show:

$$\begin{array}{rr} 5 \times 700 = & 3500 \\ 5 \times 20 = & 100 \\ 5 \times 4 = & +\ 20 \\ \hline & 3620 \end{array}$$

but we can shorten the process and write $\begin{array}{r} 724 \\ \times\ 5 \\ \hline 3620 \end{array}$. Although the pupils have become accustomed to carrying in addition problems involving reduction, carrying was much simpler there than it is in multiplication. In addition, such as $\begin{array}{r} 16 \\ 28 \\ +31 \\ \hline 75 \end{array}$, the sum of 6 units, 8 units, and 1 unit is 15 units; this is reduced to 1 ten and 5 units, and the 1 ten is added in with the tens column. In multiplication, such as

$$\begin{array}{r} 724 \\ \times\ 5 \\ \hline 3620 \end{array}$$

5 times 4 units is 20 units, which is reduced to 2 tens and 0 units. These 2 tens must be held in mind and added *after* 5 × 2 tens is found to be 10 tens. Then 10 tens + the 2 tens = 12 tens. This in turn is reduced to 1 hundred and 2 tens, and the 1 hundred held in mind until 5 × 7 hundreds is found (3500) and then added to make 3600 or 3 thousand, 6 hundred. Much time, patience, and practice are needed to establish this procedure in a pupil's mind.

The *fourth step* Larsen calls "long multiplication."* This is multiplication of any whole number by a number consisting of several digits:

$$\begin{array}{rr} & 1324 \\ & \times\ 618 \\ \hline 8 \times 1324 = & 10592 \\ 10 \times 1324 = & 13240 \\ 600 \times 1324 = & 794400 \\ \hline 618 \times 1324 = & 818232 \end{array}$$

Computations can be written in this form until an understanding of the position of partial products is established. Then the teacher can show that the form is shortened by omitting the zeros that serve as place holders in the second and third partial products, provided the rest of the digits are kept in their proper places. The fact that the right-hand figure in each partial product, if the zeros are not counted, is written under the figure being used as a multiplier is a check on correct placement. Even though reduction is involved, adding the partial products should not give trouble for the process is the same as in simple addition. It is now clear that while at first we considered multiplication as extended addition, it has taken on a form which makes it a number process in itself.

Multiplication processes will have meaning and value only when they are applied to problem situations. *When* to multiply is just as important as *how* to multiply. As each of these steps in multiplication is learned, it should be used in problems, some from textbooks, but others created by pupils within their areas of interest and ability.

* Pupils can develop this pattern if they have some facility in recognizing place value in the multiplier.

## 3. Symbols, Terminology, and Principles of Multiplication

When a child first becomes acquainted with multiplication he says, "three 2's are 6, two 4's are 8," and so on. He sees that 3 times 2 means 2 taken three times and that the symbol "×" stands for the word "times." He can then read and interpret $3 \times 2 = 6$. Just as he knows that addition and subtraction can be written in either horizontal (equation) or vertical form, he learns that multiplication can also be written either way; and by the time he reaches the second step he sees that the vertical form is useful: $\begin{array}{r} 123 \\ \times 4 \\ \hline \end{array}$ At this stage he may read this as 123 times 4 or 4 times 123. Eventually he learns the term "multiplied by," as in 123 multiplied by 4. When both the multiplicand and the multiplier are abstract numbers, either 123 times 4 or 4 times 123 is acceptable. But when the computation is $\begin{array}{r} \$123 \\ \times\ 4 \\ \hline \end{array}$, it should be read only as 4 times $123 or as $123 multiplied by 4. The teacher must take care to see that a pupil properly interprets the expressions.

There is no reason for children in the early grades to learn the terms *multiplicand*, *multiplier*, and *product*, but they should be learned in intermediate-grade arithmetic. Definitions are useful as explicit statements describing specific terms, but they should grow out of complete understanding so that the words have meaning instead of being merely parrotlike repetition.

Dealing with multiplication processes requires the following definitions. **Multiplication** is a short process for finding the sum of a number of equal addends; it may also be defined as a process for finding the product of two numbers. It always involves combining a number of groups of equal size. The **multiplicand** is the number in each group, and the **multiplier** is the number of times the group is taken. The **product** is the number that states the total of combining a number of groups of equal size.

Certain principles of multiplication* should be understood. They apply to common fractions and decimal fractions as well as to whole numbers.

**Principle 1.** *The multiplicand and the multiplier can be interchanged*

* With guidance, pupils can develop these principles.

*without affecting the product;* e.g., $3 \times 4 = 12$ and $4 \times 3 = 12$. Here the commutative law of multiplication is applied.

**Principle 2.** *The way the factors are grouped does not affect the product;* e.g., $2 \times 3 \times 4 = 24$; $2 \times (3 \times 4) = 2 \times 12 = 24$; $4 \times (2 \times 3) = 4 \times 6 = 24$. This is the associative law of multiplication.

**Principle 3.** *The sum of two numbers can be multiplied by a third number either by adding the two numbers and then multiplying their sum by the third number, or by multiplying each of the two numbers by the third number and adding their products;* e.g., $3 \times (20 + 4) = 3 \times 24 = 72$; or $(3 \times 20) + (3 \times 4) = 60 + 12 = 72$. This involves applying the distributive law of multiplication with respect to addition.

**Principle 4.** *Every multiplication computation can be checked by addition.* However, the procedure is not practical with larger numbers.

**Principle 5.** *The product will indicate units of the same kind as the multiplicand, and the multiplier will be an abstract number.* For example, "If 1 dime is worth 10 cents, what are 4 dimes worth?" They are worth 4 times 10 cents or 40 cents. The multiplier merely indicates the number of times the size or quantity of the group named as the multiplicand is to be taken.

**Principle 6.** *To multiply by a number we can multiply by its factors;* e.g., $25 \times 6 = 25 \times 2 \times 3$.

**Principle 7.** *The product is unchanged if one of two factors is multiplied by a number, provided the other factor is divided by that number.* This is the principle of compensation in multiplication. As an illustration, the product of 25 and 16 ($25 \times 16$) can be quickly determined mentally by multiplying 25 by 4 and dividing 16 by 4; the computation then becomes $100 \times 4$.

## 4. Learning the Primary Multiplication Combinations

The primary multiplication combinations, as previously stated, consist of two single-digit factors. If the zero combinations are included—there is not unanimous agreement as to whether they should be—there are 100 such combinations.

Useful in learning the combinations are cards, preferably made by the pupils. One side contains the combination, e.g., $\begin{array}{r} 3 \\ \times 4 \\ \hline \end{array}$ and also $\begin{array}{r} 4. \\ \times 3 \\ \hline \end{array}$

On the back of the card there is a visual aid in the form of dots or x's grouped to show three 4's and also four 3's:

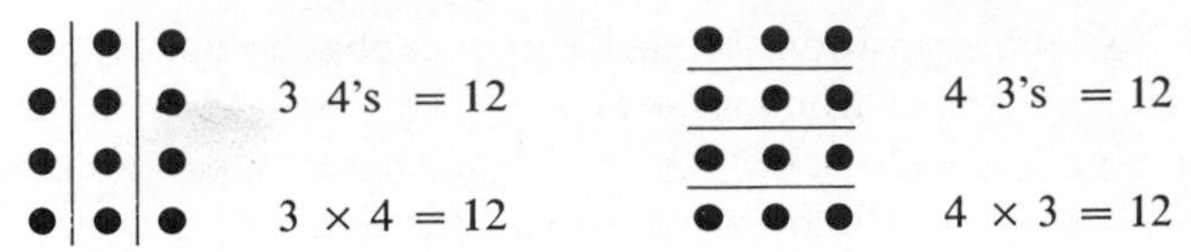


These cards enable the teacher to set apart troublesome combinations for further study.

The old method of teaching the combinations involved flash-card drill; the combinations were usually memorized without much attention being paid to relationships. If every pupil makes a multiplication table like the one below, he will have his own ready reference while learning to use and memorizing the 81 primary combinations, excluding the 19 zero combinations. There is little need for the zero combinations until pupils discover they are required in such problems as

$$\begin{array}{r} 136 \\ \times\ 20 \\ \hline \end{array}$$

In scoring points in a game a child can make three tries and get a 0 score each time; in this case 3 × 0 will be comprehensible to him. But 0 × 0 is not, nor is 0 times a number; that is, these computations cannot be demonstrated with counters. However, the simple rule that any number times 0 equals only 0, that 0 times any number equals only 0, and that 0 times 0 equals only 0 will serve the pupils' immediate needs. Actually the pupil has no use for the 1's as combinations until he begins multiplication with a two-digit multiplier.

| | 1 | 2 | 3 | 4 | 5 | 6 | 7 | 8 | 9 |
|---|---|---|---|---|---|---|---|---|---|
| 1 | 1 | 2 | 3 | 4 | 5 | 6 | 7 | 8 | 9 |
| 2 | 2 | 4 | 6 | 8 | 10 | 12 | 14 | 16 | 18 |
| 3 | 3 | 6 | 9 | 12 | 15 | 18 | 21 | 24 | 27 |
| 4 | 4 | 8 | 12 | 16 | 20 | 24 | 28 | 32 | 36 |
| 5 | 5 | 10 | 15 | 20 | 25 | 30 | 35 | 40 | 45 |
| 6 | 6 | 12 | 18 | 24 | 30 | 36 | 42 | 48 | 54 |
| 7 | 7 | 14 | 21 | 28 | 35 | 42 | 49 | 56 | 63 |
| 8 | 8 | 16 | 24 | 32 | 40 | 48 | 56 | 64 | 72 |
| 9 | 9 | 18 | 27 | 36 | 45 | 54 | 63 | 72 | 81 |

There is some opposition to teaching the tables as such; it is based on the fact that many children arrive at $3 \times 6$ by first saying the table up to that combination. However, there is wide acceptance of tables when properly used, especially by adherents of the meaning theory; they say that having a child construct the tables himself* helps him to organize his learning, which in turn leads to the development of meanings and generalizations. But all agree that if the pupil is to become competent in arithmetic, he must eventually *know* the combinations, attention being given first to accuracy and then to speed.

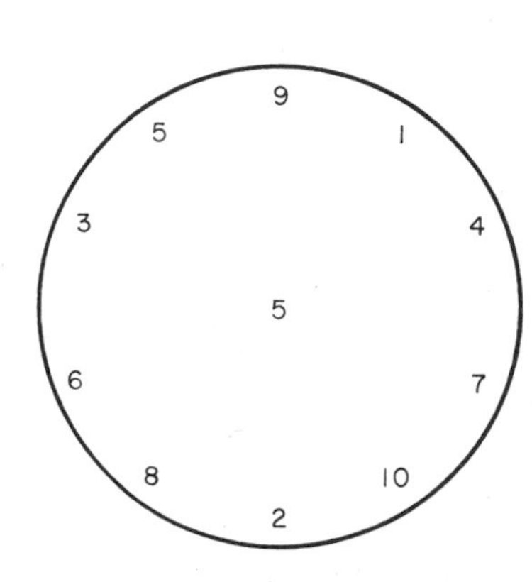

**Fig. 6.** Circle for Multiplication Practice.

After the child understands the combinations and has used them in many problem situations, periods of well-motivated practice should be provided. This practice can take varied forms. Flash cards are useful. The circle arrangement like that in Fig. 6 is very flexible because the figure in the middle can be readily changed. A few decades ago the 10's, 11's, and 12's were learned as part of the tables. The 10's are very easy and may well be included; brighter pupils can learn the 11's and 12's with little difficulty.

Most of the practice used for multiplication is of the synthetic type—thinking two factors together into a product. For the sake of variety, and as a very definite aid in later work in division, some of it might be of the analytic type—breaking products up into their factors. Speed in answering should be the purpose in this type of exercise. As an illustration, for 24, responses should be $3 \times 8$, $8 \times 3$, $6 \times 4$, and $4 \times 6$; some child might add $2 \times 12$ and $12 \times 2$. Spitzer[1] recommends "basic product drill cards" for this. Some years ago teachers attempted to have their classes master the multiplication combinations in the third grade; under the present practice this is not expected until the end of the fourth grade.

* This or some other procedure can be used for this purpose.

[1] Herbert F. Spitzer, *The Teaching of Arithmetic*, Houghton Mifflin, Boston, 2nd. ed., 1954, p. 141.

The teaching of reversals ($3 \times 4 = 12$ and $4 \times 3 = 12$) should not be attempted too early. Some authorities maintain that pupils should discover the reversals for themselves as they make the tables. However, the principle mentioned earlier in this chapter, that the multiplicand and the multiplier can be interchanged without affecting the product, can be pointed out in multiplication experience as early as the second or third grade.

## 5. Multiplication by Multiples of 10

Pupils should have enough experience in multiplying by the usual long way so that they can discover and appreciate the short-cut generalizations for these types of problems. After multiplying thus:

```
   269          325
  ×100        ×1000
  -----       ------
   000          000
  000          000
 269          000
 -----       325
 26900       ------
             325000
```

they easily see that $269 \times 100$ gives 269 plus 2 zeros, and that $325 \times 1000$ gives 325 plus 3 zeros. Thus it becomes clear that when they multiply by 100 they can quickly find the product by adding 2 zeros to the multiplicand and that when they multiply by 1000, they add 3 zeros. A quick way to multiply by 200 is to multiply the multiplicand by 2 and add the 2 zeros, thus:

```
   269
 × 200
 -----
 53800
```

. Practice with multiples of this sort usually produces the desired understanding and facility.

## 6. Use of Equations

The use of equations in connection with addition combinations was recommended in an earlier chapter as an introduction to equations which are used to increasing advantage in upper-grade arithmetic. The multiplication equation paves the way for many types of problems, particularly in percentage and its applications.

Subtraction is considered the inverse of addition. Thus we add 3 and

2 and get 5 ($3 + 2 = 5$); but we can "undo" this combination, take the 3 away and have the 2 left ($5 - 3 = 2$). If we know any two of the terms in an addition or subtraction equation we can find the third one. Likewise what is combined by multiplication can be taken apart by division. Multiplication is a process of combining equal groups; division is a process of separating a group into equal parts.

Since five 6's are 30 ($5 \times 6 = 30$), the question, "How many 6's are there in 30?" implies $30 \div 6$, or five 6's make 30. With a few such examples carefully worked out, pupils are ready for the following generalizations:* (1) When two factors of a number are known, their product is obtained by multiplication; e.g., $5 \times 6 = ?$ becomes $5 \times 6 = 30$. (2) When a product and one of its factors are known, the other factor is found by division. For example, in $5 \times ? = 30$, 5 is one factor; the other factor is found by dividing 30 by the known factor, $30 \div 5 = 6$. We may substitute 6 for the question mark in the equation, i.e., $5 \times 6 = 30$.

With the concept that a product in multiplication is obtained by multiplying two factors—e.g., $5 \times 6 = 30$—it is simple to find any one of the three numbers when the other two are known. In solving such equations the close relationship between multiplication and division becomes clear.

In this book multiplication equations are used as basic in solving several types of upper-grade problems. A few elementary textbooks have recently pointed out the value of these equations.

## 7. Checking Multiplication

There is no quick and simple way to check multiplication computations.† Doing the computation again may or may not provide an adequate check, because an error made the first time can easily be repeated.

Casting out 9's is one means of checking. The procedure is basically the same as that described in Chapter 11, as far as finding the excesses is concerned. But in multiplication, when the excesses of 9's in the multiplicand and the multiplier have been determined, they should tally with

* They can help to develop these generalizations.
† Encourage pupils to suggest possible ways of checking and try them out.

the excesses in the product when multiplied together, as shown here:

$$\begin{array}{rrr} & \text{Excesses} & \\ 245 & 2 & \\ \times 116 & \times 8 & \\ \hline 1470 & 16 & 7 \\ 245\phantom{0} & & \\ 245\phantom{00} & & \\ \hline 28420 & 16 & 7 \end{array}$$

Another procedure in common use involves checking by reducing to a digit, thus:

$$\begin{array}{rrrr} & & \text{Sum of Digits} & \\ 245 & 11 & 1 + 1 = \phantom{0}2 & \\ \times 116 & 8 & \times 8 & \\ \hline 1470 & & 16 & 1 + 6 = 7 \\ 245\phantom{0} & & & \\ 245\phantom{00} & & & \\ \hline 28420 & 16 & 16 & 1 + 6 = 7 \end{array}$$

Gross errors can be detected by estimating the answer. Hence in every computation and problem solution pupils should be taught to think whether their answer makes sense. In the above computation, 245 multiplied by 100 gives 24500. Since 245 is being multiplied by a number a little larger than 100, for 28420 to be somewhat larger than 24500 is reasonable. If the pupil had obtained 18420 as the answer, such estimation would leave no doubt that it was incorrect.

Applying the distributive law of multiplication with respect to addition, discussed earlier in this chapter, makes possible another fairly simple checking procedure. For example,

$$\begin{array}{r} 421 \\ \times\ 25 \\ \hline 2105 \\ 842\phantom{0} \\ \hline 10525 \end{array}$$

Since $25 \times 421 = (20 \times 421) + (5 \times 421)$, this problem can be checked as follows:

$$\begin{array}{rr} 421 & 421 \\ \times\ 20 & \times\ \ 5 \\ \hline 8420 & 2105 \end{array}$$

$$\begin{array}{r} 8420 \\ +2105 \\ \hline 10525 \end{array}$$

According to Principle 6 in Section 3 above, to multiply by a number we can multiply by its factors. This makes possible the following method of checking in dealing with smaller numbers:

```
  65        Check:    65
×48                 ×  8
----                ----
 520                 520
260                 ×  6
----                ----
3120                3120
```

It is always possible to check by interchanging the multiplicand and the multiplier:

```
  65                  48
×48                 ×65
----                ----
 520                 240
260                 288
----                ----
3120                3120
```

Multiplication can also be checked by dividing the product by one of its factors, either the multiplier or the multiplicand; the quotient will be the other factor. However, this is so time-consuming as to be hardly practical.

## 8. Successful Learning in Multiplication

When learning the multiplication processes progresses from the manipulative to the symbolic and thinking stage, with counters being used as long as they are required for understanding, and with pupils being given time necessary for comprehension, they will learn *how* to multiply. When these processes are all related to social situations, and especially when pupils are encouraged to make up problem situations that call for the processes, they will learn *when* to multiply.

## COMPETENCE CHECK

1. Explain why, in multiplying by a number consisting of several digits, each partial product is set one place farther to the left than the preceding one.
2. Why do we add the partial products to get the result in multiplication?
3. Make a set of basic product cards using Spitzer's design.
4. Make a multiplication wheel based on Wheat's whirligig as shown by Spitzer.

5. In multiplying 614 × 125 one person got 76570 as the answer. He said it was correct because he cast out 9's and it checked. Does it check? Is it correct? Explain your findings.
6. Do the following examples and check each one in three different ways:

$$\begin{array}{r} 649 \\ \times 110 \\ \hline \end{array} \qquad \begin{array}{r} 320 \\ \times\ 16 \\ \hline \end{array} \qquad \begin{array}{r} 426 \\ \times\ 72 \\ \hline \end{array} \qquad \begin{array}{r} 9001 \\ \times\ 200 \\ \hline \end{array}$$

7. Write a few questions you might use to test a pupil's mathematical understandings in multiplication, computational ability in multiplication, and competence in multiplication vocabulary.
8. Formulate a generalization for multiplying by 10 or its multiples.

## OPTIONAL ASSIGNMENTS

1. In a study reported by Hunnicutt and Iverson, Brownell and Carper, indicate that maturity of thought process is an important index of true learning. Discuss their method of determining children's thought processes in learning the multiplication combinations, and some of their findings.
2. For which of the following do you think objective tests in multiplication are possible: rate; accuracy; maturity of thought process?
3. To what extent does Jackson agree with the use of multiplication equations proposed in this chapter?

## REFERENCES


Hunnicutt, C. W., and Iverson, William J., *Research in the Three R's*, Harper, New York, 1958. pp. 383–393.

Jackson, Humphrey G., "Ideas for Your 'Bag of Tricks,'" *Arithmetic Teacher*, November, 1958, pp. 265–266.

chapter 14

# Division and Its Applications

## I. Difficulty of Division

Division is considered the most difficult of the fundamental processes. Although, as we shall point out, there are some stages that are inherently difficult, the concept of division is not beyond the ability of primary-grade children when it concerns their daily experiences. A small child given six cookies to divide with two other children manages the process, though he does not say, "$6 \div 3 = 2$; so we each get 2 cookies." If he goes to the store with 10 pennies and decides to buy as many pieces of 2-cent candy as he can get, he can see that he is getting a square deal when the clerk gives him 5 pieces and tells him each piece takes 2 of his pennies, though he has no conception of $10 \div 2$. When he is aided by the manipulation of concrete objects, he comprehends both of these situations, though one involves the partition concept of division and the other the measurement concept. Both Osborn[1] and Gunderson[2] agree that the second grade is not too early, by means of concrete objects, to lay the foundations for division.

Because it is within their experience, first- and second-grade children should have some manipulative experiences in division, even though they are far from ready for the division algorism, either $10 \div 2$ or $2\overline{)10}$. Dramatization is effective here; for example, "There are 32 children in our room. How many groups of 3 can we have, because only 3 can look at the specimen at one time?" The children will see that there are 10

[1] W. J. Osborn, "Levels of Difficulty in Long Division," *Elementary School Journal*, April, 1946, pp. 441–447.

[2] A. G. Gunderson, "Thought Patterns of Young Children in Learning Multiplication and Division," *Elementary School Journal*, April, 1955, pp. 453–461.

groups of 3 children, with 2 children left over (remaining as not in a group).

This gradual concrete-to-semiconcrete experience enables pupils, when they do multiplication like two 3's are 6 and see this in objects or marks—**ooo ooo** or XXX XXX—to answer the question, "How many 3's are there in 6?" very easily, though it is a division and not a multiplication process.

After they have had many such questions as "How many 2's in 4?, How many 3's in 9?, How many 2's in 6?" they will be ready for the forms $2\overline{)4}$, $3\overline{)9}$, $2\overline{)6}$, and will understand that this is a short way of asking the same questions. Here again they should first use concrete and then semiconcrete aids.

The algorism $4 \div 2$ is much more difficult, because it requires the pupils to read backward (right to left) and still say, "How many 2's in 4?" if they are to comprehend its meaning in terms of past experience. The concept "divided by" is difficult even when written in words; it is infinitely more difficult when the symbol "÷" is used. Learning to translate this symbol into the meaningful process of separating groups into smaller groups of equal size requires time.

Long division is a difficult process because it involves multiplication and subtraction as well as division, and also "trial" divisors; furthermore, the child must remember the correct form to put it all down in. But with careful introduction even long division can be less frustrating to pupils and less conducive to headaches for the teacher than it commonly was in the past.

## 2. Understanding the Concepts of Division

As was said previously, division is one of the two processes for separating groups. Groups are combined by addition and multiplication, and separated by subtraction and division. Hence, just as subtraction is considered the inverse of addition, so division is considered the inverse or "undoing" process of multiplication. We put three 4's together and have 12. We may want to take the group apart and find how many 4's there are in 12, or we may want to break it into groups other than 3.* Just as we did multiplication first with manipulative aids, we do division this way first. And just as we found it very useful

* Let pupils experiment with this.

to remember the basic combinations in multiplication, we find it essential to *know* them for division.

For division, however, an additional ability must be learned. For example, in such a problem as $7\overline{)58}$, the child must be able to determine what other factor with 7 will give a product *close* to but not more than 58. With larger and larger divisors, this question increases in difficulty. These are difficulties of a mathematical nature for which understanding must be established if the pupil is to know *how* to divide. But he must acquire an additional concept of an applicational nature if he is to know *when* to divide.

### 3. Measurement and Partition Concepts

Few elementary arithmetic textbooks have dealt with measurement and partition as separate and different concepts from the standpoint of knowing why division is indicated. Authorities are not completely agreed as to which concept should be presented first, and apparently there is little research evidence in support of one being more easily comprehended than the other. In the writer's opinion, however, the measurement concept seems simpler; it should therefore be introduced first and be thoroughly understood before the partition idea is introduced.

Hill's study[3] supports this point of view. Hill found that measurement-type situations were used in the initial presentation of division in ten of the eleven text series at third-grade level which he examined. According to him, "There is some evidence that children in grades three through six prefer to solve measurement rather than partition-type problems."[4]

Spitzer[5] likewise advocates that beginning problems in division be of the measurement type because they can readily be illustrated by drawings.*

* Have pupils do some illustrations.

[3] Edwin H. Hill, *A Study of Preferences and Performances of Third, Fourth, Fifth, and Sixth Grade Children on Two Types of Division Problems*, unpublished Doctoral Dissertation, State University of Iowa, 1952.

[4] *Ibid.*, p. 91.

[5] Herbert F. Spitzer, *The Teaching of Arithmetic*, Houghton Mifflin, Boston, 2nd ed., 1954, pp. 149–150.

The measurement concept is so named because such a question as "How many 4-cent stamps can be bought for 20 cents?" involves using 4 cents as the unit of measurement to determine how many groups (stamps) of that size unit are contained in 20 cents. As another illustration, "If Jim earns 75¢ an hour, how long will he have to work to earn $3.75 he needs to buy a gift for his mother, a clock that costs $3.75?" The unit of measurement this time is 75¢. Here the question is how many times that unit is contained in $3.75.

This type of division has a very close relationship to subtraction. Jim could obtain the answer to his question by a series of subtractions,* thus:

| | |
|---|---|
| $3.75 | total cost |
| − .75 | earned first hour |
| 3.00 | left to earn |
| − .75 | earned second hour |
| 2.25 | left to earn |
| − .75 | earned third hour |
| 1.50 | left to earn |
| − .75 | earned fourth hour |
| .75 | left to earn |
| − .75 | earned fifth hour |

In five hours he will have enough. But finding the answer by subtraction may be a very long process. An alert pupil finds that he can save time by asking how many 75¢'s there are in $3.75 and finding the answer by division.

Both of these illustrations involve finding how many groups (or measuring units of a certain size) there are in the total amount to be divided. In this type of problem, *division is the process of finding the number of groups in a whole when the groups are of equal size and the size of the groups is known.* In the partition type of problem, *division is the process of finding the size of the equal groups when the number of groups is known.*

An early experience with the partition type of problem occurs when a child is given a number of cookies or pieces of candy to divide among a group. He invariably knows how to proceed; he distributes them: "One for Bill, and one for Dick, and one for me." Then another cookie

* Pupils should experiment with this procedure.

around, and another one for each; for if Mother is wise she has given him cookies that can be divided evenly. Here again is the one-to-one correspondence technique. Later in his experience the child will know that if there are three children, each will get $\frac{1}{3}$ of the total,* but he can distribute the cookies long before he can compute $\frac{1}{3}$ of 9. Unlike the measurement type of problem, the partition type cannot be solved by a series of subtractions. For example, if 8 cookies are to be divided among 4 boys, to consider subtracting the number of boys from the number of cookies is absurd.

Division is really the process of taking a given product apart when one of its factors is known, and finding the other. This situation may be illustrated thus:

| Number of Groups | | Size of Groups | | Total |
|---|---|---|---|---|
| 6 boxes of crayons | | 12 crayons in each box | | 72 crayons |
| 6 | × | 12 | = | 72 |
| How many boxes | | 12 crayons in each box | = | 72 crayons |
| ? | × | 12 | = | 72 |

$72 \div 12 = 6$, the number of groups or boxes

Here the 12-crayon measurement unit is applied to the total and the situation is therefore the measurement type. But when the situation is:

| 6 boxes of crayons | | how many crayons in each box | | 72 crayons |
|---|---|---|---|---|
| 6 | × | ? | = | 72 |

$72 \div 6 = 12$, the size of the group

this is a partition type of computation. The product, 72, is divided by the known factor, which this time is the number of groups, 6, to find the size of each group, 12.

Making the transition from the measurement to the partition type of problem by using multiplication equations will make clear the relation of the two types. The pupil knows that both types of problem call for division, and he also knows what he is to find in each case.

Some textbook writers indicate that in any partition type of computation a fractional procedure should be used. In the above situation, for example, if 6 boxes contain 72 crayons, each box contains $\frac{1}{6}$ of the 72 crayons or 12 crayons. This is a perfectly legitimate procedure,

* Let pupils find this out by manipulation.

*provided* the pupil has advanced far enough to understand the use of fractional parts. However, if the equation type of solution has been well taught, children on a lower level can learn to recognize the process needed before they learn much about fractional computation.

Moser[6] points out one questionable outcome of the fractional algorism $\frac{1}{6}$ of 72 which a child is to compute by division. In the next grade, he says, the teacher tells the child he gets $\frac{1}{4}$ of 16 by multiplication, and thus the partitive idea dangles in his mind and contributes to his confusion. But "the ease with which children take to the missing term idea in multiplication and its helpfulness to them in problem solving situations needs to be studied more completely in actual experimentation."[7]

Moser reports that at the time he wrote (1952), the State Teachers College at Towson, Maryland, was conducting some experiments which were then in an exploratory stage. He writes as follows about finding the missing term, and discovering that multiplication and division are two ways of writing relationships involving the same set of factors: "This is the goal that all of us have been working toward for years, albeit with not too conspicuous success. It is time to experiment with a different approach to see whether the efficiency cannot be improved." And he goes on to say: "The primary purpose of this paper has been to interest teachers in thinking about an area which seems to have profited less from the change from mechanical to meaning theory than any of the other operations with whole numbers. There is reason to believe that a better job can be done than we now do and it is my personal opinion that teaching children to distinguish between the two kinds of division is a good way to begin."[8]

The present writer agrees with Moser's opinion that we can provide more effective teaching and more satisfactory learning in this area of arithmetic. Manipulative aids that are concrete and movable, like disk counters or sticks, should be used in introducing both the measurement and partition types of division computation. A pupil who can recognize these two types has gone a long way toward knowing *when* to divide, which is a most important aspect of teaching division as one of the fundamental processes.

[6] H. E. Moser, "Can We Teach Pupils to Distinguish the Measurement and Partition Ideas in Division?" *Mathematics Teacher*, February, 1952, pp. 94–97.
[7] *Ibid.*, p. 97.
[8] *Ibid.*, p. 105.

Moser's article also points out what he considers a further difficulty in effectively teaching the measurement and partition ideas in division, namely, the lack of a symbolic way of writing each one to indicate the distinction, since $3\overline{)6}$ and $6 \div 3$ are used interchangeably for both types.

Spitzer suggests solving this difficulty by using $6 \div 3$ for measurement and $\frac{1}{3}$ of 6 for partition.

The present writer advocates eliminating the fractional solution in the early learning of these concepts, and believes that using equations will resolve the algorism difficulty. Call it a formula if you will, but the equation, "Number of groups × Size of group = Total amount," enables pupils to identify the known terms and to find the unknown one.* Then either $3\overline{)6}$ or $6 \div 3$ will represent dividing the product by the known factor to find the unknown factor. As will be shown in a later chapter, if this procedure is learned early in division computations, it will pave the way for the ready solution of percentage computations and problems.

## 4. Terms in Division Defined

Definitions as such are not necessary in the early work in division, but by the middle grades pupils should know the names and relationships of the parts of a computation in division, and certainly a teacher should know them. A definition is the simplest and most precise statement of the meaning of a term, but memorizing definitions without understanding them is of no value. The following are acceptable definitions for terms in division: **Division** is the process of finding one of two factors when the other factor and the product of both are known. The **dividend** is the given product. The **divisor** is the given (known) factor. The **quotient** is the factor to be found (the unknown). These definitions imply teaching the close relationship between multiplication equations and division equations, or between multiplication and division. For example, in $14 \times 3 = 42$, when "undoing" the multiplication, 42 (now the product) becomes a dividend, and $42 \div 3 = 14$. Either factor may be found by division if the other is known.

In many division problems, however, the dividend is not a multiple of the divisor, and there is a remainder. The **remainder** is the amount by

* Help pupils to develop this equation.

which the dividend exceeds the highest multiple of the divisor that is less than the dividend. To younger children, the remainder is the amount left over when the division does not come out even. In a problem such as $29 \div 3$, the quotient is 9 and the remainder is 2. In higher grades the answer may be given as $9\frac{2}{3}$, but it is not correct to call $\frac{2}{3}$ a remainder. The quotient is $9\frac{2}{3}$.

## 5. Principles of Division*

**Principle 1.** *The division process is the inverse of a multiplication process.* Hence the dividend is always assumed to be the product of two factors.

**Principle 2.** *The dividend is equal to the product of the divisor and the quotient, plus the remainder.* For example, in $36 \div 9 = 4$, the product of the quotient, 4, and the divisor, 9, is 36 and there is no remainder. However, in $38 \div 9 = 4\frac{2}{9}$, the quotient is 4 and there is a remainder of 2. In this case $4\frac{2}{9}$ times $9 = 38$, or $4 \times 9 + 2 = 38$. This is known as the basic division relation.

**Principle 3.** *If the dividend and the divisor are both multiplied (or divided) by the same number, the quotient is not changed.* Thus $72 \div 6 = 12$. When both 72 and 6 are divided by 2 we have $36 \div 3 = 12$, and when both are multiplied by 3 we have $216 \div 18 = 12$.

## 6. The Short Division Procedure

There has been considerable discussion as to whether long division or short division should be taught first. The writer believes that this depends entirely upon how the two procedures are approached. Some maintain that short division is more difficult than long division because more of it must be done mentally. For example, in $2\overline{)36}$ (quotient 18), we put a 1 above the 3 to indicate that there is one 2 in 3; we carry the remainder, 1 ten, to the 6 as 10 units and combine it with 6 units to make 16 units. How many 2's in 16 units? There are 8 and 8 is written over the 6 in the units place.

According to Spitzer,[9] pupils have no need for short division until they

* Pupils should help develop these principles.

[9] Herbert F. Spitzer, "Arithmetic Counselor Column," *The Instructor*, January, 1958, p. 53.

come to multiplying fractions, as in $6\frac{1}{2} \times 4\frac{1}{2} = \frac{13}{2} \times \frac{9}{2} = \frac{117}{4} = 29\frac{1}{4}$. Then it can be taught as a short cut, for usually this work comes in the sixth grade.

Wheat expresses a similar opinion about short division: "It should come late, if at all, in the course."[10]

Since place value has been considered in teaching the other three fundamental processes, it is logical to apply it to division as soon as two-digit dividends are used; obviously, however, the first steps should not involve remainders.

When pupils have mastered the division facts and have learned the simple algorism, $\begin{array}{r} 2 \\ 3\overline{)6} \end{array}$, as meaning how many 3's in 6, they are using short division, not long division, as in $\begin{array}{r} 2 \\ 3\overline{)6} \\ \underline{6} \end{array}$ A logical next step is $3\overline{)60}$. This implies how many 3's in 6 tens, or how many 3's in 60, and the answer is 20, shown as $\begin{array}{r} 20 \\ 3\overline{)60} \end{array}$. This is still in short division form.

For $3\overline{)36}$ it is easy to say: "How many 3's in 3?" and record it as $\begin{array}{l} 1 \\ 3\overline{)36} \end{array}$, then how many 3's in 6 and put 2 over the 6, thus, $\begin{array}{r} 12 \\ 3\overline{)36} \end{array}$. But to do this is to drift away from the idea of place value and meaning and to rely on memorizing the form. Place value *does* introduce complications into division.

## 7. Long Division Procedures

When, in such a computation as $5\overline{)1565}$, we say there are no 5's in 1, we do not mean there are no 5's in 1000, which the 1 really stands for; on the contrary, there are two hundred 5's in 1000. Consequently it is best not to complicate division with place value at this point, but rather learn the form and clarify the meaning of the answer after it is obtained. Hence, in estimating quotients, we shall use the absolute value rather than the positional value of the digits in the divisor and the dividend.

[10] H. G. Wheat, *How to Teach Arithmetic*, Row, Peterson, Evanston, 1951, p. 155.

To proceed, there are no 5's in 1 so we take 15. There are three 5's in 15 and we place the 3 over the 5 to show that we have used the first two digits of the dividend. There is one 5 in 6 with 1 left over, and three 5's in 15.

```
   313
 5)1565
   15
   --
     6
     5
     -
     15
     15
     --
```

This computation can be and is perhaps best shown as follows:

```
      3
     10
    300
 5)1565
   1500
   ----
     65
     50
     --
     15
     15
     --
```

How many 5's in 1500? There are 300; therefore 3 goes in the hundreds place. We still have 65 and must see how many 5's there are in 65. There are least ten 5's in 65, so we write 10 in the quotient. Ten 5's are 50 so we have 15 left. We must see how many 5's it contains. This is 3 and we write it in the quotient, making the total quotient 313 (3 hundreds, 1 ten, and 3 units).

The first computation obviously is shorter and is therefore worth learning.

Actually for this step in division the partition idea makes possible better reasoning. For example, in 

```
  314,
2)628
```

$\frac{1}{2}$ of 600 is 300 (3 is written in the hundreds place); $\frac{1}{2}$ of 2 tens is 1 ten, and $\frac{1}{2}$ of 8 units is 4 units, each quotient figure being written in its proper place. We can assume, too, that by the time pupils have reached this stage of division they will be familiar with the partition concept, even when it involves fractional parts.

Certainly a pupil should be familiar with the long division form with one-digit divisors before he is introduced to two-digit divisors. He has learned to do such computations as the following:

```
           132                69
(a)      2)264      (b)    4)278
           2                 24
           -                 --
            6                 38
            6                 36
            -                 --
             4                 2 R
             4
             -
```

He has learned that if, as in (b), the first figure of the dividend is too small to contain 4, he must consider the first two figures in the dividend as a partial dividend and ascertain how many 4's there are in 27. He is familiar enough with the decimal system and place value to know that since the remainder, 3, is in the tens place, it has a value of 30 units which combines with the 8 units, making 38 units. In these 38 units there are nine 4's with 2 left over, as a remainder, R.

After this step he is ready for two-digit divisors in the long division pattern, and for such computations as 13)246. Here it is evident that 2 will not contain 13, so he must ascertain how many 13's there are in 24.

There has been much discussion about how to help pupils acquire some facility in estimating the quotient figure. In general, the one-step rule—some call it the apparent method—gives a pupil a measure of proficiency; brighter pupils will learn to do sufficient mental calculations so they avoid repeated erasing and starting over. The one-step rule says simply to use only the first figure of the divisor to get an estimated partial quotient. For example in 34)1280, how many 3's there are in 12 gives the correct quotient figure more often than not. In this case, however, it fails. There are four 3's in 12, but $4 \times 34$ is 136 which is too large, so $3 \times 34$ must be used.

If the pupil always uses this procedure, when corrections are needed he can always make them by using 1 less, or in a few cases more than 1 less, than his estimated quotient. In

```
      3
  34)1280
     102
     ---
      260
```

his estimate of the first quotient figure is 4 which he finds is too large, so he uses 3. In the second figure he estimates 8 and finds it too large, so he tries 7. In other words, his revision is always downward. But if he is taught to use the two-step rule, also called the increase-by-one method (this rule states that if the units figure of the divisor is 6 or more, the tens figure should be increased by one in making an estimation), revision either upward or downward may be involved and the procedure is therefore more complex. With the one-step rule, the pupil will soon be able to calculate 4 × 34 mentally as a trial dividend and save writing down 136 and erasing.

No new skills are involved in using three-digit divisors. Hence, if in each step of long division the pupil has learned the importance of accuracy in multiplying and subtracting, he is likely to become proficient in long division without great difficulty.

## 8. Difficulties with Zero in Division

At appropriate steps in the division processes, special attention must be given the difficulties with zero: (1) zero in the divisor, as in $10\overline{)46}$; (2) zero in the dividend, as in $2\overline{)306}$; and (3) zero in the quotient, as in $15\overline{)164}$. These should be introduced one at a time and practice should be provided for adequate understanding.

## 9. Checking Division Computations*

There are certain points in the division procedure which pupils should check as they come to them, before it comes time to check the correctness of the answer. (1) Check all multiplication and subtraction as they work. (2) After each subtraction check to see that the remainder is not as large as the divisor. (3) After the first quotient figure is placed correctly, see that a quotient figure appears over each successive figure in the dividend.

A pupil who has a thorough understanding of the use and meaning of the multiplication-division equation—that one factor × another factor = a product; and inversely, that the product divided by either factor gives the other factor; and that any dividend is really the product of the divisor (one of the factors) and the quotient (the other factor)—will realize that one simple check for division is to multiply the quotient by the divisor to see if this gives the dividend. He will need to be shown or

* Ask pupils to propose ways of checking and try them out.

helped to discover, that if there is a remainder, he must add it to the quotient-divisor product to obtain the dividend. For example:

```
      25             25
  25|649           × 25
     50            ----
    ---             125
    149             50
    125            ----
    ---             625
     24           + 24
                   ----
                    649
```

For higher-grade pupils casting out 9's is a good check. Instead of the quotient × divisor + remainder = dividend, it is the excess of 9's in the quotient × the excess in the divisor + the excess in the remainder = the excess in the dividend. Thus:

```
     25
 25|649     excess in quotient          7
    50      excess in divisor         × 7
   ---                                ---
   149                                 49
   125      excess in remainder       + 6
   ---                                ---
    24                                 55     1
            excess in dividend                1
```

As is true of all mathematics processes, of even greater importance than the mechanical procedures just described is ability to estimate the correctness of an answer, or at least the reasonableness of it. As an illustration we use the following problem: "We used 14 gallons of gas for a trip of 252 miles. How many miles did we get on each gallon of gas?" (For such problems it will be well beforehand for pupils to ask their parents or other people about gasoline mileage for various types of cars.) A pupil who gets 5 miles for his answer should know that it is unreasonable. So also should the one who gets 50 miles. Similarly, in such a computation as 15|160, if he gets 8 for an answer, he should quickly recognize that 160 is more than 10 × 15, and therefore it is much more than 8 × 15.

All types of division computations should be closely related to social situations which call for the particular computation process, lest all the emphasis be on computation to the neglect of understanding when the process should be used.

Division *is* difficult, particularly from the mechanical standpoint. Instruction in it should be spread over several grade levels, the most difficult steps being delayed at least to fifth grade. Careful teaching at each new level is required. Furthermore, not all pupils will grasp the various procedures with equal facility.

If pupils are having difficulty, the teacher will find it profitable to have them describe orally each step of their work. He may thereby discover some little point that he has not suspected has been misunderstood. For example, in describing orally his procedure in computing $2\overline{)35}$, one pupil said, "How many 2's in 3? One. Put the 1 over the 3 and there is 1 left over to carry. Put that 1 with the 5 and that makes 6. 2's in 6 are 3. Put the 3 over the 5." It's amazing how easily a teacher's instructions are misinterpreted.

## COMPETENCE CHECK

1. How is division the inverse of multiplication?
2. Explain the measurement and partition concepts in division. Give illustrations of them.
3. Which of them, in your opinion, is simpler? Why?
4. Discuss pro and con using the multiplication-division equation in acquiring proficiency in division.
5. List several difficulties involved in the mechanics of division.
6. Prepare a short diagnostic test and show how it is a means of identifying the types of difficulty involved in division.
7. Which position for the quotient is preferable? Why?

   1. In short division:

   $$5\underline{|65},\ \text{ over } 13 \quad \text{or} \quad \begin{array}{r} 13 \\ 5\overline{)65} \end{array}$$

   2. In long division:

   $$26|4810|\underline{185} \quad \text{or} \quad \begin{array}{r} 185 \\ 26\overline{)4810} \end{array}$$

8. Discuss the value of the following procedure which some authorities advocate as an aid to estimating the quotient in the early stages of division:

$$\begin{array}{r} 45 \\ 16\overline{)720} \\ \underline{64\phantom{0}} \\ 80 \\ \underline{80} \end{array} \qquad \begin{array}{l} 1 \times 16 = 16 \\ 2 \times 16 = 32 \\ 3 \times 16 = 48 \\ 4 \times 16 = 64 \\ 5 \times 16 = 80 \end{array}$$

By making a table of the multiples of 16 the pupil can find the largest multiple that does not exceed 72, namely, 64. His first quotient figure then is 4. Since $5 \times 16 = 80$, he sees that his second quotient figure is 5.

## OPTIONAL ASSIGNMENTS

1. What are the one-step rule and the two-step rule that Swain and others use in determining trial digits in division?
2. What is Flournoy's conclusion about the two methods of estimating quotients?
3. Make an evaluatory report on Geary's article, "Arithmetic–Division."

## REFERENCES


Flournoy, Frances, "Children's Success with Two Methods of Estimating the Quotient Figure," *Arithmetic Teacher*, March, 1959, pp. 100–104.

Geary, Catherine, "Arithmetic-Division," *Grade Teacher*, November, 1958, p. 40.

Hill, Edwin H., *A Study of Preferences and Performances of Third, Fourth, Fifth, and Sixth Grade Children on Two Types of Division Problems*, unpublished Doctoral Dissertation, State University of Iowa, 1952.

Hill, Edwin H., "Teachers! Two Kinds of Division," *Journal of Education*, May, 1955, p. 16.

Spitzer, Herbert F., *The Teaching of Arithmetic*, Houghton Mifflin, Boston, 2nd ed., 1954, pp. 149–150.

Swain, Robert L., *Understanding Arithmetic*, Holt, Rinehart & Winston, New York, 1957.

chapter 15

# Multiples, Factors, Divisors, Powers, and Roots

## 1. Useful Aids to Division and to Fractions

Multiples, factors, and divisors are used most commonly in connection with the reduction of fractions in various computations. But they are also of special use in connection with division, wherefore a chapter dealing with them is appropriate here.

Note that the last several chapters were concerned with number *operations*. However, numbers, multiples, factors, and the like are in the field of number *structure*, some elements of which are definitely in the area of higher mathematics. But we shall not go beyond our depth.

## 2. Factors Basic to Many Arithmetic Processes

Factors have been referred to frequently in earlier chapters. A **factor** of a number is an exact divisor of the number, or we may say that a factor of a given number is one of two or more numbers which, when multiplied together, produce the given number.

If arithmetic is taught by the procedures recommended in this book, pupils will become acquainted with the term "factors" as soon as they learn the multiplication algorism in the equation form, $4 \times 6 = 24$. Here are two factors and their product. As has been pointed out, any one of these three terms can be found if the other two are known.

Factors also play a part in division. For example, in $4\overline{)38}$, the first step is to determine what other factor with 4 will give a product close to 38, but not more than 38.

## 3. Prime and Composite Numbers

The number 1 is called the **unit**. Every other natural number is divisible by itself and 1. Any natural number that can be divided only by itself and 1 is called a **prime number**. The others are called **composite numbers**. Numbers are said to be *prime to each other* or *relatively prime* when they have no common divisor except 1.

The first few primes are 2, 3, 5, 7, 11, 13, 17, 19, 23, 31, 37. Obviously there is no regular pattern of intervals, nor is there any formula for determining them. Finding out whether a number is prime usually involves testing divisors; it is not necessary to try any except prime divisors.

For example, to determine whether 67 is a prime number, we try dividing it by 2, 3, 5, 7, and so on. But how far must we go? A rule helps to answer this question: To find whether a number ($N$) is prime, test the primes in turn as divisors of $N$, but do not test beyond $\sqrt{N}$, that is, not beyond the largest natural number whose square is less than or equal to $N$. In the case of 67, we need go no further than 7 because 121, the square of 11, the next prime, is not less than or equal to 67. Therefore, 67 is prime. There are only 25 primes below 100; beyond this, the higher the numbers, the less frequent the primes.

## 4. Greatest Common Divisor (GCD)

The **greatest common divisor** of a given group of numbers is the largest natural number that is a divisor of each number in the group. It is used most frequently in reducing fractions to their lowest terms. It is usually found by deriving it from the common factors of both numbers. For example, $\frac{120}{375} = \frac{3 \times 40}{3 \times 125} = \frac{(3 \times 5) \times 8}{(3 \times 5) \times 25}$: The GCD is $3 \times 5$ or 15, for 25 and 8 are prime to each other; therefore $\frac{8}{25}$ represents he fraction $\frac{120}{375}$ in its lowest terms.

Another frequently used method for finding the GCD is continued division, thus:

$$\begin{array}{r|l} 2 & 84 - 148 - 72 \\ \hline 2 & 42 - \ \ 74 - 36 \\ \hline & 21 - \ \ 37 - 18 \end{array}$$

Since 37 is a prime number, there is no common divisor for 21, 37, and 18. However, since 84, 148, and 72 have been divided by 4 ($2 \times 2$), 4 is their GCD. The rule for this process is: Divide all the numbers by any common divisor; continue dividing the quotients by any common divisor until the remaining quotients have no common divisor. The GCD is *the product of all the common divisors.*

## 5. Least Common Multiple (LCM)

The **least common multiple** of a given group of numbers is the smallest number that is divisible by each number in the group. For example, 30 is the least common multiple of 6, 10, and 15.

As in the case of the GCD, one method of finding the LCM is by factoring, but the procedure is somewhat different. As an illustration, the LCM of 16, 24, and 36 may be found as follows:

$$\begin{aligned} 16 &= 2 \times 2 \times 2 \times 2 \\ 24 &= 2 \times 2 \times 2 \times 3 \\ 36 &= 2 \times 2 \times 3 \times 3 \end{aligned}$$

The LCM, by definition, is divisible by 16 and therefore has the factor $2^4$; it is divisible by 24 and therefore by its factors, $2^3$ and 3; it is divisible by 36 and therefore by its factors, $2^2$ and $3^2$. The smallest number which contains all these factors—$2^4$ and $3^2$, or $2 \times 2 \times 2 \times 2 \times 3 \times 3$—is 144. Hence the LCM of 16, 24, and 36 is 144.

As was true of the GCD, the LCM can also be found by continued division of a slightly different form.

$$\begin{array}{r|l} 2 & 16 - 24 - 36 \\ \hline 2 & \phantom{1}8 - 12 - 18 \\ \hline 2 & \phantom{1}4 - \phantom{1}6 - \phantom{1}9 \\ \hline 3 & \phantom{1}2 - \phantom{1}3 - \phantom{1}9 \\ \hline & \phantom{1}2 - \phantom{1}1 - \phantom{1}3 \end{array}$$

In this case the division continues as long as *any two* of the quotients have a common factor. The LCM is *the product of all the divisors and the remaining quotients.* Here $2 \times 2 \times 2 \times 3 \times 2 \times 1 \times 3$ or 144 is the LCM. This process is more difficult of rationalization than the other three given above for finding the GCD and the LCM. The rule for finding the LCM is: Divide by any divisor common to all the numbers; repeat the process until the quotients have no common divisor; then divide by any prime divisor common to two of the quotients, and bring down any undivided quotient; continue until no two quotients have a common divisor. The product of all the divisors and the remaining quotients is the LCM. The only practical value of the LCM is in its use as a common denominator in adding and subtracting fractions.

## 6. Value of Simple Rules for Divisibility

When a pupil begins division he uses divisors for the first time; but in reducing and multiplying fractions, and in cancelling, he needs to use exact divisors. In these computations as well as in both the factoring and the continued division processes for finding the GCD and the LCM, much time can be saved if divisibility can be quickly discerned. Learning some simple rules* for divisibility helps to make this possible. The following are the most commonly used rules:

1. A number is divisible by 2 if its units digit is 2, 4, 6, 8, or 0.
2. A number is divisible by 5 if its units digit is 5 or 0.
3. A number is divisible by 10 if its units digit is 0.
4. A number is divisible by 4 if its two right-hand digits form a number divisible by 4, or if it ends in 2 zeros.
5. A number is divisible by 3 if the sum of its digits is divisible by 3.
6. A number is divisible by 9 if the sum of its digits is divisible by 9 or if the excess of 9's is 0.

## 7. Powers and Roots

The use of exponents was introduced in Chapter 8 in connection with place value in our number system, and their use in number systems other than a base-10 system was presented in Chapter 9. We saw in those chapters that in our base-10 number system any digit moved one place to the left increases 10-fold in value; for example, when read from right to left, $10^4$, $10^3$, $10^2$, $10^1$, and $10^0$ represent 1, 10, 100, 1000, and 10,000.

Negative exponents are discussed in Chapter 17 and we shall see that digits decrease 10-fold in value with each move to the right; for example, when read from left to right, $10^0$, $10^{-1}$, $10^{-2}$, and $10^{-3}$ represent 1, $\frac{1}{10}$, $\frac{1}{100}$, and $\frac{1}{1000}$.

* Let the pupils try to formulate some of them.

**Exponents** are symbols that show powers of numbers, as the above illustrations indicate. A **power** of a number is the product obtained by using the number as a factor a given number of times. Thus $10^3$ is read 10 to the third power (or 10 cubed) and equals $10 \times 10 \times 10$ or 1000. Note that powers of 10 with positive exponents are greater than 1, and those with negative exponents are less than 1. Exponents make it possible to write very large and very small numbers with far fewer figures than are needed without them. For example, $10^{12}$ is a much more convenient way of writing 1,000,000,000,000 than writing 12 zeros. Likewise, $10^{-6}$ is a more convenient form than $\frac{1}{1{,}000{,}000}$.

Mathematicians and scientists use exponents widely, but most of us rarely use higher than the second power. However, we use squares (numbers to the second power) frequently, for they are involved in many area measurements, but we do not commonly use exponents. We simply say that the area of a 4-in. square is $4 \times 4$ or 16 sq. in. But we use exponents in stating the formula for finding the area of any square, $A = s^2$.

Computing powers of numbers is a synthesizing arithmetical computation, for it involves putting groups together. Just as for the synthesizing operations of addition and multiplication there are the corresponding analytic operations of subtraction and division, so for finding powers of numbers there is the inverse process of finding the roots of powers.

To *square* a number we use it as a factor twice; e.g., $4^2 = 4 \times 4$ or 16. To *cube* a number we use it as a factor three times; thus $4^3 = 4 \times 4 \times 4$ or 64. The **square root** of a number is one of its two equal factors. The **radical sign** ($\sqrt{\ }$) is the symbol used to indicate the square root of a number: $\sqrt{16} = 4$. We shall study only the square root at this point.

## 8. Computing the Square Root

The squares of many simple numbers can be determined mentally, as in $5 \times 5$, $10 \times 10$, etc. Similarly the square root of many numbers can be determined mentally on the basis of multiplication tables. For example, 10 used as a factor twice gives 100; hence the square root of 100 is 10. Likewise, the square root of 64 is 8, of 81 it is 9, etc.

But for numbers larger than those for which we remember the

multiplication tables, there are processes for determining the square root. The simplest of these procedures is factoring. For example,

$$\begin{array}{r|l} 2 & 324 \\ 2 & 162 \\ 3 & 81 \\ 3 & 27 \\ 3 & 9 \\ & 3 \end{array} \qquad 2 \times 2 \times 3 \times 3 \times 3 \times 3 = 324$$

By the principle of commutation $(2 \times 3 \times 3) \times (2 \times 3 \times 3)$ also equals 324; hence $18 \times 18 = 324$. Since 18 is one of the two equal factors of 324, it is the square root of 324. If the prime factors of a

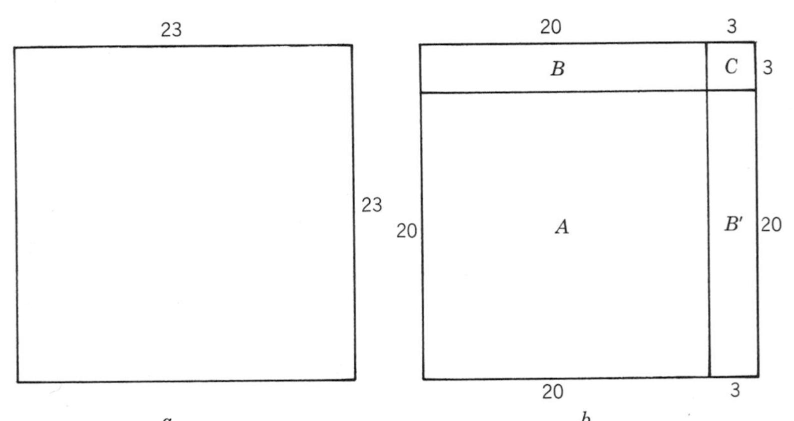


**Fig. 7.** Square Root by Algorism.

number cannot be grouped into equal pairings, its square root obviously is not a whole number.

For numbers whose square roots cannot be easily determined by inspection or factoring, the fairly simple algorism discussed in the following paragraphs may be used.

We saw above that, for example, $23^2 = 23 \times 23$; and in Chapter 13 that, for example, $23 \times 23 = (20 + 3) \times (20 + 3)$. Fig. 7*a*, represents $23 \times 23$ or 529 square units; *b* represents $(20 + 3)^2$ or $(20 + 3) \times (20 + 3)$ or 529 square units. We see by inspection that the area represented in *b* is equal to that represented in *a*. The area of *b* is equal to $20^2(A) + 3^2(C) + 2 \times (20 \times 3)$ ($B$ and $B'$). In 23, 2 stands for two

10's or 20, and 3 for 3 units. A formula for the area of $b$, then, might be written as $20^2 + 2(20 \times 3) + 3^2$; in words this would be tens squared + 2 times the tens times the units + units squared. The general formula would be $t^2 + 2tu + u^2$.

$$\begin{array}{lr} 20^2 & = 400 \\ 2 \times 20 \times 3 & = 120 \\ 3^2 & = \phantom{00}9 \\ \hline & 529 \text{ square units} \end{array}$$

The first step in finding the square root of any number is to point off the number, beginning at the decimal point, into periods of two digits each, e.g., 5ˈ29. The number of periods tells the number of digits in the square root; hence the square root of 529 will be a two-digit number. The square of any one-digit number will have no more than two figures since $9^2 = 81$. The square of any two-digit number will not have more than four figures since $99^2 = 9801$.

In 5ˈ29 the first period, 5, contains the $t^2$, and 2 is the largest number

$$\begin{array}{r|l} & \phantom{0}2\;\;3 \\ & \overline{5ˈ29} \\ & 4 \\ 40 & \overline{1}\;29 \\ & 1\;29 \\ & \overline{\phantom{1\;29}} \end{array}$$

it can be, so 2 is placed in the answer as the tens figure. The $2^2$, or 4, is subtracted from the 5 with 1 remaining, and the next period is brought down. The resulting number, 129, contains $2tu + u^2$. Since $2t = 40$, 40 is used as the trial divisor. It would appear that 129 contains it 3 times. Assuming that $u$ is 3, $2 \times 20 \times 3$ (120) represents $2tu$. If $u$ really is 3, $u^2$ is 9, and $2tu + u^2$, or $(2 \times 20 \times 3) + 9, = 129$. Therefore, $u$ is 3, the units figure in the root; checking, we have $23^2 = 529$.[1]

In computing the square root of a decimal number, such as 1247.186, the numeral is set off into periods of two digits each, in each direction from the decimal point, thus: 12ˈ47.18ˈ6.

If in computing square root, there is a remainder after the last desired figure in the answer is found, the computation can be checked by squaring the answer and adding the remainder to it.

[1] For a somewhat different algebraic explanation, see Robert L. Swain, *Understanding Arithmetic*, Holt, Rinehart & Winston, New York, 1957, pp. 223–224.

A short-cut rule that can be used after the process has been learned is as follows; we use 9846 to illustrate it.

```
             9  9
           -------
           98 | 46
           81
           --
  180      17  46
+   9      17  01
-----      ------
  189          45
×   9
-----
 1701
```

The largest square is 9 × 9 or 81. Subtract and bring down the next period. Double and multiply by 10 whatever part of the answer (9) has thus far been found; use this number (180) as a trial divisor. Add the apparent quotient (9) and then multiply by it.

The square root of a common fraction is the square root of the numerator divided by the square root of the denominator. For example, $\sqrt{\frac{64}{144}} = \frac{8}{12} = \frac{2}{3}$. To check: $\frac{2}{3} \times \frac{2}{3} = \frac{4}{9} = \frac{64}{144}$.

## 9. Applications of Square Root

The most common use of the square root is in determining the side of a square whose area is known, as in finding the length of a square field which contains 160 acres.

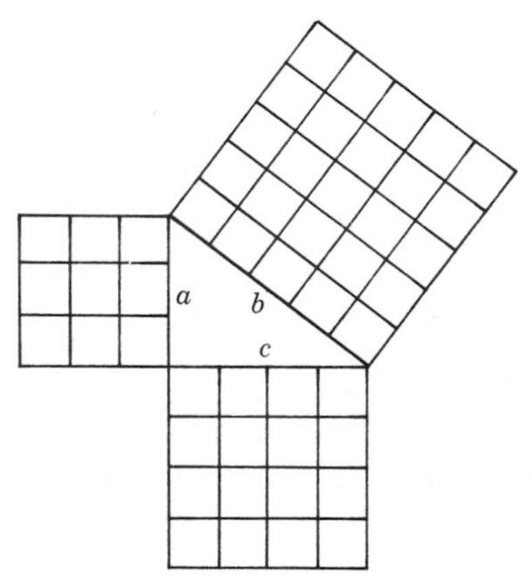


**Fig. 8.** Illustration of the Pythagorean Theorem.

In certain types of problems the application of the Pythagorean theorem calls for computing the square root. This is an important theorem in plane geometry; by means of it many practical problems can be solved. It states that the square on the hypotenuse of a right triangle is equal to the sum of the squares on the other two sides.* Thus in Fig. 8, $a^2 + c^2 = b^2$. By means of this theorem, when the

* Pupils should be able to formulate the theorem from a diagram like that in Fig. 8.

lengths of any two sides of a right triangle are known, the length of the third side can be found. In this diagram, $a = \sqrt{b^2 - c^2}$.

Mathematicians and others who frequently need to compute square roots commonly use tables of square roots to save time. However, there is no reason why pupils of average or better ability in the upper grades should not know the procedure, even though later they may use tables.

## COMPETENCE CHECK

**1.** Why are all prime numbers except 2 odd numbers?
**2.** Find the prime factors of 164; of 940.
**3.** Define and illustrate:

1. Factor
2. Multiple
3. Exact divisor
4. Least common multiple
5. Greatest common divisor
6. Prime number
7. Composite number

**4.** State the six rules for divisibility in this chapter. Give an illustration of each.
**5.** When are two numbers said to be relatively prime?
**6.** In what kind of computation is it useful to know whether two numbers are prime to each other?
**7.** Which of the following numbers are prime: 87; 91; 137? How do you know?
**8.** Reduce to the lowest terms: $\frac{185}{300}$; $\frac{176}{198}$.
**9.** Add $\frac{6}{25} + \frac{7}{80} + \frac{8}{16}$.
**10.** Use the rules of divisibility in: $\frac{45}{20} \times \frac{7}{8} \times \frac{36}{90} \times \frac{4}{5}$.
**11.** Explain exponents.
**12.** Explain the use of negative exponents.
**13.** Write each of the following in three forms:

$8^{-2}$ $3^4$ $12^0$ $10^{-1}$

**14.** Explain how computing powers of numbers is a synthesizing type of arithmetical computation, and computing roots an analytic type.
**15.** Find the square of each of the following:

16.25 10.01 $\frac{3}{4}$ .125

**16.** Explain the formula $t^2 + 2tu + u^2$.

**17.** How many digits will there be in the square roots of each of the following:

1622 14.267 97 129,265

**18.** Find and check the square root of each of the following:

279 14.22 21,641

**19.** State the Pythagorean theorem. Where did it get its name?

**20.** Find the length of the third side of the triangle shown here.

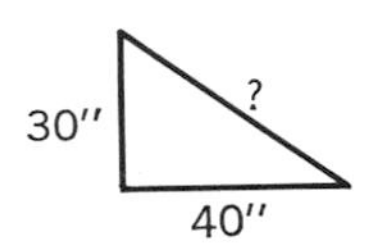


**21.** If $c$ is one edge of a cube, what will $c^3$ represent?

## OPTIONAL ASSIGNMENTS

1. From Swain or other sources, find out what a perfect number is.
2. Report on some of the interesting number lore—for example, numerology —that has accompanied the study of number theory.
3. Following Taylor and Mills, or some other source, construct the sieve of Eratosthenes. Why is this method of finding the prime numbers from 1 to 100 so named?
4. Taylor and Mills show how sets of Pythagorean integers may be determined, that is, integers that are in the right relationship to be the three sides of right triangles. Which do you think is the simplest method? Illustrate it.

## REFERENCES

Goodman, Frederick L., "Prime Numbers and Factoring," *Arithmetic Teacher*, November, 1959, pp. 274–275.

Taylor, E. H., and Mills, C. N., *Arithmetic for Teacher Training Classes*, Holt, Rinehart & Winston, New York, 4th ed., 1955, chap. 8.

Swain, Robert L., *Understanding Arithmetic*, Holt, Rinehart & Winston, New York, 1957, chap. 7.

chapter 16

# Operations with Common Fractions

## I. Historical Development of Use of Fractions

The word *fraction* comes from the Latin word *frangere*, meaning "to break"; hence the term is used to refer to parts. In early mathematical history a fraction was regarded as a broken number.

In reality a fraction is a new number created to augment the integers. There is no integer that satisfies the definition of 1 divided by 2; that is, there is no integer which when multiplied by 2 gives 1, such as $1 \div 2 = ?$ or $? \times 2 = 1$. It therefore became necessary to expand the number system if all computations in division were to have answers. That fractions are new numbers supplementing the integers is clear when they are shown marking points between the integers, thus:

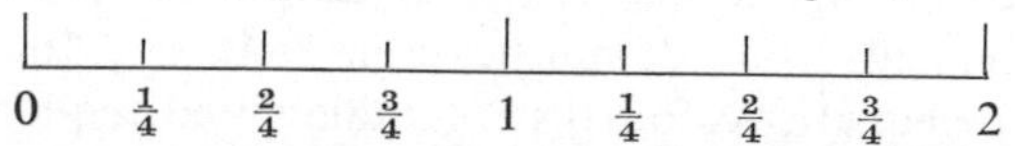


Fractional notation arose gradually with the increasing need for greater precision than is possible with natural numbers. Thus the demands of various number operations have brought about an evolution of number ideas.

The early forms of fractions were cumbersome and involved various symbols.[1] Their difficulty for computations arose from the need to operate with a *pair* of numbers as though the pair were a single number.

Of the fractional forms, unit fractions—those with numerators equal to 1, as in $\frac{1}{2}$, $\frac{1}{4}$, and $\frac{1}{5}$—were used almost exclusively for centuries. It was not until early in the thirteenth century that general fractions came

[1] For illustrations see Robert L. Swain, *Understanding Arithmetic*, Holt, Rinehart & Winston, New York, 1957, pp. 135–136.

into widespread use. From then on, the rules we now use for adding, subtracting, multiplying, and reducing fractions were in common use. Not until several centuries after that, however, was the rule for dividing fractions—invert the divisor and multiply—devised.

## 2. Fractions as Primary-Level Concepts

Though early conceptions of computations with fractions plagued mathematicians of the time, modern arithmetic procedures have brought concepts of simple fractions within the comprehension of primary-grade children. Children in the first grade are now introduced to parts of wholes, first by words accompanied by manipulation and visual aids. They know all about one-half an apple or one-half a candy bar, or even one-half a pie, but many such articles should be cut both by the teacher and by the children themselves. Flannel boards are valuable here for showing half a circle and half a square or rectangle.

Children then go on by easy steps creatively, using manipulation and telling stories about such parts; for example, "I had an apple and cut it in two. Then I had two halves. I gave one of the halves to Jane and have one half left."

Later they go on to one-third and then two-thirds, always with words, because fraction numerals and algorisms come much later. Most arithmetic textbooks and workbooks today provide for the early introduction of fractions in some such simple form.

The children having learned that only like things can be added, the teacher's statement, with demonstration, that one fourth and one fourth make or equal two fourths is familiar, and the idea is comprehensible when fourths of a circle are used in illustration. Likewise the children can comprehend the idea that one fourth and three fourths are four fourths, and that this is enough to make a whole circle or a whole pie.

If the child becomes thoroughly familiar with the *language* of fractions first, the algorism he learns later, $\frac{1}{4} + \frac{1}{4} = \frac{2}{4}$, will not be likely to be confusing to him. He knows that the 4 is used only to tell what kind of part is indicated.*

The first concepts about fractions should be based on parts of a unit, as we saw above. Fractional parts of a collection of units, a group, are presented somewhat later. Some arithmetic authorities say that for

* Guide him so he will discover this.

a child to understand parts of a group his mental age should be one or two years beyond that required for understanding parts of a unit.[2] By this time he will be thoroughly aware that when anything is divided into halves there will be two equal parts. Then he can be shown that when 6 pieces of candy are divided evenly (equally) into two portions there will be 3 pieces in each portion, and therefore that one-half of 6 is 3.

By manipulation and experience, pupils will learn to divide 6 into two equal parts or into three equal parts, and to designate the parts respectively as one-half of 6 or one-third of 6. Again the use of language symbols should be well established before the algorisms, $\frac{1}{2}$ of $6 = 3$ or $\frac{1}{3}$ of $6 = 2$, are used. Children should become very familiar with the language of fractions, and create number situations and stories which use it. When meanings and understandings are thus established, mathematical symbols for these concrete situations can be used readily. These primary concepts build a sound foundation for later work in computing with fractions in the middle and upper grades.

## 3. Terminology of Fractions

As pupils progress from primary-level to higher-level concepts of fractions, they should become familiar with the terms used.

1. Fractions may be said to have three main functions: (1) to express one or more of the equal parts of a unit or a group of units—as in $\frac{2}{3}$ of an apple or $\frac{2}{3}$ of the 24 pupils in the classroom; (2) to indicate an unperformed division—as in $\frac{3}{4}$; and (3) to express a ratio—as in 3 to 4 in $\frac{3}{4}$.
2. In a fraction the numeral below the line, the **denominator**, tells the number of parts into which the whole has been divided; thus $\frac{1}{4}$ shows that something has been divided into 4 parts. The numeral above the line, the **numerator**, tells how many of these parts we are dealing with;

thus in 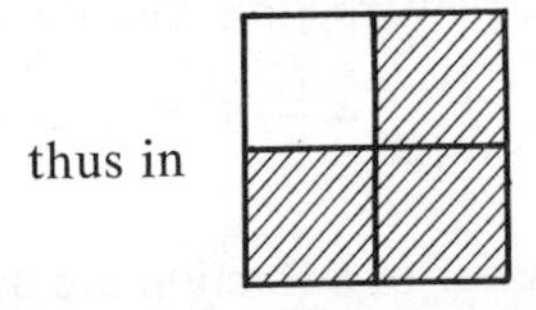 $\frac{3}{4}$ of the square is shaded, which indicates that the square has been divided into 4 equal parts, and

[2] J. T. Johnson, "Are Ratios Fractions?" *Elementary School Journal*, March, 1948, pp. 374–378.

that we are dealing with 3 of those parts. The numerator and the denominator are known as the **terms** of a fraction.

3. Fractions are classified in form as **simple** and **complex**, and in value as **proper** and **improper**. A **simple fraction** is one whose terms are integers—as in $\frac{2}{3}$ or $\frac{4}{5}$. A **complex fraction** is one with a fraction or a mixed number in one or both of its terms—as in $\frac{3\frac{1}{2}}{\frac{4}{5}}$. A **proper fraction** is one that is less than a unit; its numerator is less than its denominator—as in $\frac{7}{8}$. An **improper fraction** is one that is equal to or greater than a unit; its numerator is equal to or greater than its denominator—as in $\frac{4}{4}$ or $\frac{5}{4}$. A **mixed number** is a numeral composed of an integer and a fraction—as in $6\frac{1}{2}$.

## 4. Higher-Level Concepts of Fractions

Before beginning general computation with fractions children should have had a great deal of experience with equivalent fractions by manipulating parts of circles or rectangles on a flannel board or on their desks. Such work deals with fractional parts of units. The teacher can demonstrate equivalence by having the pupils cut one circle into halves, and other circles of equal size into fourths, sixths, eighths, and so on, and then lay 2 eighths on 1 fourth, or 3 fourths on 6 eighths, and write down the many equivalents they find. This prepares the children for changing fractions to common denominators. Having acquired some facility in adding and subtracting like fractions, they will be ready for adding and subtracting unlike fractions and for finding uses for such computations in their own experience.

By this time pupils, with teacher guidance, should be able to formulate some generalizations concerning fractions; for example:

1. When the numerator and denominator of a fraction are both multiplied by the same number, the new fraction is equivalent to (equal to) the other fraction. In $\frac{3 \times 2}{4 \times 2} = \frac{6}{8}$, the value of the fraction has not been changed.
2. When the numerator and denominator of a fraction are divided by the same number, the value of the fraction is unchanged; e.g., $\frac{6 \div 2}{8 \div 2} = \frac{3}{4}$. These are mechanical processes, but proof

that they are true should be demonstrated by means of concrete or semi-concrete aids.

## 5. Reduction of Fractions

It is sometimes necessary or desirable in using fractions in computation to change the form of a fraction, for example, changing $\frac{1}{4}$ to $\frac{2}{8}$. Any process which changes the form without changing the value is called **reduction**; the forms $\frac{1}{2}$, $\frac{2}{4}$, and $\frac{4}{8}$ may be regarded as different names for the same number. We may *choose* the form in which we express the number. In $\frac{1}{2} - \frac{1}{4}$ we have unlike fractions. We may reduce them both to fourths or, if we choose, to eighths. In either case we shall have like fractions and can then do the subtraction.

Reduction of fractions* is of several types.

### *Reduction to lowest terms*

A fraction is in its lowest terms when the numerator and the denominator are prime to each other, that is, when they have no common divisor except 1. To reduce a fraction to its lowest terms we divide both numerator and denominator by their highest common divisor, e.g., $\frac{30 \div 15}{75 \div 15} = \frac{2}{5}$. As we said at the end of Section 3, this does not change the value of the fraction. The reduction may be done in several steps instead of using the *highest* common divisor immediately, e.g., $\frac{30 \div 3}{75 \div 3} = \frac{10 \div 5}{25 \div 5} = \frac{2}{5}$. If no common divisor is immediately apparent, the following principle may be used: Any common divisor of the numerator and the denominator of a fraction is a divisor of their difference (or their sum); for example, in $\frac{30}{75}$ the difference is 45. If 30 and 75 have any common factors, those numbers will also be factors of 45. Hence one or more of the factors of 45 (3, 5, 9, 15) will be factors of both 30 and 75. In this case, 3, 5, and 15 are common factors of 30 and 75. This principle is one application of the distributive law of multiplication.

---

* Guide pupils to develop these procedures.

### *Reduction to higher terms*

Changing a fraction to higher terms means changing it to an equivalent fraction with a larger denominator. This is done by multiplying both numerator and denominator by the same integer. As indicated in Section 3, this does not change the value of the fraction. This type of reduction is used chiefly in adding and subtracting fractions and will be discussed more fully in a later section. For example, if we want to add $\frac{1}{2}$, $\frac{1}{4}$, and $\frac{1}{8}$, we must change the fractions to like fractions, because only like things can be added. In this case we need to change $\frac{1}{2}$ and $\frac{1}{4}$ to eighths. Since we multiply the denominator 2 (in $\frac{1}{2}$) by 4 to get 8 $\left(\frac{1}{2 \times 4} = \frac{}{8}\right)$, we must also multiply the numerator by 4 if we are to leave the value unchanged. The procedure is $\frac{1 \times 4}{2 \times 4} = \frac{4}{8}$; for $\frac{1}{4}$, it is $\frac{1 \times 2}{4 \times 2} = \frac{2}{8}$. We can now add $\frac{4}{8}$, $\frac{2}{8}$ and $\frac{1}{8}$.

### *Reduction of an improper fraction to a mixed number*

Reducing an improper fraction to a mixed number involves merely doing the indicated division; thus, $\frac{42}{6} = 7$, or in case of a remainder, $\frac{135}{4} = 33\frac{3}{4}$. It is customary in arithmetic to express an answer as a whole number or a mixed number rather than as an improper fraction.

### *Reduction of an integer to an improper fraction*

It is seldom necessary to reduce an integer to an improper fraction. However, the pupil who knows that $\frac{4}{4} = 1$ whole, $\frac{3}{3} = 1$ whole, and so on, readily grasps the related fact that 3 whole apples have three times as many parts as 1 whole apple has, hence $3 \times \frac{4}{4}$ or $3 \times \frac{3}{3}$. These concepts should of course be explained first by visual and manipulative means.

### *Reduction of a mixed number to an improper fraction*

Too often reducing a mixed number to an improper fraction is taught by having pupils memorize and apply the following rule: To change a mixed number to an improper fraction, multiply the integer by the denominator of the fraction, add the numerator, and write the result over the denominator. If we support the idea of meaning and understanding in the learning of arithmetic, we will not begin this form of reduction with the rule. Rather, we will show the pupil that in some computations it is simpler to deal with $\frac{15}{4}$ than with $3\frac{3}{4}$—for example, in multiplying mixed numbers such as $3\frac{3}{4} \times 2\frac{1}{2}$. This is much more readily computed as $\frac{15}{4} \times \frac{5}{2}$. There is probably little purpose in teaching this type of reduction until the multiplication of fractions is introduced; but whenever it is taught, the pupil should *understand* the process.

This type of reduction follows logically the reduction of an integer to an improper fraction. Instead of having 2 whole apples and $\frac{1}{2}$ an apple to divide among several people, the child sees the advantage of having all halves. He sees that 2 apples are reduced to 4 halves, $\frac{4}{2}$, and that the additional $\frac{1}{2}$ makes 5 halves, $\frac{5}{2}$.

In the case of $3\frac{3}{4}$, there are $\frac{4}{4}$ in one whole (an apple, or whatever concrete thing is being used) and in 3 whole ones there are three times as many fourths, or $\frac{12}{4}$. This $\frac{12}{4} + \frac{3}{4}$ gives a total of $\frac{15}{4}$ as being equivalent to $3\frac{3}{4}$. Given an adequate amount of this type of computing the pupil discovers that what really happens—for example, in $3\frac{1}{4}$—is $\frac{4 \times 3 + 1}{4}$. He becomes aware of this as a short cut and he explains it by stating the rule given above, but now he knows *why* $4 \times 3 + 1$ is the total number of fourths.

## 6. Addition and Subtraction of Fractions*

The addition of fractions includes several types.

1. Like fractions with no reduction, such as $\frac{1}{5} + \frac{2}{5} = \frac{3}{5}$.
2. Mixed numbers with like fractions and no reduction, such as:

$$\begin{array}{r} 6\frac{1}{5} \\ +3\frac{3}{5} \\ \hline 9\frac{4}{5} \end{array}$$

* With guidance pupils can figure out these processes without demonstrations by the teacher.

3. Mixed numbers with like fractions and with reduction, such as:

$$\begin{array}{r} 6\frac{1}{4} \\ +3\frac{3}{4} \\ \hline 9\frac{4}{4} = 1 \\ +1 \\ \hline 10 \end{array}$$

Here when $\frac{4}{4}$ is reduced to 1, it is added in with the units column.

4. Mixed numbers with unlike fractions that are reduced to like fractions, with no carrying, as in:

$$\begin{array}{rr} 6\frac{1}{4} & \frac{1}{4} \\ +3\frac{1}{2} & \frac{2}{4} \\ \hline 9\frac{3}{4} & \frac{3}{4} \end{array}$$

5. Mixed numbers with unlike fractions that are reduced to like fractions, with carrying, as in:

$$\begin{array}{rl} 6\frac{1}{4} & \frac{2}{8} \\ +3\frac{7}{8} & \frac{7}{8} \\ \hline 9 & \frac{9}{8} = 1\frac{1}{8} \\ +1\frac{1}{8} & \\ \hline 10\frac{1}{8} & \end{array}$$

The subtraction of fractions involves processes that are closely related to those in addition. In only one case—mixed numbers in which the fraction of the subtrahend is larger than that of the minuend—are the processes really different from those in addition. In $\begin{array}{r} 6\frac{3}{8} \\ -3\frac{7}{8} \\ \hline \end{array}$ there are like denominators, but $\frac{3}{8}$ is not large enough for $\frac{7}{8}$ to be taken away. This indicates the need for borrowing, or reducing 1 unit of the minuend to eighths, since this is the denominator it is convenient to work with. This situation is not basically different from that in which borrowing is used in whole numbers, with which the pupils are already familiar. Thus $6\frac{3}{8}$ becomes $5\frac{3}{8} + \frac{8}{8}$ or $5\frac{11}{8}$, and the above problem in subtraction is now:

$$\begin{array}{r} 5\frac{11}{8} \\ -3\frac{7}{8} \\ \hline 2\frac{4}{8} \text{ or } 2\frac{1}{2} \end{array}$$

In $\begin{array}{r} 6\frac{1}{3} \\ -3\frac{5}{6} \\ \hline \end{array}$ there are unlike denominators. The first step is to make the denominators alike; it is then obvious that $\frac{5}{6}$ cannot be subtracted from $\frac{2}{6}$. Again 1 unit is borrowed and reduced, this time to sixths, since this is the denominator we want to work with. The problem now is:

$$\begin{array}{l} 5\frac{2}{6} + \frac{6}{6} = \frac{8}{6} \\ -3\frac{5}{6} \\ \hline \end{array} \quad \text{or} \quad \begin{array}{r} 5\frac{8}{6} \\ -3\frac{5}{6} \\ \hline 2\frac{3}{6} \text{ or } 2\frac{1}{2} \end{array}$$

## 7. Multiplication of Fractions

No computations with whole numbers have much resemblance to multiplication of fractions. But if the first steps in adding fractions are understood, the first step in multiplying them will not be difficult. The relationship is the same as that between adding and multiplying whole numbers. For example, $3 + 3 + 3 + 3$ gives the same result as four 3's, or 12; $\frac{1}{4} + \frac{1}{4} + \frac{1}{4}$ is the same as three $\frac{1}{4}$'s or $\frac{3}{4}$. This can readily be demonstrated if visual aids such as flannel boards are used. As in addition, the denominator merely indicates the kind of parts; only the numerator is used in the computation. For example, $\frac{1}{4} + \frac{1}{4} + \frac{1}{4}$, or 3 times 1 part of the kind we call fourths, is 3 of those parts, the same as 1 and 1 and 1 or 3 times 1 of anything else. Hence, as long as the multiplier is a whole number the computation is fairly simple.

When the fractional part used as the multiplicand is not a unit fraction, as in $2 \times \frac{2}{3}$, the procedure is the same, $\frac{2}{3} + \frac{2}{3}$, or 2 times $\frac{2}{3}$. Here again 2 and 2 are 4 parts, and 2 times 2 parts are 4 parts, in this case 4 thirds or $\frac{4}{3}$.

Too many textbooks introduce this step by using $2 \times \frac{2}{3}$ and the reverse, $\frac{2}{3} \times 2$, without differentiation. As long as both factors are abstract numbers the result is the same for both. But when problem situations are involved, confusion may easily arise. To illustrate $2 \times \frac{2}{3}$ the problem might be: "Jim has $\frac{2}{3}$ of his apple left and Tom has $\frac{2}{3}$ of his left. How much do they both have?" Obviously they have $\frac{2}{3} + \frac{2}{3}$ or 2 times $\frac{2}{3}$, which is $\frac{4}{3}$, or $1\frac{1}{3}$ apples in all. But with $\frac{2}{3}$ as the multiplier, we generally interpret $\frac{2}{3}$ times a quantity as $\frac{2}{3}$ of it. Thus $\frac{2}{3}$ of 2 apples is a somewhat different concept than 2 times $\frac{2}{3}$ of an apple, even though the two processes have the same numerical result. Therefore, care should be taken to see that pupils understand the two different concepts.

Having had previous experience in changing integers and mixed numbers into fractions, as in $3 = \frac{12}{4}$ and $3\frac{1}{2} = \frac{7}{2}$, the pupil can see $4 \times 3\frac{1}{2}$ as $4 \times \frac{7}{2}$ or $\frac{28}{2}$ or 14.* He should also be shown or helped to discover that it is possible to compute $4 \times 3\frac{1}{2}$ thus:

$$\begin{array}{r} 3\frac{1}{2} \\ \times 4 \\ \hline 12 \\ +2 \\ \hline 14 \end{array} \qquad 4 \times \frac{1}{2} = 2$$

Multiplying a fraction by a fraction is a difficult new concept, and should be introduced with some visual aid like the diagram shown below for the following problem: "Mr. Adams rented a vacant lot for Tom and three of his friends, Bill, Jim, and Jack, to make gardens on so they could earn money for a Scout trip. Each boy had $\frac{1}{4}$ of the lot. Tom decided to plant $\frac{1}{2}$ of his part to corn. What part of the whole lot was his corn plot?"

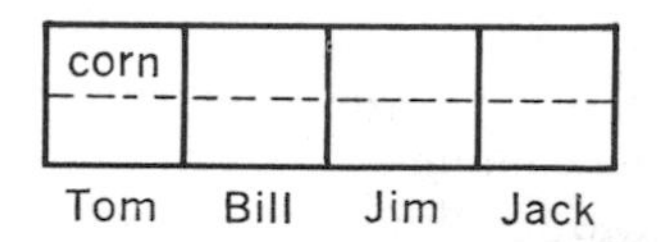


* Pupils should be given the opportunity to discover this for themselves.

The diagram shows that $\frac{1}{2}$ of $\frac{1}{4}$ of the lot is $\frac{1}{8}$ of it. The pupils have worked this out by diagrams in earlier work in fractions. The new experience here is solving the problem by algorism and proving it by diagram.

Since it is clear that $\frac{1}{2}$ of $\frac{1}{4} = \frac{1}{8}$, and it can be shown by similar diagrams that $\frac{1}{2}$ of $\frac{1}{6} = \frac{1}{12}$, $\frac{1}{3}$ of $\frac{1}{2} = \frac{1}{6}$, and so on, the pupils may discover that the product of the numerators gives the numerator of the answer, and the product of the denominators gives the denominator of the answer. In this way they have learned the mechanics of the computation. Teachers who want their pupils to understand the algorism can point out that the larger the denominator of a unit fraction, the smaller is the value of the fraction. When a circle is divided into eighths, there are twice as many parts as when the same circle is divided into fourths, but they are only half as large. By the same principle, when the denominator of $\frac{1}{6}$ is multiplied by 2 and changed to 12 ($\frac{1}{12}$), the size of the part ($\frac{1}{12}$) is only half as large as the $\frac{1}{6}$.

Instead of saying, "To find $\frac{1}{2}$ of a given fraction, double the denominator of that fraction, or to find $\frac{1}{3}$ of it, multiply the given denominator by 3," writing the algorism $\frac{1}{2} \times \frac{1}{4}$ places the numbers to be multiplied in proximity and $\frac{1}{2} \times \frac{1}{4}$ becomes $\frac{1 \times 1}{2 \times 4}$ or $\frac{1}{8}$.

Thus far the illustrations have dealt only with unit fractions. But suppose we want to find $\frac{1}{2}$ of $\frac{3}{4}$. Again we change the size of the parts, but not the number of parts; hence, $\frac{1}{2}$ of $\frac{3}{4}$ is $\frac{3}{8}$. But what happens if the first fraction is not a unit fraction but instead we want to find $\frac{2}{3}$ of $\frac{3}{4}$? As before, $3 \times 4$ makes the parts twelfths and therefore only a third as large as the fourths were; also as before, the number of parts is not disturbed, except that taking 2 parts of anything ($\frac{2}{3}$) gives twice as much as taking 1 part ($\frac{1}{3}$) of it. Since $\frac{1}{3}$ of $\frac{3}{4}$ is $\frac{3}{12}$, if we want $\frac{2}{3}$ of $\frac{3}{4}$ we shall have 2 times as much as $\frac{3}{12}$, or $\frac{6}{12}$. We must multiply these parts by 2. Writing it as $\frac{2}{3} \times \frac{3}{4}$ makes it easy to multiply the two numerators and the two denominators, and their position indicates what numbers we are to multiply. Any algorism is merely a way of writing what we have found to be true.

## 8. Division of Fractions

Neither multiplication nor division of fractions is presented in all its forms before the sixth grade in most modern elementary arithmetic texts. Division is admittedly the most difficult of the four fundamental processes, with fractions as well as with integers.

The division of fractions involves three main types of computation:

1. Whole numbers divided by fractions, such as $6 \div \frac{1}{3}$.
2. Fractions divided by whole numbers, such as $\frac{1}{2} \div 4$.
3. Fractions divided by fractions, such as $\frac{3}{4} \div \frac{1}{2}$.

In the writer's opinion, they should be introduced in this order.

In the first place $4 \div \frac{1}{3}$ is a measurement type of division; this is a simpler concept than the partition type.* Furthermore, such a problem can be solved by serial subtraction as was done in Chapter 14 for this type of division of integers, as illustrated in (a). It can be verified by drawings, e.g., by using a number line as in (b). There are 12 $\frac{1}{3}$'s in 4.

a.

$$\begin{array}{r} 4 \\ -\frac{1}{3} \\ \hline 3\frac{2}{3} \\ -\frac{1}{3} \\ \hline 3\frac{1}{3} \\ -\frac{1}{3} \\ \hline 3 \\ -\frac{1}{3} \\ \hline 2\frac{2}{3} \\ -\frac{1}{3} \\ \hline 2\frac{1}{3} \\ -\frac{1}{3} \\ \hline 2 \\ -\frac{1}{3} \\ \hline 1\frac{2}{3} \\ -\frac{1}{3} \\ \hline 1\frac{1}{3} \\ -\frac{1}{3} \\ \hline 1 \\ -\frac{1}{3} \\ \hline \frac{2}{3} \\ -\frac{1}{3} \\ \hline \frac{1}{3} \\ -\frac{1}{3} \\ \hline \end{array}$$

b.

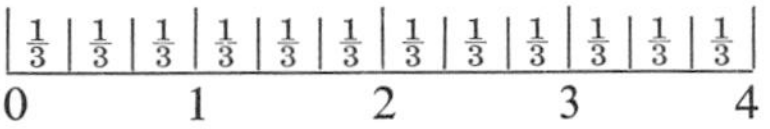

| $\frac{1}{3}$ | $\frac{1}{3}$ | $\frac{1}{3}$ | $\frac{1}{3}$ | $\frac{1}{3}$ | $\frac{1}{3}$ | $\frac{1}{3}$ | $\frac{1}{3}$ | $\frac{1}{3}$ | $\frac{1}{3}$ | $\frac{1}{3}$ | $\frac{1}{3}$ |
|---|---|---|---|---|---|---|---|---|---|---|---|

0 1 2 3 4

This can be verified by drawings as in (c). There are 12 $\frac{1}{3}$'s in 4.

c.

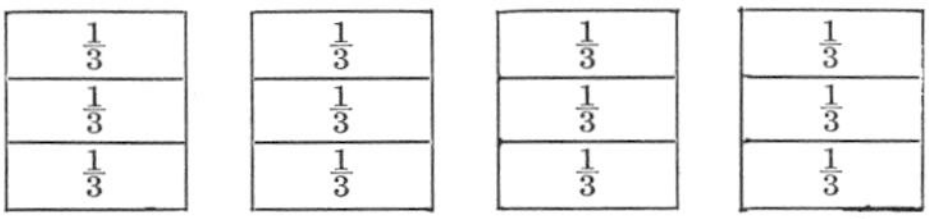

| $\frac{1}{3}$ | $\frac{1}{3}$ | $\frac{1}{3}$ | $\frac{1}{3}$ |
|---|---|---|---|
| $\frac{1}{3}$ | $\frac{1}{3}$ | $\frac{1}{3}$ | $\frac{1}{3}$ |
| $\frac{1}{3}$ | $\frac{1}{3}$ | $\frac{1}{3}$ | $\frac{1}{3}$ |

This is readily solved by the common-denominator method which is used in many of the newer elementary textbooks in arithmetic as a first step in the division of fractions by computation; this is shown in (d).

d. $4 = \frac{12}{3}$ $\quad \frac{12}{3} \div \frac{1}{3}$ is as $12 \div 1$ or 12.

Hence $4 \div \frac{1}{3} = 12$.

Note that the drawing in (c) above actually changed the whole number (4 rectangles) into thirds (12 of them), and therefore is a graphic illustration of method (d). Many computations should be provided using the common-denominator procedure; they should include real life situations like "Four candy bars cut into thirds will serve how many children?"

* With some manipulative experimentation pupils can find a solution.

In such problems it is well to begin with a unit fraction as the divisor. The next step can be like $4 \div \frac{2}{3}$. Here $4 = \frac{12}{3}$ and $\frac{12}{3} \div \frac{2}{3}$ is like $12 \div 2$ or 6. Then the pupil begins to see a short cut: he has always multiplied the whole number by the denominator of the fraction and divided by the numerator of the fraction thus, $4 \times 3 = 12$; $12 \div 2 = 6$, or $4 \times 3 \div 2$. Since this is the procedure, $\frac{4 \times 3}{2}$ indicates the computation, and after some experimentation he will conclude that $4 \times \frac{3}{2}$ has changed his division problem into a simple multiplication problem. By induction he has arrived at the rule: To divide by a fraction, invert the divisor and multiply. Or in more academic language: To divide a number by a fraction, multiply the number by the reciprocal of the fraction.[3]

Now the pupil is ready to do the problems by one method and check by another. After he has mastered the first type of computation reasonably well, he is ready for the second type, fractions divided by whole numbers, such as $\frac{1}{2} \div 4$. This type can also be introduced by the common denominator method, but it involves a more difficult concept, for $\frac{1}{2} \div \frac{8}{2}$ is like $1 \div 8$ or $\frac{1}{8}$. However, the pupil is now ready to apply the rule for all division of fractions, thus, $\frac{1}{2} \div 4 = \frac{1}{2} \times \frac{1}{4}$ or $\frac{1}{8}$. Moreover, he can show the solution by a drawing:

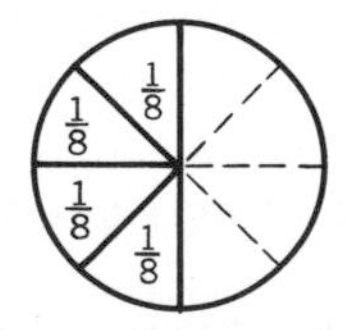


An illustrative problem is: "If $\frac{1}{2}$ a pie is divided among 4 boys, what part of the whole pie will each one get?"

In their work with whole numbers pupils have learned that when any number is divided by 4, the solution may be found by taking $\frac{1}{4}$ of the given number. Likewise in the fractional problem $\frac{1}{2} \div 4$, the computation can be expressed as $\frac{1}{4}$ of $\frac{1}{2}$ and as $\frac{1}{4} \times \frac{1}{2}$; in the latter, as was pointed out previously, the division operation is converted to a multiplication process.

[3] Two numbers are said to be reciprocals if their product is 1; for example, $4 \times \frac{1}{4}$ or $\frac{2}{3} \times \frac{3}{2}$. The reciprocal of any number $N$ is equal to $\frac{1}{N}$; e.g., $1 \div \frac{2}{3} = \frac{3}{2}$.

For the third type, fractions divided by fractions, as in $\frac{3}{4} \div \frac{1}{2}$, the common denominator method can also be used first: as $\frac{3}{4} \div \frac{2}{4}$ or $3 \div 2$ or $1\frac{1}{2}$. Drawings are very difficult to use for this type; rationalization of the process is also difficult, except that it involves a measurement type of problem and can be solved by serial subtraction. Moreover, when the divisor is a unit fraction, such as $\frac{1}{2}$, the children can be shown that if $\frac{3}{4}$, or any other number, is divided by $\frac{1}{2}$, the answer will be twice as large as when the number is divided by 1. Thus when $\frac{3}{4}$ is divided by 1, the answer is $\frac{3}{4}$; when $\frac{3}{4}$ is divided by $\frac{1}{2}$, the answer is twice as large—$\frac{3}{4} \times \frac{2}{1}$ or $\frac{6}{4}$. Obviously this is equivalent to using the inversion or reciprocal rule, and $\frac{3}{4} \div \frac{1}{2}$ becomes $\frac{3}{4} \times \frac{2}{1}$ or $\frac{6}{4}$ or $1\frac{1}{2}$.

Problems involving social utility are rarely of this type, unless we use mixed numbers instead of common fractions in such a problem as, "How many milk shakes can I make from $6\frac{1}{2}$ cups of milk, if I use $1\frac{1}{2}$ cups for each milk shake?"

Some maintain that pupils in the fifth and sixth grades cannot be expected to understand all the rationale of inverting the divisor in dividing fractions, but that they can be taught the mechanical procedure for doing it.[4] Since the division of fractions is rarely called for in everyday life, there seems to be no reason to introduce it until pupils are sufficiently mature to comprehend it. The writer believes that sixth-grade pupils can comprehend the process as it is presented in this chapter. Furthermore, she agrees with arithmetic authorities who say that if pupils are to attain proficiency in elementary arithmetic as a background for further courses in mathematics, they need to know some types of computation that may not be directly involved in their daily experiences.[5]

With this idea in mind, the writer believes that pupils should be introduced to complex fractions, such as:

$$\frac{\frac{2}{3} \text{ of } 4\frac{1}{2}}{2\frac{1}{3} \div 8}$$

[4] J. Allen Hickerson, *Guiding Children's Arithmetic Experiences*, Prentice-Hall, New York, 1952, p. 236; L. J. Brueckner and Foster E. Grossnickle, *How to Make Arithmetic Meaningful*, Holt, Rinehart & Winston, New York, 1947, p. 344; Foster E. Grossnickle, "How to Use a Fractional Divisor," *Journal of Education*, October, 1954, pp. 17–19.

[5] Cf. Herbert F. Spitzer, "How Will the New Emphasis on Science Affect Arithmetic Teaching?" *The Instructor*, April, 1959, p. 6.

No new processes are involved.* Recognition of the long line as indicating division calls for simplifying both the entire numerator and the entire denominator by performing the indicated computation, and then dividing the simplified numerator by the simplified denominator, thus:

$$\left.\begin{array}{l}\frac{2}{3} \text{ of } 4\frac{1}{2} = \frac{2}{3} \times \frac{9}{2} = 3 \\[2ex] 2\frac{1}{3} \div 8 = \frac{7}{3} \times \frac{1}{8} = \frac{7}{24}\end{array}\right\} \qquad \frac{3}{\frac{7}{24}}$$

$$3 \div \frac{7}{24} = 3 \times \frac{24}{7} = \frac{72}{7} = 10\frac{2}{7}$$

Mixed numbers have been given little attention in discussing division of fractions because pupils have become accustomed to changing mixed numbers to improper fractions for multiplication, and computation with them is no different from that with proper fractions.

These experiences with fractional computations give rise to four additional principles that older pupils can derive.

1. Multiplying the numerator of a fraction by a number *multiplies* the fraction by that number; e.g., $\frac{1 \times 3}{3} = \frac{3}{3}$.
2. Dividing the numerator of a fraction by a number *divides* the fraction by that number; e.g., $\frac{4 \div 2}{8} = \frac{2}{8}$.
3. Multiplying the denominator of a fraction by a number *divides* the fraction by that number; e.g., $\frac{1}{4 \times 2} = \frac{1}{8}$.
4. Dividing the denominator of a fraction by a number *multiplies* the fraction by that number; e.g., $\frac{3}{8 \div 2} = \frac{3}{4}$.

## 9. Cancellation

Since cancellation is simply multiplication of fractions, it should be given some attention here. No new computational ideas are involved and most pupils have little difficulty with it. Cancellation is a procedure for decreasing the size of numbers that have to be worked with. For example, in multiplying $\frac{16}{24} \times \frac{9}{40} \times \frac{8}{32}$ without any cancellation the

* Give pupils an opportunity to pool their thinking and decide on the steps to be taken to obtain a solution.

answer will be $\frac{1152}{30720}$, a rather formidable-looking fraction. Reducing it to lowest terms involves several steps and thereby increases the chance of errors.

Cancellation applies the principle relating to fractions which states that if the numerator and denominator are divided by the same number, the value of the fraction is unchanged; that is, the ratio of the numerator to the denominator remains the same.* Also involved is the rule which says that the product of two fractions is obtained by multiplying the two numerators for the numerator of the product, and multiplying the two denominators for the denominator of the product. Thus $\frac{16}{24} \times \frac{9}{40} \times \frac{8}{32}$ in the form that indicates this multiplication is: $\frac{16 \times 9 \times 8}{24 \times 40 \times 32}$. This three-factor numerator is the indicated dividend, and the three-factor denominator is the divisor.

One principle of factoring states that a factor of a number is a factor of any of its multiplies. Therefore, any factor of 16, 9, and 8 is also a factor of 1152, and likewise any factor of 24, 40, and 32 is also a factor of 30,720. Obviously it is much more convenient to divide the numerator and the denominator by their *common factors* while they are in the three-factor form than when they are in the product form, $\frac{1152}{30720}$. Furthermore, another principle of division says that dividing the dividend and divisor by the same number does not change the quotient. When pupils see the various principles being applied, they are on their way to understanding number relationships.

The most common error in cancellation problems is failing to record the quotient when dividing by common factors. For example, in $\frac{6}{7} \times \frac{7}{8}$ pupils assume that when they cross out the 7's they do away with them; this is due to their not really understanding the applications of the above principles. The correct procedure is to say that we divide both the numerator and the denominator by 7. When we divide the 7 in the numerator by 7 the quotient is 1 and the 7 in the denominator also results in a quotient of 1; these 1's should be recorded. Recording quotients other than 1 gives much less difficulty. Correctly written, then, the computation is: $\frac{\overset{3}{\cancel{6}}}{\underset{1}{\cancel{7}}} \times \frac{\overset{1}{\cancel{7}}}{\underset{4}{\cancel{8}}} = \frac{3}{4}$. Since whether the 1's are

* Encourage pupils to discover this.

recorded does not affect the answer, this procedure may be dispensed with after the pupils really understand all the steps and the reasons for the procedure.

## 10. Fractions in Part-Whole Relationships

In general there are three types of computation involving fractions in part-whole relationships.

1. Finding a part of a number, such as $\frac{3}{4}$ of 12.
2. Finding what part one number is of another, such as what part of 12 is 9?
3. Finding a number when a fractional part of it is given, such as $\frac{3}{4}$ of what number is 9?

Thirty-seven years ago Brown and Coffman[6] were dealing with those types by using equations thus:

1. $\frac{3}{4}$ of $12 = ?$
2. ? part of $12 = 2$
3. $\frac{3}{4}$ of $? = 9$

Unfortunately this procedure was shelved during some of the attempts to modernize arithmetic. The present writer believes, however, that equations are the simplest and most understandable procedure for teaching such computations—provided the pupils become proficient in using multiplication and division equations while working with whole numbers.

With this knowledge of the solution of equations, the first type above: $\frac{3}{4}$ of $12 = ?$ merely becomes: $\frac{3}{4} \times 12 = ?$; here two factors are known, the product is to be found. The second type when simplified becomes: ? of $12 = 9$, or: $? \times 12 = 9$. Here the product and one factor are known; the solution is obtained simply by dividing the product by the known factor to find the other factor: $9 \div 12 = \frac{9}{12}$ or $\frac{3}{4}$. Likewise in the third type: $\frac{3}{4}$ of $? = 9$, the product and one factor are known and the other factor is obtained by division: $9 \div \frac{3}{4} = 9 \times \frac{4}{3}$ or 12.

The teacher should never let able pupils be satisfied with one method of solution. He should encourage them to find other methods and to check their first solution by another method. In these computations many arithmetic textbooks present only the unitary analysis method for

[6] Joseph C. Brown, and Lotus D. Coffman, *The Teaching of Arithmetic*, Row, Peterson, Evanston, 1924.

the first and third types; but since this method is not readily applicable to the second type, the pupils have been left to juggle possibilities (is it $\frac{9}{12}$ or $\frac{12}{9}$?) hoping they can trust their memory.

The unitary analysis method of solving the first type is as follows: What is $\frac{3}{4}$ of 12? $\frac{1}{4}$ of $12 = 3$; $\frac{3}{4}$ of $12 = 3 \times 3$ or 9. For the third type: $\frac{3}{4}$ of a number $= 9$; $\frac{1}{4}$ of the number is $\frac{1}{3}$ as much as $\frac{3}{4}$ of it, or $\frac{1}{3}$ of 9, or 3; $\frac{4}{4}$ of the number is 4 times as much as $\frac{1}{4}$ of it, so $\frac{4}{4}$ of the number is $4 \times 3$ or 12. The second type might be solved thus: What part of 12 is 9? What part of 12 is 1? It is $\frac{1}{12}$ of 12. Then 9 is 9 times as large a part as 1 is; therefore, $9 \times \frac{1}{12}$ or $\frac{9}{12}$ or $\frac{3}{4}$.

It should be obvious that recalling these processes as well as understanding them, is much more difficult than using equations. Furthermore, the same three types appear in the form of decimal fractions and percentages; hence using equations with common fractions will enable the pupil to use them readily in these other situations.

Using a fractional form to express ratio should, in the writer's opinion, be reserved for the upper grades, though some of the new elementary arithmetic text series include it in work for the middle grades. Instead of "What part of 9 is 6?" the question becomes "What is the ratio (relation as determined by measurement) of 9 to 6?" or, in simpler figures, "What is the ratio of 1 to 4?" This may be answered by saying that 1 is $\frac{1}{4}$ as much as 4, or that 4 is 4 times as much as 1.

The fact that number has several aspects—for example, series meaning, collection meaning, ratio meaning, and relational meaning—was mentioned in Chapter 9. As we saw there, *ratio meaning* indicates a comparison developed through measurement. It is closely related to multiplication, division, and fractions. Thus in measuring a 1-inch line in comparison with a 4-inch line, we find that the 1-inch line is $\frac{1}{4}$ of the 4-inch line, and that the 4-inch line is 4 times the length of the 1-inch line. This aspect of number is definitely a more difficult concept than the other three mentioned above, and its presentation may well be delayed until ratio meaning is called for in certain measurement problems and in drawing to a scale.

The importance of visual aids and manipulation in dealing with fractional parts cannot be emphasized too strongly. Moreover, verbal problems applying each successive process in fractions should be provided. As was pointed out earlier, pupils should compose illustrative computations and problems; for when they can write suitable problems, it is more than probable that they will better comprehend the problems written by others.

In short, common fractions need not be the stumbling block that they too commonly are in elementary arithmetic if they are properly presented and are developed by means of these successive processes.

## COMPETENCE CHECK

**1.** Define or explain each of the following, and give an illustration:

1. Terms of a fraction
2. Simple fraction
3. Complex fraction
4. Proper fraction
5. Improper fraction
6. Mixed number
7. Unit fraction
8. A fraction in the lowest terms
9. Integer
10. Reciprocal of a number
11. Equivalent fractions
12. Common fraction
13. Rationalization of fractions
14. Ratio meaning of fractions

**2.** Write five principles or generalizations derived from your study of fractions.

**3.** Why do we add numerators, but not denominators, in adding fractions?

**4.** Explain how you solve $\frac{2}{3} \times \frac{4}{5}$ and why that process gives the right answer.

**5.** Solve "8 is what part of 12?" by using equations. Also solve it by the unitary analysis method.

**6.** Make a diagram to illustrate your solution of "$\frac{3}{4}$ of what number equals 21?"

**7.** Explain or demonstrate how you would show the equivalence of $\frac{1}{2}$, $\frac{3}{6}$, and $\frac{6}{12}$ on a flannel board.

**8.** How are fractions reduced to higher terms?

**9.** Give an example of subtracting fractions with no reduction, and with reduction and also borrowing.

**10.** What does dividing the denominator of a fraction do to the value of the fraction? Illustrate.

**11.** What three types of computation are there in the division of fractions?

**12.** Explain and illustrate the common denominator method of dividing fractions.

**13.** Explain and illustrate the inversion method.

**14.** Show two ways of solving $2\frac{3}{4} \times 5$.

**15.** Demonstrate with a fractional number line each of the following:

$$\frac{3}{4} + \frac{1}{8}; \qquad \frac{7}{8} - \frac{1}{4}; \qquad 3 \times \frac{2}{3}; \qquad 6\frac{1}{2} \div 4.$$

**16.** Explain and illustrate: "A fraction may be considered as representing the quotient of two numbers."

**17.** Explain cancellation and the two principles involved.

**18.** Why is cancellation a misleading name for the process?

## OPTIONAL ASSIGNMENTS

1. Do the basic laws of arithmetic—commutative, associative, and distributive laws—apply to fractions? Give illustrations to support your answer.
2. What is Spitzer's answer to the question he uses as a title, "How Will the New Emphasis on Science Affect Arithmetic Teaching?"

## REFERENCES


Grossnickle, Foster E., "How to Use a Fractional Divisor," *Journal of Education*, October, 1954, pp. 17–19.

Spitzer, Herbert F., "How Will the New Emphasis on Science Affect Arithmetic Teaching?" *The Instructor*, April, 1959, p. 6.

chapter 17

# Operations with Decimal Fractions

## 1. Introduction

Pupils with a good comprehension of the meaning and use of common fractions should not find much difficulty in understanding and using decimal fractions and percentages. Their forms are different, but essentially all of them represent parts of wholes or of groups which may be identical in value; for example, a certain part of anything may be written as $\frac{3}{4}$ of it, .75 of it, or 75 per cent of it.

## 2. Wide Use of Decimal Fractions

Every school child learns to recognize and use money values, such as \$2.50, \$10.75, and so on, long before he is introduced to decimal computation in any other form. He knows how to add the amounts he spends, e.g.,

```
 $3.50
   .25
 +1.25
 -----
 $5.00
```

and in most schools he has learned to keep the decimal points in a straight line before he leaves the third grade, but he knows it only as a mechanical operation.

Although decimal numbers are most frequently used in reading and writing amounts of money, we have only to scan a newspaper to see the extent to which they are used in many other types of information: precipitation, .65 inch; in sports,

```
Newton      .800
Centerville .500
Lincoln     .450
```

and the 100-yard dash in 10.5 seconds; barometric pressure, 29.65 inches of mercury. At the service station we pay for 8.6 gallons of gas; our tax rate is .021, and so on. Furthermore, decimals are also widely used in all sorts of technical work for greater precision of measurement.

Obviously, some ability to interpret and compute with decimal fractions is essential to understanding many social situations in our environment. Nevertheless, our schools have provided much less than adequate teaching in the area of decimal fractions and mixed decimals. After a survey test given to 936 pupils in five school systems in Ohio, Guiler reports that a large proportion of the pupils showed weakness in handling decimals; for example, 66% in multiplying decimals; 83.9% in dividing them; 33% in adding and subtracting; 60.7% in changing fractions to decimals; 82.7% in changing mixed numbers to decimals; and over 80% in placing the decimal point in dividing decimals.[1] The present writer believes that decimals can be taught more effectively than these test results indicate.

### 3. Decimal Fractions a Continuation of the Number System

Decimal fractions are used when it is convenient to have denominators in powers of 10, as in $\frac{6}{10}$ (.6), $\frac{3}{1000}$ (.003), or $\frac{14}{10000}$ (.0014). They have several advantages over common fractions. For example, $\frac{1}{10} + \frac{2}{100} + \frac{6}{1000}$ can be added much more quickly as

$$\begin{array}{r} .1 \\ .02 \\ +.006 \\ \hline .126 \end{array}$$

than as common fractions. Moreover, $\frac{465}{1{,}000{,}000}$ is less cumbersome written as .000465, and computation with it is easier. Though a notation system for decimal fractions did not come into general use until near the end of the sixteenth century, mathematics and science could never have attained their present development without it. In fact, the development of the decimal system may be called another milestone in the intellectual progress of mankind, much as the development of zero was.

In Chapter 16 we saw that common fractions are a very useful addition to the natural number series because they indicate numbers between the integers. So also decimal numerals permit a useful extension of our system of notation.

The decimal system was discussed as a basic concept in Chapter 8.

[1] W. S. Guiler, "Difficulties in Decimals Encountered by Ninth-Grade Pupils," *Elementary School Journal*, March, 1946, pp. 384–393.

We noted there that our number system is called a decimal system because it has a base of 10. We saw that a numeral increases tenfold in value with each successive place it moves to the left, and that the successive powers of 10 are of great importance in our number system.

Of great importance, too, are the decimal numerals. They decrease tenfold in value with each successive place they occupy to the right of the units place. Thus, as is true of integral numbers, each digit in decimal numerals has two values, intrinsic value and place value. For example, the 3 in .003 has intrinsic value anywhere it appears as being less than 4 and more than 2. In this number it has place value also. It is in the third place to the right of the decimal point and hence has a value of only 3 thousandths of a unit. As we know, .04 is read 4 hundredths. Here zero serves the same purpose that it does in integral numbers; it is a place holder; it tells us there are no tenths and keeps the 4 in the hundredths place.

In discussing place value in Chapter 8, the tenfold increase in value as digits move to the left was shown as $10^5$, $10^4$, $10^3$, $10^2$, $10^1$, $10^0$. The decimal point is used to separate the integral portion of a given number from the part whose value is less than 1; thus 1.5 is 1 whole and $\frac{5}{10}$ of another. To show that decimal numbers decrease tenfold with each move to the right, we indicate the values thus: $10^{-1}$, $10^{-2}$, $10^{-3}$, $10^{-4}$, $10^{-5}$, etc.

A word of explanation about negative exponents is needed here. In order to write numbers that are much smaller than 1, it was necessary to extend the meaning of exponents. This was done by using negative exponents, such as $10^{-1}$, which means "take the reciprocal." Hence $10^{-1}$ is interpreted as the reciprocal of $10^1$, which is $\frac{1}{10^1}$, or $\frac{1}{10}$. By the same reasoning, $10^{-2} = \frac{1}{10^2}$ or $\frac{1}{100}$; $10^{-3} = \frac{1}{10^3}$ or $\frac{1}{1000}$, and so on. The series $10^{-1}$, $10^{-2}$, $10^{-3}$, $10^{-4}$ may thus be written as $\frac{1}{10}$, $\frac{1}{100}$, $\frac{1}{1000}$, $\frac{1}{10000}$. We recognize that the denominators are the same as the names of the respective decimal places—tenths, hundredths, thousandths, and ten-thousandths—and we see that for any given fraction, the number of zeros in the denominator of the common fraction is the same as the number of *places* in the fraction written as a decimal; e.g., $\frac{1}{10} = .1$; $\frac{1}{1000} = .001$.*

* Let the pupils discover this.

Another and perhaps simpler way to indicate values to the right of the decimal point is $(\frac{1}{10})^1$, $(\frac{1}{10})^2$, $(\frac{1}{10})^3$, $(\frac{1}{10})^4$, $(\frac{1}{10})^5$, and so on. This corresponds with the power of 10 in the integral part of the number thus:

$$10^4 \quad 10^3 \quad 10^2 \quad 10^1 \quad 10^0 \quad . \quad \left(\frac{1}{10}\right)^1 \quad \left(\frac{1}{10}\right)^2 \quad \left(\frac{1}{10}\right)^3 \quad \left(\frac{1}{10}\right)^4 .$$

Note that the ones place, *not* the decimal point, is the center of our number system, and that the first place to the left of 1 is $10 \times 1$, whereas the first place to its right is $\frac{1}{10} \times 1$.

Note also that regardless of where we start, even with an order far to the right of the decimal point, digits increase tenfold in value with every move to the left, and decrease tenfold in value with every move to the right.* The following, a diagrammatic representation of the number 2,222,222.222222, illustrates these number relationships:

| millions | hundred thousands | ten thousands | thousands | hundreds | tens | ones | tenths | hundredths | thousandths | ten-thousandths | hundred-thousandths | millionths |
|---|---|---|---|---|---|---|---|---|---|---|---|---|
| 2 | 2 | 2 | 2 | 2 | 2 | [2] | 2 | 2 | 2 | 2 | 2 | 2 |
| $2(10)^6$ | $2(10)^5$ | $2(10)^4$ | $2(10)^3$ | $2(10)^2$ | $2(10)^1$ | $2(10)^0$ | $2(10)^{-1}$ | $2(10)^{-2}$ | $2(10)^{-3}$ | $2(10)^{-4}$ | $2(10)^{-5}$ | $2(10)^{-6}$ |

Presented in another form, this becomes:

$$\begin{aligned}
2(10)^6 &= 2{,}000{,}000. \\
2(10)^5 &= 200{,}000. \\
2(10)^4 &= 20{,}000. \\
2(10)^3 &= 2{,}000. \\
2(10)^2 &= 200. \\
2(10)^1 &= 20. \\
2(10)^0 &= 2. \\
2(10)^{-1} &= .2 \\
2(10)^{-2} &= .02 \\
2(10)^{-3} &= .002 \\
2(10)^{-4} &= .0002 \\
2(10)^{-5} &= .00002 \\
2(10)^{-6} &= .000002 \\
\hline
& \quad 2{,}222{,}222.222222
\end{aligned}$$

* With guidance pupils can work this out.

Here we see that because the ones, or units, place is the center, 7 places are needed to write millions, and only 6 to write millionths. In further objectifying the relationship between places to the left of the decimal point and those to the right, the teacher should provide some types of visual aids for the pupils. Visual aids are discussed later in this chapter.

### 4. Reading and Interpreting Decimal Fractions

In reading decimal fractions the series of digits is read as if they were an integral number and the name of the order of the right-hand digit is added; thus .42169 is read as forty-two thousand, one hundred sixty-nine hundred-thousandths. Actually we are changing the various values to hundred-thousandths and adding them together:

| | | | |
|---|---|---|---|
| 4 tenths (.4) | 40,000 | hundred-thousandths | .40000 |
| 2 hundredths (.02) | 2,000 | " " | .02000 |
| 1 thousandth (.001) | 100 | " " | .00100 |
| 6 ten-thousandths (.0006) | 60 | " " | .00060 |
| 9 hundred-thousandths (.00009) | 9 | " " | .00009 |
| | 42,169 | " " | .42169 |

The above figures make clear the reason for giving the decimal fraction the name of the last order that appears. This is similar to what was said in an earlier chapter, that in reading integral numerals, the values are all converted to units. For example, for the number 4265 we have:

| | |
|---|---|
| 4000 | units |
| 200 | " |
| 60 | " |
| + 5 | " |
| 4265 | " |

Here the word "units" is understood, but not stated in reading the number. In decimals, we must name the part of the unit indicated by the last digit to show that the complete decimal is only a fractional part of a unit. Hence 16.25, which is read 16 and 25 hundredths, means 16 units and $\frac{25}{100}$ of another unit. A decimal like 16.25 is called a **mixed decimal,** comparable to $16\frac{1}{4}$, a mixed number.

In complex decimals, such as $0.08\frac{1}{3}$, the $\frac{1}{3}$ is not given an order name but is merely attached to the digit preceding it and read 8 and $\frac{1}{3}$ hundredths; similarly, $0.206\frac{2}{3}$ is read 206 and $\frac{2}{3}$ thousandths. Therefore, such a form as $.\frac{1}{3}$ or $.\frac{1}{7}$ is never used.

That adding zeros at the right of a decimal fraction does not change its value is readily made clear.* For example, .4 and .40 are equivalent because $\frac{4 \times 10}{10 \times 10} = \frac{40}{100}$. But placing a zero between the decimal point and the first decimal digit *does* change the value; thus .4 and .04 are not equivalent because $\frac{4 \times 10}{10 \times 10} = \frac{40}{100}$, not $\frac{4}{100}$.

### 5. Various Symbols for the Separatrix

A dot, which we call the **decimal point,** is used in this country as the **separatrix**—the mark which separates the integral number from the fractional part—in writing numerals involving decimals. However, there is not world-wide agreement on the symbol for the separatrix, just as is true about the manner of pointing off the periods of integers. Although England, like the United States, uses a dot (decimal point), it is written above the line: 3·25. In many European countries a comma is used, as in 3,25; other countries use $3^{25}$, or $3_{25}$, or 3, 25 (note the space).[2]

### 6. Need for Illustrations and Visual Aids

If pupils are to understand the parts of units represented by decimal numerals, they will need visual representations of them. But the difficulty of depicting anything divided into a thousand or ten thousand or a million parts makes illustration almost impossible. Graph paper is valuable here, for 100 squares, 10 squares long and 10 squares wide, can be marked off, and the big square can be used to represent 1 unit. Thus the pupils readily see that one row of 10 squares is $\frac{1}{10}$ of the unit, and one of the small squares is $\frac{1}{100}$ of the unit. Many practice problems can be based on a diagram like that in Fig. 9, to show equivalents in tenths and hundredths visually—for example, $\frac{3}{10} = \frac{30}{100}$—and to check up on what the children already know about changing the denominators of fractions.

Also useful are place-value pockets like those used in primary grades for learning tens (a bundle of 10 units) or hundreds (a bundle of 10 tens), but with pockets added to the right in which are placed, for

* Let pupils explore this situation.

[2] Cf. Robert L. Swain, *Understanding Arithmetic*, Holt, Rinehart & Winston, New York, 1957, p. 156.

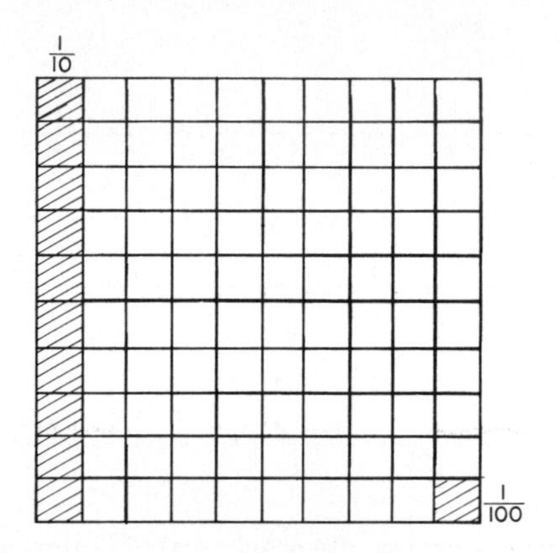


**Fig. 9.** Decimal Parts.

example, 1 tab marked $\frac{1}{100}$ in the hundredths place, 10 tabs thus marked in the tenths place, since $\frac{10}{100} = \frac{1}{10}$, and so on.*

Another effective visual aid for use on a flannel board is a set of cardboard squares and rectangles consisting of a 10-inch square, a strip 1 by 10 inches ($\frac{1}{10}$ of the large square), and a 1-inch square ($\frac{1}{10}$ of the strip and $\frac{1}{100}$ of the square). Patches of sandpaper on the back of the cardboard pieces will hold them on the flannel board.

For individual desk work, sets consisting of a 5-inch square and the $\frac{1}{10}$ and $\frac{1}{100}$ parts of it permit manipulation for such learnings as $1 = \frac{10}{10} = \frac{100}{100}$, $\frac{1}{10} = \frac{10}{100}$, and $\frac{5}{10} = \frac{50}{100}$.

A number line could be a visual aid, but our system of linear measurement (inches, feet, and yards) is of no help in connection with decimals. However, a line 100 inches long can be marked into decimal parts and used, like the square in Fig. 9, to show equivalents. A 5-inch line can be divided as indicated (top of page 196), and the pupils shown that $\frac{2}{10} = \frac{1}{5}$; $\frac{4}{10} = \frac{2}{5}$; $\frac{5}{10} = \frac{1}{2}$, and so on.†

This is an opportune time to explain the metric system of linear measurement and its values and convenience. For example, if there were 10 inches instead of 12 in a foot, we would not have to write 6 ft. 8 in., or $6\frac{2}{3}$ ft.; we would write simply 6.8 ft. and would find computation with it much simpler.

* Encourage pupils to explore these possibilities.

† Challenge the pupils to experiment with and make a decimal number line before they are shown the form.

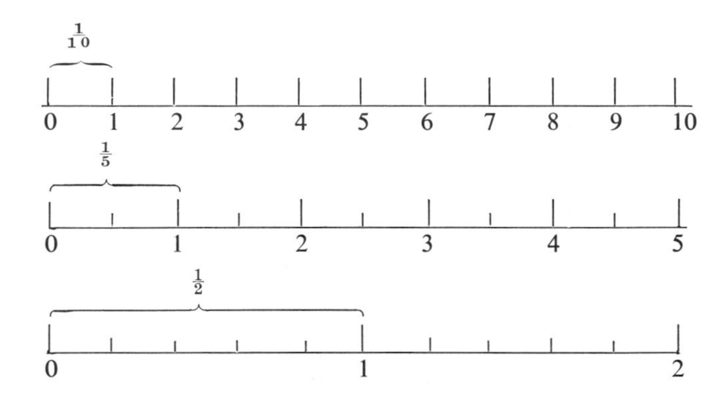


A clinical thermometer, usually marked at .2° intervals, is a useful aid, as are also speedometers, on which miles and tenths of a mile are indicated. Reading such instruments and computing the intervals between points on them provide children with valuable practice with decimals.

Some teachers introduce work with decimals by using our money system, but the value of this seems doubtful. In the first place, pupils have no way of *seeing* that a dime is a tenth of a dollar, or a penny a tenth of a dime. They must believe it because people and books *say* it is so. Furthermore, the familiar nickel, quarter, and half-dollar do not fit into the decimal plan and are therefore not discussed.

## 7. Reduction of Decimal Fractions

As was mentioned in Section 1 above, parts of wholes may be expressed either as common fractions or as decimal fractions, the choice of form depending merely on which is more convenient for the particular computation. For example, if we want to find .75 of 160, we can do it very quickly mentally if we convert the .75 to $\frac{3}{4}$ and find $\frac{3}{4}$ of 160. But if we want to find $\frac{3}{4}$ of \$16.75, it is probably simpler and less conducive to error if we multiply \$16.75 by .75. Eventually pupils should learn to recognize the advantages, in a given situation, of reducing a common fraction to a decimal or a decimal to a common fraction, and the visual aids mentioned in Section 6 should provide them with practice in dealing with equivalents in different forms.

We first consider reducing a common fraction to a decimal fraction. Since a common fraction represents an unperformed division, we obtain a decimal fraction when we do the indicated division. For example, when $\frac{3}{4}$ is divided, we get

$$4\overline{)3.00}\quad \begin{array}{r} .75 \\ 2\,8 \\ \hline 20 \\ 20 \\ \hline \end{array}$$

. Since this procedure involves placing the decimal point in the division of decimals, it should be postponed until placing the decimal point has been taught. As shown here, *some* common fractions can be reduced to *simple* decimal fractions.

Incidentally, only simple common fractions which in the lowest terms have powers of 2 or 5, or both, as factors of the denominator can be reduced to simple decimal fractions. Other common fractions can be reduced only to complex decimal fractions. Thus when $\frac{7}{9}$ is divided, we have

$$9\overline{)7.00}\quad \begin{array}{r} .77\frac{7}{9} \\ 6\,3 \\ \hline 70 \\ 63 \\ \hline 7 \end{array}$$

. In such cases it is seldom necessary to compute with the exact decimal fraction, that is, to include the fractional remainder $\frac{7}{9}$ in the computation. Usually the division is carried to the desired accuracy and rounded off, i.e., .778 from $.77\frac{7}{9}$. In doing this, the pupils must understand that they have an approximate result, whereas $\frac{7}{9}$ as a common fraction gives an exact answer.

In some cases common fractions can readily be reduced to decimal fractions by changing the denominator to some power of 10,* e.g., $\frac{6 \times 4}{25 \times 4} = \frac{24}{100}$ or .24. An efficient pupil will learn to see the opportune form for a fraction and the simplest way to get the fraction into the form called for by the particular computation.

Reducing a decimal fraction to a common fraction is in general simpler than reducing a common fraction to a decimal fraction. When decimal fractions are read orally, they cannot be distinguished from common fractions; for example, four tenths is either $\frac{4}{10}$ or .4, and sixteen hundredths is either $\frac{16}{100}$ or .16. Hence all that is necessary to reduce simple decimal fractions to common fractions is to write them

* This is a place for pupils to do some reasoning and find the method.

with the denominator that is indicated by the place name of the decimal —.4 to $\frac{4}{10}$—and then, if desired, reduce them to the lowest terms. However, when there are more decimal places and reading the number is more difficult, a helpful rule is that there will be as many zeros in the denominator of the common fraction as there are decimal places in the decimal fraction.* For .0216, then, $\frac{216}{10000}$ is readily determined. Not quite so simple to reduce are complex decimal fractions, such as $.66\frac{2}{3}$. This also may be written $\frac{66\frac{2}{3}}{100}$, but it must be simplified by doing the indicated division, namely, $66\frac{2}{3} \div 100$, or $\frac{\overset{2}{\cancel{200}}}{3} \times \frac{1}{\cancel{100}} = \frac{2}{3}$. The interchange between common and decimal fractions is used frequently, as is also the conversion of either to percentage. The latter is discussed in the next chapter.

## 8. Addition and Subtraction of Decimal Fractions

Adding and subtracting decimal fractions and decimal mixed numbers involve few new concepts and usually give little difficulty. Pupils who early learned the importance of keeping columns of digits straight in adding integers, so as to have units under units, tens under tens, and so on, will readily grasp the importance of a tenths column, a hundredths column, etc., and will also realize that this arrangement puts the decimal points in a straight column. In adding

$$\begin{array}{r} 4.2 \\ 6.5 \\ +3.1 \\ \hline 13.8 \end{array}$$

they can check as follows to be satisfied that their decimal answer is correct:†

$$\begin{array}{r} 4\frac{2}{10} \\ 6\frac{5}{10} \\ +3\frac{1}{10} \\ \hline 13\frac{8}{10} \end{array}$$

* Let pupils discover this.
† Guide your pupils so they will discover this.

In $\begin{array}{r} 6.01 \\ 2.25 \\ 1.3 \\ +\ .001 \\ \hline 9.561 \end{array}$ zeros can be added as place holders, thus: $\begin{array}{r} 6.010 \\ 2.250 \\ 1.300 \\ +\ .001 \\ \hline 9.561 \end{array}$. For beginners, this will insure that figures are in the right columns. Few real-life situation problems call for the addition of "ragged" decimals like those in the first column, but the result is the same in both columns —there are in all only 1 thousandth, 6 hundredths, and 5 tenths.

If pupils understand the decimal system in general, carrying in adding decimals will be done, as far as mechanics is concerned, just as it was with integers. For example, in $\begin{array}{r} 3.61 \\ 2.491 \\ +\ .163 \\ \hline 6.264 \end{array}$, the total in the thousandths column is 4; in the hundredths it is 16 and we "put down the 6 and carry the 1." There are 12 tenths, so we "put down the 2 and carry the 1 to the next column (units)."

Rationalizing the addition of decimals involving reduction, or carrying, will give some trouble. It is much more difficult to see that $\frac{16}{100}$ makes $\frac{1}{10}$ and $\frac{6}{100}$ over than it is to see that 16 units makes 1 ten and 6 units over. To rationalize* the addition in the problem in the preceding paragraph, we say that the total in the thousandths column is 4; in the hundredths column it is 16 hundredths, but $\frac{10}{100} = \frac{1}{10}$, so $\frac{16}{100}$ is reduced to 1 tenth and 6 hundredths over, and the 1 tenth is added in the tenths column. Thus there are $\frac{12}{10}$, enough for one unit, $\frac{10}{10}$, and 2 tenths which are added in their respective columns. For these reasons this process should be undertaken in very simple steps. For example, in $\begin{array}{r} 2.5 \\ 1.3 \\ +1.2 \\ \hline 5.0 \end{array}$, show that 10 tenths ($\frac{10}{10}$) make a unit to be added in with the 2, 1 and 1 in the units column. Similarly, with $\begin{array}{r} 1.65 \\ +2.15 \\ \hline 3.80 \end{array}$, show that $\frac{10}{100}$ makes $\frac{1}{10}$ that is added in with the 6 tenths and the 1 tenth, for a total of 8 tenths.

---

* Challenge able pupils to do this.

When adding decimals becomes as simple as adding integers, subtraction in a form that requires no reduction should be introduced first, e.g., $\begin{array}{r} 2.64 \\ -1.12 \\ \hline 1.52 \end{array}$. Reduction is introduced later, as in $\begin{array}{r} 2.43 \\ -\ .15 \\ \hline 1.28 \end{array}$, when 1 tenth $(\frac{1}{10})$ is reduced to ten hundredths $(\frac{10}{100})$, and there are 13 hundredths from which to subtract 5 hundredths, with only 3 tenths left from which to subtract 1 tenth. Actually the rationalization for subtracting decimals is easier than it is for adding them, because it is easier to reduce 1 tenth $(\frac{1}{10})$ to hundredths than to reduce 16 hundredths to tenths which leaves some hundredths as a remainder.

Subtracting a decimal fraction from a whole number, $\begin{array}{r} 6.\phantom{000} \\ -\ .125 \\ \hline 5.875 \end{array}$, involves a new and somewhat difficult step. In working with integers, there are never fewer digits in the minuend than in the subtrahend; hence such a problem as this raises a difficulty at sight. If in adding and subtracting decimals up to this point, pupils have been accustomed to filling in the decimal places with zeros as in $\begin{array}{r} 2.1\phantom{00} \\ .45\phantom{0} \\ +\ .625 \\ \hline \end{array}$, making $\begin{array}{r} 2.100 \\ .450 \\ +\ .625 \\ \hline \end{array}$, they will at once fill them in in the present problem, obtaining $\begin{array}{r} 6.000 \\ -\ .125 \\ \hline \end{array}$, and will be ready to apply the usual reduction (borrowing) procedure.

Some teachers ask: "Why worry about the rationalization process? Just teach pupils to add and subtract." A teacher who is not interested in having his pupils acquire meaning and understanding in arithmetic does not "worry" about the rationalization process; he merely teaches the mechanics of the process. It is the result of this mechanical, drill type of teaching that is responsible for our saying: "Let's teach arithmetic better."

## 9. Multiplication of Decimal Fractions

In the drill procedure used for many years pupils learned to multiply such numbers as 24.16 × 1.312, thus:

$$
\begin{array}{r}
24.16 \\
\times 1.312 \\
\hline
4832 \\
2416\phantom{0} \\
7248\phantom{00} \\
2416\phantom{000} \\
\hline
31.69792
\end{array}
$$

As for placing the decimal point in the product, they simply memorized the rule: Add the number of decimal places in the multiplicand and the number in the multiplier (in this case a total of 5), and point off in the product that many places from the right. Though the pupil had no idea *why* this rule worked, with enough practice and a good memory he was able to multiply decimals, but he had only a superficial knowledge of the process.

Those who advocate the meaning theory of arithmetic want the pupil to know *why* the rule works by knowing how it is derived.* There are various procedures for accomplishing this. One beginning step may involve showing the solution in terms of equivalent common fractions; e.g., $3 \times .4 = 3 \times \frac{4}{10} = \frac{12}{10} = 1\frac{2}{10} = 1.2$. Hence $3 \times .4 = 1.2$. Another example, $.4 \times .6 = \frac{4}{10} \times \frac{6}{10} = \frac{24}{100} = .24$. Still another, $.8 \times .16 = \frac{8}{10} \times \frac{16}{100} = \frac{128}{1000} = .128$. Then a new situation is introduced: $.4 \times .15 = \frac{4}{10} \times \frac{15}{100} = \frac{60}{1000} = .060$. Here, in order to get 60 into the thousandths place, it is necessary to put a zero as a place holder in the tenths place.

At this point the teacher may call attention to the fact that in each of these examples the number of zeros in the fractional denominator of the product is equal to the number of places in the denominator of the multiplicand plus the number of places in the denominator of the multiplier.† As we saw earlier, in writing common fractions and their equivalent decimal fractions, such as .125 for $\frac{125}{1000}$, there are always as many decimal places required as there are zeros in the denominator of the common fraction. Hence the rule for adding the number of decimal places is further justified. Doing a number of such problems will convince the pupil that he can place the decimal point by counting places and be sure it is correct.

More advanced pupils can, by experimenting, develop further

* A challenge for able pupils.
† Guide pupils to discover this.

generalizations to aid in placing the decimal point. For example, after doing many such problems as $3 \times .2 = .6$ ($3 \times \frac{2}{10} = \frac{6}{10}$); $.3 \times .2 = .06$ ($\frac{3}{10} \times \frac{6}{10} = \frac{6}{100}$); and $.3 \times .45 = .135$ ($\frac{3}{10} \times \frac{45}{100} = \frac{135}{1000}$) they will conclude that:

ones × tenths = tenths
tenths × tenths = hundredths
tenths × hundredths = thousandths

As in every other computational process, pupils should be taught to check problems. In working with decimals, in addition to the usual checks, they need to learn to determine by estimation whether their answer is reasonable.* For example, quick inspection shows that $3.9 \times 25 = 145$ is wrong, because $3 \times 25$ is 75; 3.9 is almost 4 and $4 \times 25$ is 100; hence any answer larger than 100 is wrong. The answer is more than 75 and less than 100, but close to 100; therefore, 97.5 is probably correct.

```
   25
 × 3.9
  ---
  225
  75
 ----
 97.5
```

Even in multiplying numbers with many more digits, such as 208.145 × .5129, a pupil should learn to recognize that the last of the following answers: 10.67575705, 1067.575705, and 106.7575705, is nearest to the correct answer because .5129 is only slightly over one-half, and half of 208 is 104; therefore, 106.7575705 is a reasonable answer.

## 10. Division of Decimal Fractions and Mixed Decimals

If division of integers has been well learned, much of the difficulty associated with division of decimals will be avoided. A thorough review of long division with integers and with answers involving remainders should precede division of decimals.

As in multiplying decimals, the rule for placing the decimal point should be derived inductively and by similar reasoning. If the pupil works in division with equivalent common fractions whose denominators are multiples of 10, as he did in multiplication, he will better understand where to place the decimal point.

The first step should involve division by whole numbers. In $\frac{6}{10} \div 2$

* Encourage practice in these estimations.

the pupil should recall that the 10 merely identifies the size of the parts, and that $\frac{6}{10} \div 2$ is like 6 cookies $\div$ 2, which is equivalent to saying $\frac{1}{2}$ of $\frac{6}{10}$ $(\frac{3}{10})$, or $\frac{1}{2}$ of 6 cookies (3 cookies). Hence $.6 \div 2$ $\left(2\overline{).6}^{\,.3}\right)$ is .3. Since this quotient is tenths, the decimal point must indicate this. Likewise, $\frac{24}{100}$ or $.24 \div 2$ $\left(2\overline{).24}^{\,.12}\right)$ is half of 24 hundredths, or 12 hundredths (.12). In these examples, when the digits in the quotient are properly placed, the decimal point in the quotient is directly over the one in the dividend. In $6\overline{).24}^{\,.04}$, $\frac{1}{6}$ of 24 hundredths is 4 hundredths; but to indicate this, a zero place holder must be put in the tens place, and again the point is directly above the one in the dividend. These examples, together with many others, will convince pupils that as long as the divisor is an integer the placement of the decimal point will be the same.

For the second step, in which both the dividend and the divisor contain a decimal fraction, the best procedure, in the writer's opinion, and the one generally used in current textbooks, is to convert the divisor to a whole number and proceed as in the first step.

In connection with equivalent common fractions discussed in Chapter 16, one generalization developed was that the numerator and the denominator of any fraction may be multiplied or divided by the same number (except 0) without changing the value of the fraction. Thus, $\frac{2 \times 2}{3 \times 2} = \frac{4}{6}$; $\frac{1 \times 3}{2 \times 3} = \frac{3}{6}$; $\frac{5 \times 10}{10 \times 10} = \frac{50}{100}$. Therefore, $\frac{5}{10}$ (.5) is equivalent to $\frac{50}{100}$ (.50) ; $.5\overline{)40}$ is equivalent to $5\overline{)400}^{\,80}$, for $\frac{40 \times 10}{.5 \times 10} = \frac{400}{5} = 80$.

Here some practice is needed in determining what power of 10 should be used to multiply in converting the multiplier to a whole number. Practice exercises like $.3\overline{)\quad}$, $.45\overline{)\quad}$, and $.125\overline{)\quad}$ are valuable. The alert pupil will discover rather quickly that he multiplies by whatever power of 10 has the same number of zeros as there are decimal places in the divisor. However, he must never lose sight of the fact that, with $\frac{2}{5}$ for example, if he multiplies the divisor, 5, by a given number, he must multiply the dividend, 2, by the same number, as in $\frac{2 \times 4}{5 \times 4} = \frac{8}{20}$. Thus

$\frac{2 \times 10}{.5 \times 10} = \frac{20}{5}$, and $.5\overline{)2}$ is equivalent to $\underline{.5 \times 10}\overline{)2 \times 10}$ or $5\overline{)20.}^{\;4.}$ Here again the decimal point in the quotient is directly over the one in the dividend. In $3.5\overline{)7.0}$, multiplying each by 10 gives $35\overline{)70.}$ When a pupil has learned *why* he can legitimately move the decimal point, he will readily move the one in the divisor to the end of the number and the one in the dividend the same number of places. To save confusion and keep an accurate record of the original location of the decimal point as well as its new location, the caret (‸) is used to indicate the new location in the solution, thus, $.16\overline{)1.28}$ and the solution

$$\begin{array}{r} 8. \\ .16_\wedge\overline{)1.28_\wedge} \\ \underline{1\ 28} \end{array}$$

A good rule in dividing decimals is to get the decimal point properly located in the divisor, dividend, and quotient before beginning the numerical computation.

In the third step, in some decimal division computations one or more zeros must be annexed to the dividend to obtain the desired answer; for example, in order to get a needed decimal answer, $2\overline{)1.}$ must be written

$$\begin{array}{r} .5 \\ 2\overline{)1.0} \\ \underline{1\ 0} \end{array}$$

Since 1 cannot be divided by 2 for an integral answer, the 1 is changed to $\frac{10}{10}$ (1.0 written decimally); 10 tenths divided by 2 gives 5 tenths,

$$\begin{array}{r} .5 \\ 2\overline{)1.0} \\ \underline{1\ 0} \end{array}$$

Likewise, in order to secure a mixed decimal answer, $4\overline{)5}$ must be written:

$$\begin{array}{r} 1.25 \\ 4\overline{)5.00} \\ \underline{4\phantom{00}} \\ 10\phantom{0} \\ \underline{8\phantom{0}} \\ 20 \\ \underline{20} \end{array}$$

Although no new mechanics are involved here, if the process is to be rationalized, the pupil must understand that 5 units is the same when written 5 units, 0 tenths, and 0 hundredths (5.00), or 500 hundredths (5.00).

Some decimal division problems do not come out even and remainders must be considered. It is common practice in such cases to carry out the division to the desired degree of accuracy and then round off the quotient by using the *nearest* digit in the last place. If the remainder is less than one-half after the final digit of the quotient is obtained, it is customary to drop it; when it is more than one-half, the next higher digit is used for the final figure in the quotient; thus:

```
      .290 6/9
  9 ⟌ 2.616
      1 8
      ---
        81
        81
        --
         6
```

If accuracy to the nearest thousandth is desired, the above quotient becomes .291. If accuracy to the nearest hundredth is adequate, the quotient of the following will be .82.

```
       .81 9/11
  11 ⟌ 9.00
       8 8
       ---
        20
        11
        --
         9
```

As was said in Chapter 16, this type of division is the one usually used to reduce common fractions to decimals. For example:

```
              .75                  .8                .33 1/3
 3/4 = .75  4⟌3.00    4/5 = .8  5⟌4.0    1/3 = 3⟌1.00
              2 8                  4 0                 9
              ---                  ---                ---
               20                                      10
               20                                       9
               --                                      --
                                                        1
```

## 11. Short Cuts with Decimals

As was stated in an earlier chapter, short cuts in arithmetic serve a real purpose, but they should not be used until the full procedure is thoroughly understood. In Section 8 above, we saw that in adding ragged decimal fractions, such as

```
   .2
   .015
  +.21
  ----
```

, the addends should all be made

thousandths, thus:

$$\begin{array}{r} .200 \\ .015 \\ +.210 \\ \hline .425 \end{array}$$

. But when understanding has been established, it is unnecessary to do this, for the result can be obtained from the ragged pattern just as well:

$$\begin{array}{l} \phantom{+}.2 \\ \phantom{+}.015 \\ +.21 \\ \hline \phantom{+}.425 \end{array}$$

In the discussion of multiplication of decimals in Section 9 we saw that after a pupil derives the rule for locating the decimal point inductively, counting the total decimal places in both multiplicand and multiplier to determine the number of places in the product will enable him to locate the decimal point in the product quickly and with confidence.

Likewise, when he has learned a meaningful way to locate the decimal point in a quotient, he may use a short cut, particularly the rule:* To find the number of decimal places in the quotient, subtract the number of places in the divisor from the number in the dividend:

$$\begin{array}{r|l} & 21.1 \\ \cline{2-2} .15 & 3.165 \quad (3 - 2 = 1) \\ & 3\,0 \\ & \underline{\phantom{3\,}}\,16 \\ & \phantom{3\,}15 \\ & \phantom{3\,1}15 \\ & \phantom{3\,1}15 \end{array}$$

He will be ready to accept the correctness of this short cut after checking it with many problems in which he has used the caret method to locate the point.

In addition to these short cuts, pupils should acquire some facility in using a short cut for multiplying and dividing by powers of 10. Again, this should follow considerable experience in computing the long way. To illustrate:

$$\begin{array}{r} .265 \\ \times\ 10 \\ \hline 000 \\ 265\phantom{0} \\ \hline 2.650 \end{array} \qquad \begin{array}{r} 2.6 \\ \times 1\,0 \\ \hline 0\,0 \\ 2\,6\phantom{0} \\ \hline 2\,6.0 \end{array}$$

* He should be guided to develop this rule.

After a few such problems, pupils will readily discover that in multiplying any number by 10 its decimal point is simply moved one place to the right. More illustrations like the following show that in multiplying by 100 it is moved two places to the right, and so on:

```
    2.41
  × 100
  -----
    000
   000
  241
  ------
  241.00
```

Examples will also show pupils that in dividing a number by 10 and multiples of 10 the decimal point is moved one place to the left for each 0 in the divisor:*

```
       .31            .00469
10 ) 3.10     100 ) .46900
     3 0             400
     ---             ---
       10             690
       10             600
       --             ---
                      900
                      900
                      ---
```

These two multiplication and division generalizations are extremely useful in many kinds of mental computation; for example, in $2.41 \times 200$: $2 \times 2.41$ is $4.82 \times 100$ is 482; this is readily computed mentally.

Rules supply many short-cut procedures and are to be recommended, provided the pupils understand their derivation.

## 12. Decimals in Part-Whole Relationships

As was pointed out in Chapter 16, common fractions are frequently involved in the three types of computations dealing with part-whole relationships:

1. $\frac{2}{3}$ of 18 = ?
2. What part of 18 is 12?
3. 12 is $\frac{2}{3}$ of what number?

That chapter emphasized the equation method of stating all three types:

1. $\frac{2}{3} \times 18 = ?$
2. $? \times 18 = 12$
3. $\frac{2}{3} \times ? = 12$

* Let pupils discover this.

As previously pointed out, a generalized statement for solving multiplication-equation types of computations is: When both factors are known, multiply them to find the product; when the product and one factor are known, divide the product by the known factor to find the other factor.

The same three types of computation arise with decimals and the same equation procedures can be used to solve them. For example:

1. If .40 of a 15-qt. solution is water, how much water is in it?

   .40 of 15 qts. = ?  $.40 \times 15$ qts. = 6 qts. water.

2. In a 15-qt. solution there are 6 qts. of water; what decimal part of the solution is water?

   ? $\times$ 15 qts. = 6 qts.  $6 \div 15 = .40$ water.

3. If .40 of a certain solution is water and the amount of water is 6 qts., what is the total amount of solution?

   .40 of ? = 6 qts.  $6 \div .40 = 15$ qts. solution.

We saw in Chapter 16 that these types of problem can also be solved by the unitary analysis method. The three problems above can likewise be solved in that way.

1. .40 of a 15-qt. solution is water. How much water is in it?

   .01 of it is .01 of 15 qts. or .15 qt.
   .40 of it is $40 \times .15$ qt. or 6 qts. water.

2. In 15 qts. of solution there are 6 qts. of water. What part of this solution is water?

   What part of 15 qts. are 6 qts.?

   1 qt. is $\frac{1}{15}$ of 15 qts. (the amount of solution)

   6 qts. are $6 \times \frac{1}{15}$ or .40 water.

3. There are 6 qts. of water in a certain solution of which .40 is water. What is the amount of solution?

   .40 of the amount of solution = 6 qts.

   .01 of the amount of solution is $\frac{1}{40}$ of 6 qts. or .15 qt.

   1.00 of the amount of solution is $100 \times .15$ qt. or 15 qts.of solution.

## COMPETENCE CHECK

**1.** Write 165.249 and show the powers of 10 represented.

**2.** Find 12 examples of common use of decimals in newspapers.

**3.** When a given number has only decimal and no integral orders, why is it advisable to place a zero to the left of the decimal point, thus: 0.56?

**4.** Name the first ten orders to the right of the decimal point.

**5.** Write in figures:
1. one hundred sixteen and four hundred twenty-five thousandths.
2. six and forty-eight millionths.
3. eight hundred-thousandths.
4. two and one-third tenths.

**6.** Why is such a form as $.\frac{1}{6}$ never used?

**7.** Could decimal fractions be introduced before common fractions? Support your answer with illustrations.

**8.** Explain why rationalization of the reduction involved in the first of the following is easier than that involved in the second:

$$\begin{array}{r} 2.613 \\ -1.469 \\ \hline \end{array} \qquad \begin{array}{r} 2.613 \\ +1.469 \\ \hline \end{array}$$

**9.** Using centimeter paper, or paper with 10 ruled lines per inch, draw squares or rectangles to show each of the following: 4.6; 2.15; 1.75.

**10.** Show the addition of 2.45 + 1.25 by using different colors on squared paper or on a number line.

**11.** 1. Show 3.25 ÷ .5 on graph paper and compare with the algorism for 3.25 ÷ .5.
2. Show this division on a number line.

**12.** Mention two ways of locating the decimal point in division and discuss their relative merits.

**13.** A brochure concerning Minnesota's North Shore Drive shows the following mileages from Duluth:

| | |
|---|---|
| To Leif Ericson Park | 0.9 mi. |
| To Talmadge Creek | 10.7 mi. |
| To French River | 12.1 mi. |
| To Sucker River | 14.9 mi. |
| To Stony Point Lookout | 17.1 mi. |
| To Knife River | 20.0 mi. |
| To Two Harbors | 26.5 mi. |

What is the distance from French River to Two Harbors? From Talmadge Creek to Knife River?

**14.** What advantage is it to the tourist for distances to be stated as in the preceding?

15. If your car averages 16.5 miles to the gallon, how much gas will you expect to use in driving 300 miles?
16. Compose and solve two problems based on pupils' school or social environment to illustrate multiplication of decimals. Repeat for division of decimals. Check your answers by a common computational check, and also by estimation.
17. Explain and illustrate the use of a caret for locating the decimal point in the quotient of the two division computations you composed in the preceding.
18. Write each of the following numbers, correct to the nearest indicated decimal:

| | |
|---|---|
| hundredth | 3.1416 |
| thousandth | 16.10021 |
| ten-thousandth | 2.41699 |

19. Explain how the decimal system is used for recording speed and mileage on automobile speedometers.
20. When you multiply by a decimal, will the product always have a decimal in it? Support your answer by illustrative computations.
21. Compose a problem for each of the three types discussed in Section 12. Solve each problem, first by the equation method, then by another method.

## OPTIONAL ASSIGNMENTS

1. Mathematicians point out that in reality the decimal point is used to indicate which figure is units, and for that reason some advocate placing the dot *over* rather than *after* the units figure—e.g., $36\dot{4}125$, instead of 364.125. What advantages or disadvantages do you see in this procedure?
2. According to Hickerson, "Since there are so few occasions in a child's life to multiply and divide decimal fractions, these processes should not be introduced until the junior or senior high school years." Do you agree or disagree? Give your reasons.
3. Consult Larsen or other sources concerning repeating decimal fractions and give a report on it.
4. From Larsen or other sources find out how to determine the number of decimal places required for a decimal fraction to come out even when you know that the denominator makes it possible to reduce the decimal fraction to a simple common fraction.
5. Arithmetic authorities do not entirely agree on the best procedure for locating the decimal point in dividing decimals. Compare the opinions of Grossnickle, Crofts, Spitzer, and the present author as to the best method, and the ability of fifth- and sixth-grade pupils to rationalize any of these methods. What is your own opinion about this?

## REFERENCES

Crofts, Mary E., "Division of Decimal Fractions," *Mathematics Teacher*, April, 1946, pp. 178–179.

Grossnickle, Foster E., "How to Find the Position of the Decimal in the Quotient," *Elementary School Journal*, April, 1952, pp. 452–457.

Hickerson, J. Allen, *Guiding Children's Arithmetic Experiences*. Prentice-Hall, New York, 1952, chaps. 13, 14.

Larsen, Harold D., *Arithmetic for Colleges*, Macmillan, New York, rev. ed., 1954, chap. 8.

Spencer, Peter L., "Do They See the Point?" *Arithmetic Teacher*, November, 1958, pp. 271–272.

Spitzer, Herbert F., *The Teaching of Arithmetic*, Houghton Mifflin, Boston, 2nd ed., 1954, chap. 8.

*chapter* 18

# Percentage and Its Applications

## 1. Wide Use of Percentage Terms

In the moving up of arithmetic content which has taken place in recent years, computations and problems in percentage and its applications have generally been put into the seventh and eighth grades in a somewhat diluted form, partly, according to curriculum experts, because of the difficulty of these computations, and partly because children have no need for them before this level of experience. The newer programs for teaching arithmetic, however, indicate that some work with percentage concepts will be put back into fifth- and sixth-grade curriculums for two reasons: first, there is a current movement to "stiffen up" arithmetic from the first grade on; and second, in the modern school and community environment, a pupil even in the intermediate grades reads many items of information involving percentages. These reasons, it will be noted, are the reverse of those for postponing work in percentage in recent years.

To illustrate a pupil's need for some comprehension of percentage: Blake wants a Ping-pong set. He notes an after-Christmas sale that advertises "Ping-pong sets, 25% off." He asks his father what they will cost at the sale; he knows that he is charged a 3% sales tax on everything he buys. He follows his school's athletic records, and in a report about a basketball game he reads that Collins had a "hot night," shooting 52% and making 100% of his free shots. These items are on his level of interest and he should be prepared to interpret them. In his science and social studies texts he reads such items as: 60% of the population of a certain country live in one fertile valley province; only 66% of the people took the trouble to vote; the number of cars on the highway has increased 100% since a certain year. This content, aside from interpreting the percentage data, is entirely within his comprehension, and so are the percentage data if he is properly introduced to the subject.

In order to have a reasonable comprehension of such situations as the above, a pupil should have been learning that "so many per cent" means "so many out of 100." In the case of the Ping-pong set, for every $100 of cost, $25 will be taken off, or one-fourth of the cost, because $25 is $\frac{1}{4}$ of $100. The 100% on free throws means that Collins made 100 shots out of 100 chances; in other words, whatever his number of chances, he made all of them—if he had 14 chances, he made 14 shots.

The use of percentages provides a readily interpreted figure for the general reader. When we read that only 66% (66 out of every 100) of the people took the trouble to vote, we interpret it as about two-thirds of the people, or two out of three; but we would have more trouble interpreting the statement that in a community with 6450 eligible voters only 4257 voted.

## 2. No New Concepts in Percentage

As indicated in Chapters 16 and 17, common fractions, decimal fractions, and percentages are so closely related that no new computational concepts are involved when working with percentages. It is mainly a matter of using different terms, or we may say, employing somewhat different language.

Percentages, however, involve only a very limited group of fractional parts. Though any part whatsoever of wholes may be expressed in common fractions—e.g., $\frac{1}{4}$, $\frac{799}{845}$, $\frac{1}{10000}$, etc.—decimal fractions express only the parts whose denominators are some multiple of 10, such as .1 ($\frac{1}{10}$), .15 ($\frac{15}{100}$), .003 ($\frac{3}{1000}$), etc. Percentages are still further limited, for the term is used only to express parts with a denominator of 100, e.g., 6% $\left(\frac{6}{100}\right)$, $3\frac{1}{2}$% $\left(\frac{3\frac{1}{2}}{100}\right)$, and so on. The percentage idea is commonly used in the range of 1% to 100% ($\frac{1}{100}$ to 1), but it is also frequently used to indicate parts either smaller or larger than those in that range—e.g., $\frac{1}{2}$% ($\frac{1}{200}$) or 250% ($2\frac{1}{2}$).

The term *per cent*[1] is derived from the Latin *per centum*, meaning, in

[1] Authorities differ as to whether this word should be written *percent* or *per cent*. This book will use *per cent*.

free translation, *for every hundred.* Pupils can see the derivation from *centum* (hundred) and they are accustomed to the use of *per* as in 16 miles per gallon, $3 per day. Since 1% indicates one out of every hundred, 1% of anything means $\frac{1}{100}$ of it. In computations we use the term per cent just as we use hundredths—6% of one's salary means $\frac{6}{100}$ of it.

As far as manipulative or visual aids are concerned, if pupils have used the aids for decimal fractions suggested in Chapter 17, the hundred square will give them an opportunity to cover parts on it to represent 16% (16 parts), noting that 84 parts (84% of the total) are uncovered; or to color 25 parts (25%), noting 75 parts (75%) are uncolored. A new number line like the one below, which shows parts as common fractions, as decimals, and as percentages, will also be useful.*

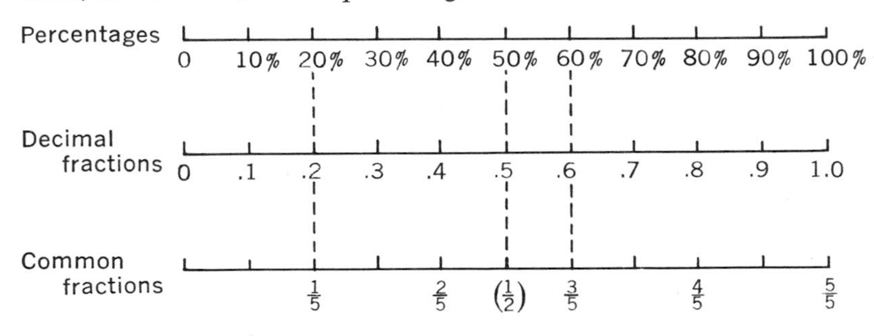


Equivalents indicated above are: $20\% = .2 = \frac{1}{5}$
$50\% = .5 = \frac{1}{2}$
$60\% = .6 = \frac{3}{5}$

### 3. Computing with Percentages

We use common and decimal fractions as abstract numbers and compute with them as such; e.g., $\frac{1}{4} + \frac{3}{8} = \frac{5}{8}$, or

$$\begin{array}{r} .16 \\ +.24 \\ \hline .40 \end{array}$$

But we do not use percentages without indicating *percentage of what.* For example, 6% + 3% has no meaning, but the following does:

6% of the pupils have grade B
+3% of the pupils have grade A
9% of the pupils have grade A or B

* Challenge alert pupils to devise such a number line.

Given percentages of the same thing can be combined, as above, or subtracted, as in:

$$\begin{array}{rl} 9\% & \text{of the pupils have grade A or B} \\ -3\% & \text{of the pupils have grade A} \\ \hline 6\% & \text{of the pupils have grade B} \end{array}$$

But no multiplication or division can be performed until the per cent sign (%) is removed and the part, e.g., 25%, is expressed as a decimal, .25, or a common fraction, $\frac{1}{4}$. For example, Jim saved 25% of his first week's earnings of $24. How much did he save? The computation must be written as .25 × $24 or as $\frac{1}{4}$ of $24 for a solution.

This is why considerable emphasis was placed on ability to convert common fractions to decimals, and vice versa, in earlier chapters. If the pupil has acquired that ability, he should have little trouble with the additional procedure of converting common fractions or decimals to percentages, or percentages to common fractions or decimals. It is to provide proficiency in these abilities that many teachers have pupils memorize such common equivalents as:

| | | | |
|---|---|---|---|
| $50\% = .50 = \frac{1}{2}$ | | | |
| $33\frac{1}{3}\% = .33\frac{1}{3} = \frac{1}{3}$ | $66\frac{2}{3}\% = .66\frac{2}{3} = \frac{2}{3}$ | | |
| $25\% = .25 = \frac{1}{4}$ | $75\% = .75 = \frac{3}{4}$ | | |
| $20\% = .20 = \frac{1}{5}$ | $40\% = .40 = \frac{2}{5}$ | $60\% = .60 = \frac{3}{5}$ | $80\% = .80 = \frac{4}{5}$ |
| $16\frac{2}{3}\% = .16\frac{2}{3} = \frac{1}{6}$ | $83\frac{1}{3}\% = .83\frac{1}{3} = \frac{5}{6}$ | | |
| $14\frac{2}{7}\% = .14\frac{2}{7} = \frac{1}{7}$ | | | |
| $12\frac{1}{2}\% = .125 = \frac{1}{8}$ | $37\frac{1}{2}\% = .375 = \frac{3}{8}$ | $62\frac{1}{2}\% = .625 = \frac{5}{8}$ | $87\frac{1}{2}\% = .875 = \frac{7}{8}$ |
| $10\% = .10 = \frac{1}{10}$ | | | |
| $8\frac{1}{3}\% = .08\frac{1}{3} = \frac{1}{12}$ | | | |
| $6\frac{1}{4}\% = .0625 = \frac{1}{16}$ | | | |
| $5\% = .05 = \frac{1}{20}$ | | | |

As previously emphasized, however, memorization should *follow* an understanding of how the equivalents are found. It is good practice to have the pupils construct the list of equivalents and then memorize it as a time-saver.

When changing common fractions to per cents, as in the above list, remember that per cents are hundredths; hence, when you change the fraction to a decimal you carry it *only to the two places* required to express hundredths. For example, converting $\frac{2}{3}$, $\frac{1}{16}$, and $\frac{3}{4}$ to per cents, we have:

$$\frac{2}{3} \qquad 3\overline{)2.00}^{\;.66\frac{2}{3}} \qquad \text{or } 66\tfrac{2}{3}\%$$
$$\begin{array}{r} 1\,8 \\ \hline 20 \\ 18 \\ \hline 2 \end{array}$$

$$\frac{1}{16} \qquad 16\overline{)1.00}^{\;.06\frac{1}{4}} \qquad \text{or } 6\tfrac{1}{4}\% \qquad\qquad \frac{3}{4} \qquad 4\overline{)3.00}^{\;.75} \qquad \text{or } 75\%$$
$$\begin{array}{r} 96 \\ \hline 4/16 \end{array} \qquad\qquad \begin{array}{r} 2\,8 \\ \hline 20 \\ 20 \\ \hline \end{array}$$

To change per cents to common fractions, we have only to write the denominator (always hundredths), remove the per cent sign, and reduce to lowest terms, thus: $40\% = \frac{40}{100} = \frac{2}{5}$.* But a few cases are more difficult. For example,

$$66\tfrac{2}{3}\% = \frac{66\frac{2}{3}}{100} = 66\tfrac{2}{3} \div 100 = \frac{\overset{2}{\cancel{200}}}{3} \times \frac{1}{\cancel{100}} = \frac{2}{3}$$

similarly:

$$\frac{1}{2}\% = \frac{\frac{1}{2}}{100} = \frac{1}{2} \div 100 = \frac{1}{2} \times \frac{1}{100} = \frac{1}{200}$$

A simpler way to convert such a percentage as $\frac{1}{2}\%$ to a common fraction is to write it as $\frac{1}{2}\% = .005 = \frac{5}{1000} = \frac{1}{200}$. A great deal of practice should be provided in writing the three equivalent forms, sometimes beginning with common fractions, sometimes with decimals, and sometimes with per cents.

### 4. Part-Whole Relationships in Percentage

As was shown in Chapters 16 and 17, many computations and problems in both common fractions and decimal fractions involve part-whole relationships, and likewise, many involve percentages. As

* Let pupils help deduce the procedure.

was also said there, at least in the writer's opinion such computations and problems are most simply and effectively solved by using the multiplication equation. To illustrate:

With common fractions:

1. $\frac{1}{4}$ of 60 = ?
2. $\frac{1}{4}$ of ? = 15
3. What part of 60 = 15

With decimals:

1. .25 of 60 = ?
2. .25 of ? = 15
3. What part of 60 = 15

With per cents:*

1. 25% of 60 = ?
2. 25% of ? = 15
3. What per cent of 60 = 15

In all these three types there is one pattern—two factors and their product ($a \times b = c$). In the first type for fractions, decimals, and per cents, the two factors are known and the product is found by performing the indicated multiplication. In the second type for all, the product and one of the factors are known; the pupils have learned that dividing the product by the known factor (as in $2 \times ? = 8$) gives the other factor. The third type is practically the same as the second, involving finding one of the two factors.

If, as this book advocates, pupils have become reasonably proficient in setting up and solving equations, they will use the equation method with confidence and have little or no difficulty with percentage problems. Here again much practice is needed, and the pupils should compose many problems involving these computations based on their own experience and social environment. They may write such problems as the following:

1. The nurse's report says 20% of the children in this school have defective teeth. There are 425 children in the school; how many of them have defective teeth?

$$20\% \text{ of } 425 = ?$$
$$.20 \times 425 = 85 \qquad \begin{array}{r} 425 \\ \times .20 \\ \hline 85.00 \end{array}$$

* Pupils should consider the problem situation and determine which form for these equations applies.

2. The children in our school pay 20¢ each for noon lunch. Our teacher says this is only 80% of the actual cost of the lunch, that the school pays the rest. What is the full cost of the lunch?

80% of ? = 20¢

80% of 25¢ = 20¢

$$
\begin{array}{r}
25.\\
.80\,\overline{)\,20.00}\\
16\,0\\
\hline
4\,00\\
4\,00\\
\hline
\end{array}
$$

Cost of lunch is 25¢.

To check:

$$
\begin{array}{r}
25¢\\
.80\\
\hline
20.00¢
\end{array}
$$

3. We had 50 words in a spelling test; Jane got 45 of them right. What mark should she have?

?% of 50 = 45

$$
\begin{array}{r}
.90 \text{ or } 90\%\\
50\,\overline{)\,45.00}\\
45\,0\\
\hline
0
\end{array}
$$

She got 90% of them right.

To check:

$$
\begin{array}{r}
50\\
.90\\
\hline
45.00
\end{array}
$$

Therefore her grade would be 90 to indicate that she got 90% of the words right.

Pupils may profitably write each problem first in terms of common fractions—stating the first problem as "$\frac{1}{5}$ of the pupils in our school"; then in terms of decimal fractions, as ".2 of the pupils in our school"; and then with a per cent as here. Doing this with many problems keeps pupils aware of the close relationship of common fractions, decimal fractions, and percentages. And we repeat that, when attacking a problem like the first one, they should be permitted to use whichever form—$\frac{1}{5}$ or .20—is faster for them and gives them more assurance in solving the problem. An alert pupil is discouraged and often frustrated by having to use .20 when he can see a quick solution with $\frac{1}{5}$.

Obviously these three types of problems will be introduced one at a time. Adequate practice should be provided, together with considerable experience in setting up the proper equation for many textbook and teacher-made problems, and some creative work, before the class proceeds to the next type. Pupils should learn to analyze the problem and to set the equation down before attempting any computation. Much will be gained if they are taught to write the equation first in words and then substitute the known numbers in the respective terms:

In our school 90% of the pupils have not been tardy or absent this month. We have 30 pupils; how many of them have had perfect attendance?

The equation in words is:

Some % of (total number of pupils) = (pupils with perfect attendance)

90% of 30 = ?

$$\begin{array}{r} 30 \\ .90 \\ \hline 27.00 \end{array}$$

.90 × 30 = 27 pupils with perfect attendance

The pupils then proceed from problems in which the equation is fairly obvious, with two of the terms provided, to the more difficult two-step type of problem in which one term of the equation is given indirectly and must be found before the equation for solution can be written. To illustrate:

Jim sold strawberries at a stand for a gardener and got 3% of the sales for his pay. One day he sold 125 boxes at 30¢ a box. What was his day's pay?

The pupil must first find the total sales for the day, 125 × 30¢ = $37.50. Then the equation becomes 3% of $37.50 = ?

In such problems as this, once the equation is set up, the solution is really mechanical; but putting the problem statement into equation terms calls for understanding and insight which are acquired gradually. Developing this kind of ability has been one of the weakest spots in the teaching of arithmetic, and lack of this ability is one of the basic reasons for the frustration many pupils experience in solving problems.

### 5. Problems Involving a Per Cent Increase or Decrease

One of these two-step percentage problems that requires careful presentation and interpretation is the problem dealing with a per cent of increase or of decrease. Here one basic principle is that such increase or decrease is always computed on the original cost, weight, salary, etc. The following are illustrative:

1. Mr. Brown came home and announced that he had just received a 10% increase in salary, which he said would change the family budget somewhat. His salary had been $350 a month. The first question at the family conference was "How much will the new salary be?" This he asked his son Jerry to compute on this pattern:

   A per cent of the original salary = increase

   10% of $350 = ?

   $$\begin{array}{r} \$350 \\ .10 \\ \hline \$35.00 \end{array}$$

   10% × $350 = $35 increase

   $350 + $35 = $385 new salary

2. A local newspaper reported that 12,260 car licenses were sold in that county in 1958. In 1959, 12,873 were sold. What was the per cent of increase?

A per cent of the original (1958) sales = increase
? % of 12,260 = increase

Two terms of the equation are unknown; hence it cannot be solved as an equation. But 12,873 − 12,260 = 613 increase

Now ?% of 12,260 = 613

$$\begin{array}{r} .05 \text{ or } 5\% \\ 12260 \overline{)613.00} \\ \underline{613\ 00} \end{array}$$

To check:

$$\begin{array}{r} 12260 \\ \underline{\times \quad .05} \\ 613.00 \end{array}$$

3. Karen sold a set of her books for $12, which her mother said was only 20% less than they had paid for the books. What was the original cost?

A per cent of the original cost = gain or loss
20% of cost = loss

Two terms are unknown so some other step is necessary.

A per cent of the cost = the selling price
?% of the cost = $12

Two terms are still unknown; but

100% of the cost = the cost
− 20% of the cost = the loss
80% of the cost = the selling price

Then

80% of ? = $12
80% of $15 = $12

$$\begin{array}{r} 15 \\ .80 \overline{)12.00} \\ \underline{8\ 0} \\ 4\ 00 \\ \underline{4\ 00} \end{array}$$

The cost was $15.

The wording of some such problems may baffle the pupil because some of the meaning is implied. In such a problem as: "Find a number which is 25% more than 120," the pupil who has been trained to note that any stated per cent is a *per cent of something* looks for the per cent *of what*. This problem does not say 25% of 120. In fact, it does not indicate the *of what*. But according to the basic principle at the beginning of this section, a per cent of increase or decrease is always based on the *original* amount. In this problem the original number is 120. Then the question is: What number is 120 plus 25% of 120?

$$25\% \text{ of } 120 = 30 \qquad 120 + 30 = 150$$

$$\begin{array}{r} 120 \\ .25 \\ \hline 600 \\ 2400 \\ \hline 30.00 \end{array}$$

Therefore, 150 is 25% more than 120.

Or the problem might be to find a number which is 125% of 120.

$$125\% \text{ of } 120 = ? \qquad 1.25 \times 120 = 150$$

$$\begin{array}{r} 120 \\ 1.25 \\ \hline 6\ 00 \\ 24\ 0\phantom{0} \\ 120\phantom{00} \\ \hline 150.00 \end{array}$$

## 6. Other Methods of Computing with Percentages

In Section 4 of this chapter, dealing with part-whole relationships, we advocated the equation method of solution, and that method has been applied in other parts of the chapter as well. But the abler students, and certainly the teacher, should realize that there are other methods of solution and be able to use them.

The unitary analysis method and the equation method of solving these types of problems were presented in Chapter 16 for fractional forms, and in Chapter 17 for decimal forms. The three types of percentage computation may also be solved by unitary analysis, as shown in the following illustrations:

1. 75% of 16 = ?
   1% of 16 is $\frac{1}{100}$ of 16 ($\frac{1}{100} \times 16$), or .16
   75% of 16 is 75 × .16, or 12
   75% of 16 = 12
2. 75% of a certain number is 12. What is the number?
   1% of the number is $\frac{1}{75}$ of 12 or $\frac{4}{25}$, or .16
   100% of the number is 100 × .16, or 16 (or $100 \times \frac{4}{25} = 16$)
   75% of 16 is 12
3. What per cent of 16 is 12?
   What per cent of 16 is 1?
   1 is $\frac{1}{16}$ or $6\frac{1}{4}\%$ of 16
   12 is $12 \times 6\frac{1}{4}\%$ or 75% of 16
   75% of 16 is 12

Prevalent in elementary arithmetic textbooks for many years have been procedures involving three *cases* of percentage, with a rule for each case. This necessitates learning and distinguishing the three terms, base, rate, and percentage. Base is the whole amount of which a part is taken, rate is the number per hundred to be taken, and percentage is the part taken. For example:

*40%* of the *pupils in our room* are *girls.*
Rate Base Percentage

Case 1. When rate and base are known, multiply to find percentage.
Case 2. When base and percentage are known, divide percentage by base to find rate.
Case 3. When rate and percentage are known, divide percentage by rate to find base.

The following computations in which the case rules are applied are the same as were used in Section 4 above, in connection with per cent in the multiplication equation.

Case 1. What is 25% of 60?
The base and rate are known; hence we multiply:

```
   60
 ×.25
 ----
  300
 120
-----
15.00
```

25% of 60 is 15

Case 2. What per cent of 60 is 15?
The base and percentage are known. Hence we divide the percentage by the base: .25 or 25%

```
      .25
 60)15.00
    12 0
    ----
     3 00
     3 00
     ----
```

25% of 60 is 15

Case 3. 15 is 25% of what number?
The percentage and rate are known. Hence we divide the percentage by the rate:

```
        60
 .25)15.00
     15 0
     ----
        0
```

15 is 25% of 60

Obviously this procedure calls for memorizing terms and rules with no rationalization, and in the writer's opinion provides far from an adequate understanding of percentage problems or even computational exercises of various types.

Closely allied to the case and rule method is the formula method. Here the pupil learns three formulas by which he finds each of the three terms, thus:

$$\text{Rate} \times \text{Base} = \text{Percentage}$$

Then, $$rb = p \qquad r = \frac{p}{b} \qquad b = \frac{p}{r}$$

Many pupils have floundered in all types of percentage computations because they did not fully understand the terms and consequently could not remember the formulas or successfully apply them.

## 7. Applications of Percentage

Many of the problems which ordinary literate people are called upon to handle involve percentage—for example, interest, discount, taxes, insurance rates, and the like. Furthermore, we need some knowledge of percentage to interpret many newspaper and magazine articles—not least among them information about sports.

Elementary pupils should have sufficient introduction to percentage and enough experience with it to serve them in interpreting their school and social environment, such as handling their own financial interests and responsibilities—putting out money at interest, and computing discounts and sales taxes—and also the content of textbooks, and of newspaper items that interest them. Much of the language of percentage, however, comes with experience; hence such problems as involve property taxes, insurance, installment buying, commissions, bonds, dividends, and the like, should be postponed until the later upper grades. By that time, an average pupil with a good arithmetic foundation and normal social development will be ready to apply the typical percentage procedures he has learned to various new problems, especially if he has learned to use equation procedures effectively.

The following examples show how readily the equation method can be applied in various problems involving percentage:

Discount

1. A \$48 chair was sold at 10% discount. What was the amount of reduction?

A per cent of the original price = the discount

10% of \$48 = ?

$$\begin{array}{r} \$48 \\ \times .10 \\ \hline \$4.80 \end{array}$$

.10 × \$48 = \$4.80 reduction

2. Tom bought for \$30 a coat marked \$36. What per cent discount did he get?

\$36 − \$30 = \$6 discount

?% of \$36 = \$6

$$\begin{array}{r} .16\tfrac{2}{3} \text{ or } 16\tfrac{2}{3}\% \\ 36\,\overline{)\,6.00} \\ 3\,6 \\ \hline 2\,40 \\ 2\,16 \\ \hline 24/36 \end{array}$$

He got a $16\frac{2}{3}$% discount.

Interest

1. What interest will \$400 draw for one year at $3\frac{1}{2}$%?

Rate × Principal × Time (years) = Interest

$3\frac{1}{2}\% \times \$400 \times 1 = ?$

$$\frac{3\frac{1}{2}}{100} \times 400 \times 1 = ? \quad 3\frac{1}{2} \div 100 = \frac{7}{2} \times \frac{1}{100} = \frac{7}{200}$$

$$\frac{7}{\cancel{200}} \times \overset{2}{\cancel{400}} \times 1 = 14$$

Therefore, \$14 is the interest.

2. How long will it take \$500 to earn \$45 interest at 5%?

$$\frac{5}{\cancel{100}} \times \overset{5}{\cancel{500}} \times ? = 45$$

$$25 \times ? = 45$$

$$\begin{array}{r} 1\tfrac{4}{5} \\ 25\,\overline{)\,45} \\ 25 \\ \hline 20/25 \end{array}$$

Therefore, $1\frac{4}{5}$ years or 1 yr. 9 mo. 18 days

Taxes

1. What tax must I pay on property assessed at \$8500 if the tax rate is $12\frac{1}{2}$ mills?

Rate × Assessed Valuation = Tax

.0125 × 8500 = ?

.0125 × \$8500 = \$106.25 tax

$$\begin{array}{r} 8500 \\ \times .0125 \\ \hline 4\,2500 \\ 17\,000 \\ 85\,00 \\ \hline 106.2500 \end{array}$$

The tax is \$106.25.

2. What is the rate of taxation in my town when I pay $75 tax on property assessed at $5000?

$? \times \$5000 = \$75$

$.015 \times \$5000 = \$75$

```
        .015
5000 | 75.000
       50 00
       25 000
       25 000
```

The tax rate is 15 mills.

Commission

A man who gets 5% commission on sales made a $350 commission one month. What was the amount of his sales?

5% of sales = $350

5% of ? = $350

5% of $7000 = $350

```
       70 00.
.05 | 350.00
      35
       0 00
```

The amount of sales was $7000.

Profit and Loss

A shoeshop bought 600 pairs of a certain type of summer shoes at $4.50 a pair. They sold two-thirds of the shipment for $7 a pair, and the rest late in the season at $4 a pair. Did they gain or lose on the 600 pairs and how much? What per cent of the selling price was the gain or loss?

```
600 pairs at $4.50 cost $2700
400 pairs at $7.00 sold for $2800
200 pairs at $4.00 sold for   800
              Total sales  $3600
                Less cost  $2700
                     Gain  $ 900
```

?% of selling price = gain

?% of $3600 = $900

25% of $3600 = $900

```
        .25 or 25%
3600 | 900.00
       720 0
       180 00
       180 00
```

There was a 25% gain.

Note: It was customary in the past to compute the per cent of gain or loss on the cost of goods. But since the original cost represents only part of the merchant's investment, and since some of his investment has not yet yielded income, many businesses now compute this per cent on the selling price because it is a definite and known amount. To prevent confusion the basis used should be stated in a problem.

## COMPETENCE CHECK

1. Write a rule for changing per cents to decimals. Change $16\frac{1}{4}\%$, $30\%$, and $4\frac{1}{2}\%$ to decimals.
2. 1. $45\%$ of $200 = ? \times 200$
   2. $6\frac{1}{4}\%$ of $48 = ? \times 48$
   3. $125\%$ of $80 = ? \times 80$
3. Express each of the following as a common fraction, a decimal fraction, and a per cent:

   $6.2\%$ $\quad\frac{9}{20}\quad$ $115\%$
4. List textbook or local uses of percentage with which elementary pupils would be familiar.
5. Write 15 to 20 groups of equivalent common fractions, decimal fractions, and per cents without using paper and pencil in computing.
6. 1. Compose a problem to illustrate each of the three types of part-whole relationship problems in percentage.
   2. Write an equation for each of the above, first only in words, then with known figures supplied.
   3. Solve these problems.
7. Why are no new computational concepts involved in solving percentage problems?
8. Discuss the relative merits of the four commonly advocated methods of computing percentages—equation, unitary analysis, three cases with rules, and formula.
9. Compose a problem and solve it by each of these four methods.
10. Do you agree that the three most difficult concepts in percentage are per cents less than 100, per cents more than 100, and per cents of increase and decrease? On what grade level do you think they belong?
11. Compose one problem of each of the five types that seem to you the most difficult types in percentage. Solve them.

## OPTIONAL ASSIGNMENTS

1. Examine several of the references to see what procedure the authors advocate in dealing with the three types of percentage computations. Report your reactions.
2. Hickerson says (p. 286): "... Most children should not attempt to compute with per cents until junior or senior high school." To what extent do you agree with him? Why?
3. What is the historical derivation of the per cent sign?
4. According to Smith, per cents over $100\%$ and under $1\%$ are not for the slow pupil. To what extent do you agree with him?
5. Scan the references and list those that advocate solving percentage problems by the equation method, by the unitary analysis method, by the three cases with rules, by formulas.

## REFERENCES

Hickerson, J. Allen, *Guiding Children's Arithmetic Experiences*, Prentice-Hall, New York, 1952, chap. 15.

Marks, John L., Purdy, C. Richard, and Kinney, Lucien B., *Teaching Arithmetic for Understanding*, McGraw-Hill, New York, 1958, chap. 10.

Smith, Rolland R., "Per Cents in the Seventh and Eighth Grades," *Journal of Education*, November, 1953, pp. 34–35.

Spitzer, Herbert F., *The Teaching of Arithmetic*, Houghton Mifflin, Boston, 2nd ed., 1954, chap. 8.

Swain, Robert L., *Understanding Arithmetic*, Holt, Rinehart & Winston, New York, 1957, pp. 165–169.

Taylor, E. H., and Mills, C. N., *Arithmetic for Teacher Training Classes*, Holt, Rinehart & Winston, New York, 4th ed., 1955, chap. 15.

Wheat, H. G., *How to Teach Arithmetic*, Row, Peterson, Evanston, 1951, pp. 267–270.

chapter 19

# Measurement

## 1. Need for and Use of Measurement

In an earlier chapter we spoke of primitive man's need for some system of counting (numeration) and of recording the count (notation). His primitive and crude systems enabled him to account for property consisting of individual items—sheep, skins, and the like. But then came the need for some means of accounting for distances more accurate than "two days' journey," for amounts of grain more accurate than "hands full" or "horns full," and for metals, whose value often depended more on weight than on quantity. Thus began the long and gradual development of what today we call measurement, from those roughly usable beginnings to the highly precise, complex, and accurate measurements used by civilized peoples today.

## 2. Historical Development of Measurement

It would be a long story to trace the development of measurement from its infancy to its modern form. However, describing a few steps in that development will give some idea of the gradual changes that occurred in past centuries.

The earliest means of measurement really involved no *units of measure*. Poles and skins and slabs were put up where they were to be used, and chopped to fit—a far cry from the procedures of today's skilled worker, with his nonshrinkable and nonstretchable steel tapeline calibrated to small fractions of an inch, and his machines for precision cutting.

When primitive man used barter he depended on his wits for an even trade; but when trade became more extensive, men wanted to know "how much" they were giving and "how much" they were getting. Although their ingenuity may have been limited, the human body was always available and they began to use its dimensions as measures of length and distance:

Length—The girth (the distance around the waist).
The cubit (from the point of the elbow to the tip of the middle finger).
The span (from the end of the thumb to the tip of the little finger when the hand is spread out).
The ell (from the middle of the chest to the tips of the fingers, with the arm outstretched).
The fathom (from finger tips to finger tips, with both arms outstretched).

Distance—The foot (distance from heel to tip of toes).
The pace (two steps).
Day's journey (distance one could travel in a day).

Such measures served for centuries but they followed no pattern of mathematical relationship; that characteristic of measuring units came later.

In addition to measures for length and distance, for which some of the more aggressive people devised measuring sticks, some means of measuring quantity was needed. Matching weights on a balance served this purpose and was used thousands of years ago. Later, certain-sized containers and agreed-upon weight units came into use, but they could hardly be called standardized.

By medieval times measures began to have more resemblance to those we use. The foot was established as a measure and the Romans divided it into twelfths, which came to be called inches. In an effort to standardize the length of an inch, a Scottish king stated that it was to be the average width of the thumbs of three men, measured at the root of the nail. Edward II of England later decreed an inch to be the length of 3 barleycorns taken from the middle of the ear and laid end to end, a foot to be 12 inches, and a yard (originally the girth or ell of a man) to be 3 feet. At various times in English history a foot ranged from $9\frac{3}{4}$ inches to 19 inches. An attempt was made to standardize a rod (now $16\frac{1}{2}$ feet) by lining up 16 men of assorted sizes and making the total length of their left feet the legal length of a rod.

All these efforts led slowly and gradually toward the agreed-upon standards of measurement of today. Many of our measures have been described and defined by Act of Congress, and precise units are stored under dust-free, constant-temperature conditions for reference. State laws provide punishment for merchants and others who give short measure beyond the legal permissible variance. This requires them to have accurate measuring instruments—scales, yard measures, etc.—as well as to use them honestly.

## 3. Purposes and Aims of Teaching Measurement in Elementary School

We are aware not only of the high degree of accuracy of measurements today, but also of the ubiquitous nature of measurement in our everyday living. A casual inventory of things in our environment that have been or can be measured by some accepted unit of measurement would include age, weight, height, body temperature, blood count, blood pressure, heart beat, breathing rate, vision, hearing, intelligence, sizes of every article of wearing apparel, rings, watches, glasses, room temperature, light, air pressure, humidity, time, money, class size, aspirin tablets, pop, pencils, pens, books, paper—and we have only begun the list.

It follows, then, that since so large a part of everyone's environmental experience involves measurement in some form, our purpose in teaching measurement information and procedures in elementary school is to orient these pupils in the many environmental situations in which some knowledge of measurement is essential.

Our aims in teaching measurement on this level are based on the expanding-concept idea, in which the child is led gradually from the simple, nonstandardized descriptions and computations to development along such lines as:

1. Formulation of concepts of the various units used.
2. Ability to choose the appropriate known and accepted unit of measurement for the object to be measured.
3. Acquisition of increasing skill in using measuring instruments.
4. Realization that the use to be made of measurement determines the degree of precision required.
5. Ability to work with denominate numbers and to handle their reduction into the units that make computation easiest.

By what procedures shall we accomplish these aims? *Not* by the long-used method of memorizing a table and then doing a few reduction problems to apply it. Rather, as in every other area of arithmetic learning discussed in this book, by emphasizing manipulative experiences at every step—in setting up the table, in reducing from one unit to others, in selecting situations in which the various measuring units will be useful, in approximating (guessing) measurements and then verifying them, and so on. Some of these procedures will be discussed further in this chapter.

## 4. First Steps in Measurement

As was said in Chapter 10, many children enter school with some number concepts already well established. These concepts include several that are related to measurement, mostly rather crude and roughly approximate in form. The teacher can easily make a survey and record individual pupils' abilities on a check sheet. As an illustration:

Does he show comprehension of simple units:
- Of distance—1 block; 2 blocks.
- Of time—1 day; 1 week.
- Of capacity—1 cupful; 1 pint; 1 quart.
- Of weight—1 pound.
- Of money—1 cent; 1 nickel; 1 dime, etc.

Does he show comprehension of the use of simple instruments of measurement:
- Of length—ruler; yardstick.
- Of time—watch; clock; calendar.
- Of capacity—measuring cup; pint measure; quart measure.
- Of weight—scales.

Beginning where the pupils are, the teacher continues to work on developing such concepts. In conversations with the pupils as well as in definitely planned experiences, he helps them increase their vocabulary of comparison, and of identification of sizes, quantities, weights, and distances. Most primary number books provide practice in using such terms as more, less, wider, longer, heavier, bigger, smaller, tallest, and so on.

Pupils will be given experience in using simple instruments for measuring, such as measuring cup, pint and quart measures, ruler, scale, clock, thermometer, and calendar. Opportunities to use real money, and toy money, if available, will be provided occasionally. Many primary teachers use a grocery store unit which provides for measuring shelves, weighing make-believe foods, selling pints and quarts (cartons), and counting money, and other similar experiences.

Among the early concepts regarding size and measurement that pupils should have are recognition of simple geometric figures, particularly squares and circles—the largest square, a smaller square, and so on.

## 5. Experience with Linear Measures

Since measuring length involves only one dimension, it is the simplest kind of measure to understand and apply. As was said in a preceding section, a primary child uses approximations of distance that serve his purpose—"I can jump farther than you can"; "I can throw the ball farther than Bobby can"; "I live a long way from school and have to come on the bus"; "My Uncle Tom lives a really long ways from here—he lives about a million miles from here." Or perhaps the child has learned to say, "I live four blocks from school," but how the four-block distance is determined he probably does not know.

As he continues his mathematical learning he sees the need for more precise measurement; e.g., at the track meet his own jump and those of others are measured to a fraction of an inch. He comes to realize that standardized units are required and that modern instruments are capable of measuring such infinitely small lengths as thousandths of an inch. But he also realizes that such great precision is not needed for most of the measurements that people in general make. Laying out a tennis court or a baseball diamond is a different matter from making a watch spring. He learns that it is physically impossible to attain perfect precision in any measurement, but that it is important to make careful measurements and to compute as accurately as possible whether he is cutting material by a dress pattern or measuring a room for new linoleum or measuring for cutting parts in a shop project.

A weak spot in teaching linear measurement in the past has been the fact that the linear table has been memorized without adequate concepts both of the size of each unit and of the relationships between the units. More effective procedures are:

1. Drawing lines 1 inch, 1 foot, and then 1 yard and 1 rod long; and then lines of various lengths in multiples of those units.

2. Walking a mile.
3. Guessing at lengths like those in (1) and verifying them by measurement.
4. Discussing appropriate uses of those units of measurements. For example, what would you use to measure:
   a. A book?
   b. The doormat?
   c. The floor?
   d. Window drapery?
5. Reducing to other units, such as,
   a. 72 inches are how many feet? How many yards?
   b. $2\frac{1}{3}$ yards are how many feet? How many inches?

Not to be overlooked is the fact that linear measure involves circles. The distance around, or the circumference, is difficult to measure; it is best measured by using a length of string, and applying the string to a measuring tape or a ruler. Measuring the circumference and deriving the radius and the diameter provide valuable experience.

## 6. Experience with Square Measures

Measures of area involve two dimensions and are therefore much more difficult of comprehension than linear measures. Part of this difficulty is also due to the fact that as a preschool and primary pupil a child had most experience with measurements of length—a shorter fishpole, a long stick, a short string. Whatever was akin to area experience usually involved bulk—a bigger piece of pie, a smaller candy bar, a big book. The child was rarely called upon to comprehend purely surface area, a "plane figure."

The simplest way to develop the concept of area is to use the idea, "How much will it take to cover it?" But no one can tell *how much* until some appropriate measuring units are selected. The teacher suggests squares, an inch each way, thus introducing the concept of a square inch.

### *Area of Rectangle*

A **rectangle** is a plane figure whose opposite sides are equal and parallel, and whose adjacent sides are perpendicular to each other.*

* Let pupils formulate descriptive definitions of the various figures.

Thus a **square** is one form of rectangle. It is a rectangle whose four sides are equal.

After sufficient manipulation, including finding out, by counting, how many square inches cover books, sheets of paper, and other square and rectangular surfaces (Fig. 10), the teacher helps the pupils

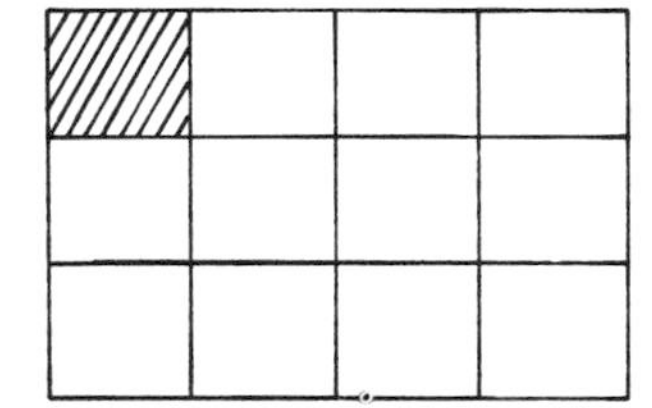

**Fig. 10.** Square units of measure.

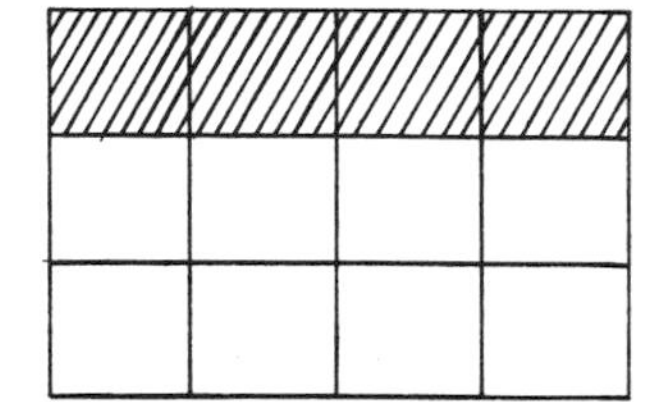

**Fig. 11.** Counting by rows.

discover a short cut for finding this number by counting the number of square inches in one row and then adding or multiplying to find the number in the several rows (Fig. 11).

Following computation of this kind, the square-foot pattern is introduced and the same procedure used as with square inches, but this

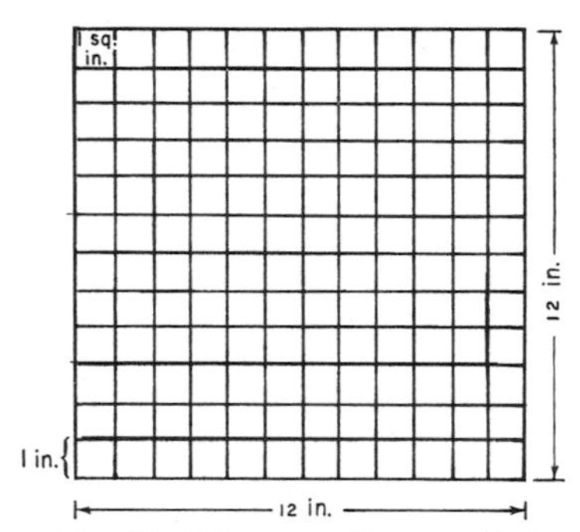


**Fig. 12.** Diagram of square foot.

time applied to floors and other larger areas. The pupils should build a square foot, using 1-inch squares, and find out for themselves that 144 square inches equal 1 square foot, as shown in Fig. 12. Since computing the areas of all other plane figures is based directly or indirectly on computing the areas of rectangles, the teacher must make sure to provide a good foundation here.

In progressing to square yards as units, a piece of wallboard, cut by teacher and pupils into a square yard, and then marked in square feet (Fig. 13), gives a vivid impression of the unit called a square yard. The writer has found more than one college student who was unable to draw a square foot or a square yard on the chalkboard or floor. The process of laying out the square yards on the floor and counting them,

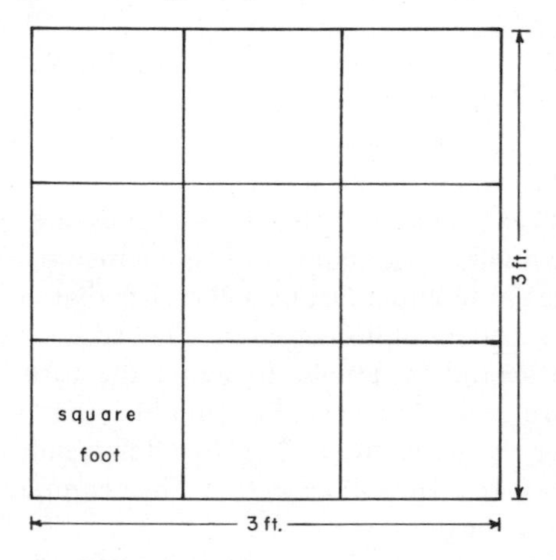


**Fig. 13.** Diagram of square yard.

measuring the floor and computing its area in square yards, and comparing the result obtained by counting with that obtained by computation provides useful experience.

The next step is to provide a rod measure and go outdoors and measure rods and square rods and discuss their uses. If feasible, the class may walk a mile to experience distance, and use the school bus for a trip around a square mile. Fortunate here are the children in open flat country who can see from corner to corner of the square mile.

Square miles involve land measurement, which in turn involves measurement in acres. The acre as a unit is mystifying to many people, and not one person in a thousand can define it in terms of dimensions, though it is widely used in newspaper articles. It is not called a "square" acre, and is never defined as a square. Even farmers who use acres most in computing never measure an acre as a square. The acre as a unit is an elusive concept, because if we try to make it a square unit, it will be *about* 209 feet on a side. Since it contains 160 square rods, each side, if the acre is square, will be between 12 and 13 rods long—not a convenient dimension.

*Any* area that contains 160 square rods is an acre; hence a strip 1 rod wide and 160 rods long—a long narrow ribbon of land $16\frac{1}{2}$ feet wide and half a mile long—is an acre. A farmer knows if he has plowed such a strip he has plowed an acre of land. If his field is a quarter of a mile long (80 rods), when he plows a strip 2 rods wide, he has plowed an acre. The gardener whose land is 40 rods by 60 rods has 2400 square rods; $2400 \div 160 = 15$ (acres of land). Pupils should measure off a square of land that is 209 feet on a side to develop the concept of "just about an acre," but they must remember that an acre can be any shape, as long as it contains 160 square rods.

After the pupil has adequate experience with measuring and counting, and sees that the number of square units in a row times the number of rows gives the area in square units, he will realize that units of length × units of width = square units of area; he soon shortens this to $l \times w = A$. He should be taught to avoid the form, 2 inches × 4 inches = 8 square inches; instead he should either write 2 × 4 sq. in. = 8 sq. in., or merely compute $2 \times 4 = 8$ and indicate the area in terms of the units used. He will learn that when computing areas, both dimensions must be in the same units.

In working with square measures, pupils have used linear measures in measuring the length and width, and perhaps in reducing them to the same units. After they have a good grasp of area measurements, the teacher should bring to their attention another use of linear units, namely, in measuring perimeter.

Questions like, "How far is it around this square?" and "What is its outside measurement?" can be answered by measuring around or walking around, or drawing a colored line around different-shaped figures, but measuring in each case. This leads to an understanding of *distance around*, for which they learn the new word **perimeter.** After some such experiences and a good number of how-to-do-it problems without numbers, they will discover, as they work with numbers, that $2l + 2w$ = perimeter, or in the case of squares, $4s$ = perimeter. They must keep in mind that whenever they want *distance around* they must go back to rulers and tapelines for measuring. Of help here is to lay a string on the perimeter of a square or rectangle, then measure the length of string needed and compare it with $2l + 2w$ = perimeter.

As was the case with linear measure, the table of square measure should be written after it is verified by counting, and then learned, only because the pupils realize that they are slowed down by having to look up measures they want to use. At each step of the way, the teacher should use problems within their experience and also from the textbook, along with many practice exercises, to help them comprehend the computations and applications of square measures.

### *Area of Triangle*

As was mentioned above, the procedure for finding the area of a rectangle is basic to that for finding the area of all other plane figures. It is not necessary to use geometric proof of the equality of triangles at this stage, for pupils will accept statements regarding such equality when based on observation and measurement, particularly if one figure is imposed on another and the two appear to be identical in form and size.

When a rectangular piece of paper is folded on the diagonal and cut into halves, as shown in Fig. 14, it is obvious that triangle *adc* equals

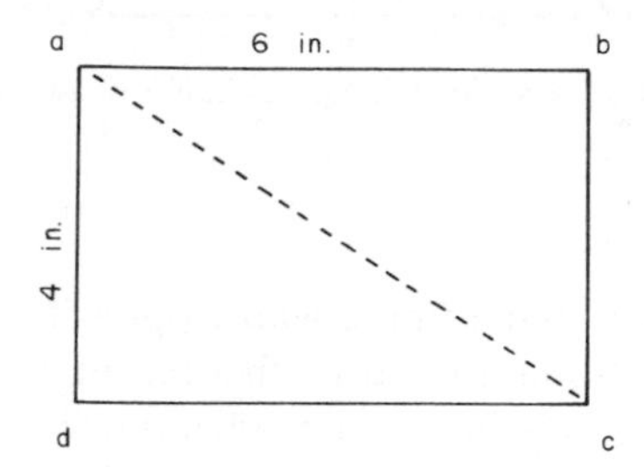


**Fig. 14.** Triangle as half a rectangle.

triangle *abc*. If sides of the rectangle are 4 inches and 6 inches, $4 \times 6$ gives the area of the rectangle *abcd*. One-half the area of that rectangle $\left(\frac{4 \times 6}{2}\right)$ is the area of either of the triangles.

Only the terms *length* and *width* have been used thus far in work with rectangles, and others now need to be introduced. With a little manipulation a pupil sees readily that if a cardboard rectangle is placed on edge it rests on one side, which may be called its **base,** and that the vertical edge (side) becomes its height, which may be called its **altitude.**

In a triangle like *cad* [c, a, d] one of its sides, *ca*, is its **altitude** (a line from the vertex to the base and perpendicular to the base). But in triangle *lmn* (Fig. 15), the altitude *mo* is not one of its sides. As shown in the figure, the area of triangle *lmn* is half the area of the rectangle *lprn*. The altitude *mo* of the triangle is also the altitude of the rectangle *lprn*. In finding the area of a triangle it is essential to know both its *base* and its *altitude*.

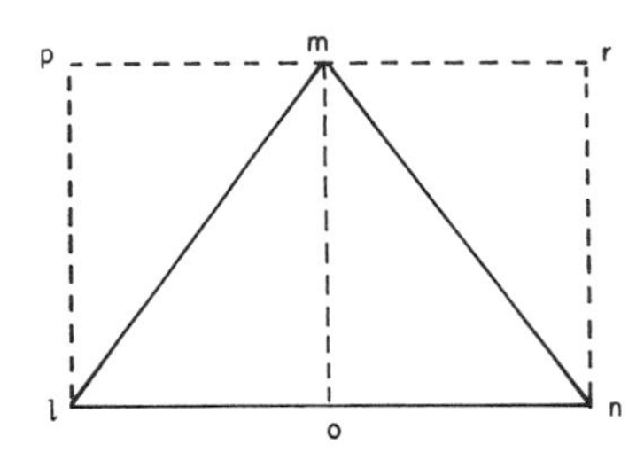


**Fig. 15.** Isosceles triangle as half a rectangle.

### *Area of Parallelogram*

A **parallelogram** is a plane figure whose opposite sides are equal and parallel. Therefore a square or any other rectangle is a parallelogram. But not all parallelograms have their adjacent sides perpendicular to each other; for example, *abcd* shown in Fig. 16 is a parallelogram.

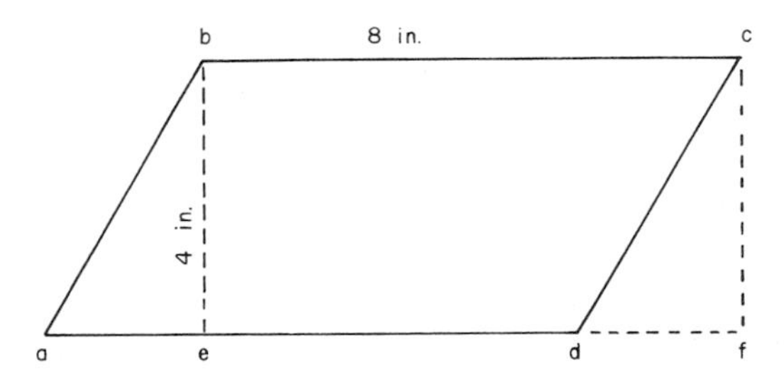


**Fig. 16.** Equivalent areas of rectangle and parallelogram.

To find the area of a parallelogram, we convert it to a rectangle equivalent in area to the parallelogram. On a piece of paper the shape of *abcd* (Fig. 16), we draw *be* perpendicular to the base; this is the altitude. We cut triangle *abe* off from the parallelogram *abcd* and lay it in the position *dcf*. We find that since the same amount of paper covers *dcf*, we obviously have a rectangle *ebcf* equivalent in area to the parallelogram *abcd*. Hence, the area of the parallelogram equals its base *ad* times its altitude *be* (8 × 4), or 32 square inches.

### *Area of Trapezoid*

Any plane figure with four sides, only two of which are parallel, is called a **trapezoid;** for example, *abcd* in Fig. 17 is a trapezoid. If a piece

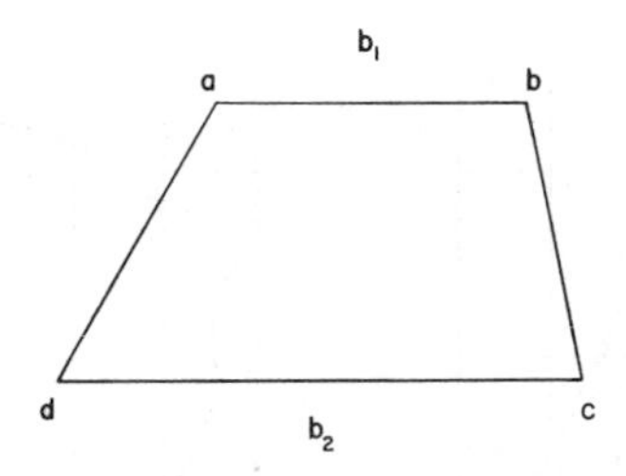


**Fig. 17.** Trapezoid.

of paper, cut like *abcd*, is used as a pattern for cutting another piece of paper, and the second piece is laid beside *abcd* in the position *befc* (Fig. 18), a parallelogram *aefd* is formed. The side *dc* + side *ab* (represented by its equal, *cf*) forms the base of the parallelogram *aefd;* its area can be found (base × altitude) by multiplying *df* by

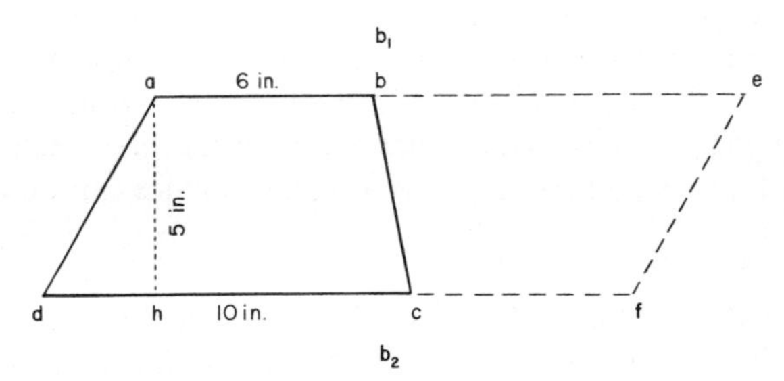


**Fig. 18.** Relationship of trapezoid to parallelogram.

*ah* (16 × 5), or 80 square inches. But the area of the parallelogram *aefd* is twice as large as that of the trapezoid *abcd;* therefore, to find the area of the trapezoid we take $\frac{1}{2}$ of (16 × 5), or 40. Or we may use ($\frac{1}{2}$ of 16) × 5 = 40. If we take $\frac{1}{2}$ of 16 we are taking one-half the combined length of *ab* and *dc*, the two bases of the trapezoid. Hence, the area of a trapezoid may be indicated as

$$A = altitude \times \left(\frac{\text{base} + \text{opposite side}}{2}\right)$$

$$A = \text{a}\left(\frac{\text{b}_1 + \text{b}_2}{2}\right).$$

One visual aid that helps to clarify surface measurements is squared paper manila sheets ruled with quarter-inch, half-inch, or inch

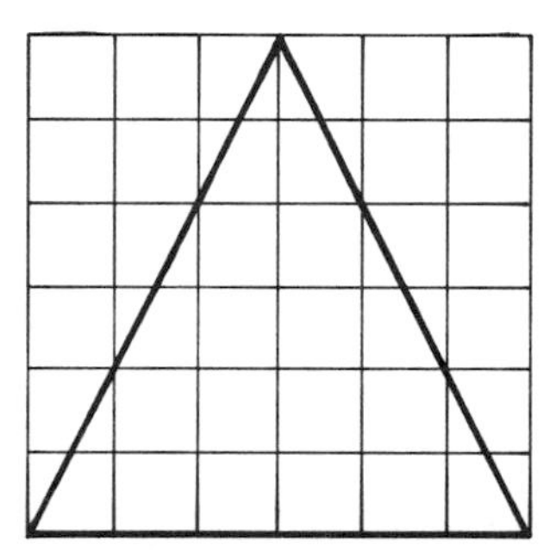

**Fig. 19.** Area of triangle on squared paper.

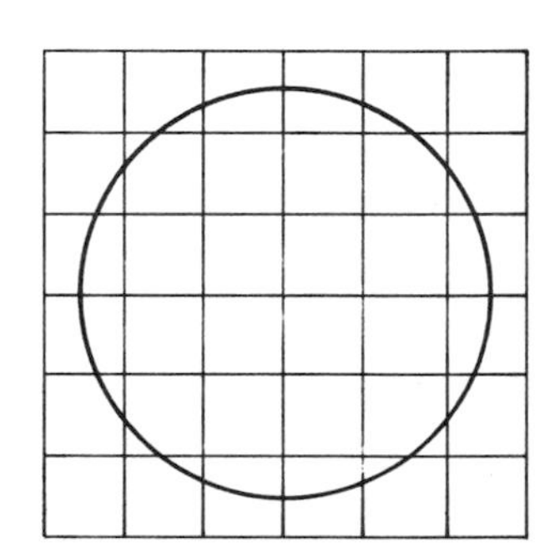

**Fig. 20.** Area of circle on squared paper.

squares. Squares, rectangles, triangles, and any other plane figures can be drawn on this paper, the basic squares representing units of any dimension. Pupils can count the squares within the figure and compare this with the number of square units they find by computation. However, it is difficult to count the number of squares within any figures except rectangles, because many squares are only partially included; this is shown in Figs. 19 and 20. Even so, rough estimates can be obtained.

### *Area of Circle*

No doubt the two uses of the word "circle" cause more confusion among pupils than teachers realize. We say a ring is a circle. We "form a circle" for a game or dance. Thus used, the word circle may be defined as a closed curve, every point on which is equally distant from a point within, called the *center*. But the teacher hands out paper and says, "When the pattern comes down your row to you, draw and cut out a circle from the paper I have just given you." Every pupil knows he is not to cut out a *ring* of paper, but a piece bounded by the curved line we have just defined as a circle; we shall come to call this the *circumference* of the circle just cut out. Finding the area of a circle is a much more advanced mathematical process and more difficult of explanation than finding the area of any of the other plane figures thus far described.

With some difficulty, but with considerable satisfaction, the area of a circle can be represented in the form of a rectangle as an aid in verifying

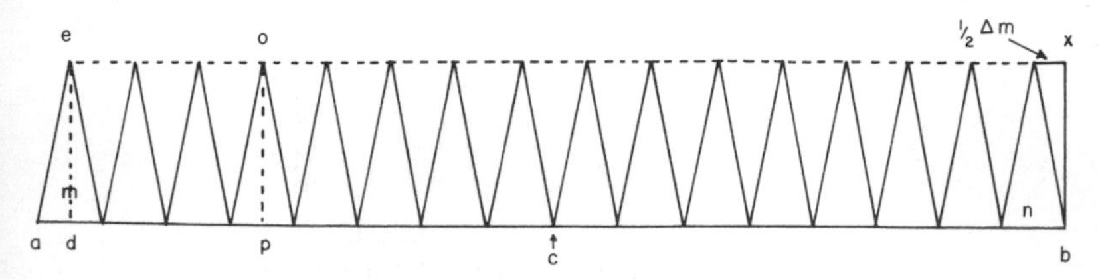


**Fig. 21.** Area of circle.

it. A good demonstration can be given with a piece of muslin, on which the circumference of a circle with a 7-inch diameter has been stitched on a sewing machine. Using a protractor, and with the teacher's help, the pupils can cut the circle of cloth into sixteenths, cutting from the center of the circle to the circumference, but not through the stitching, except at one point, so that the triangular sections can be stretched out as shown in Fig. 21.

Before this demonstration, the pupils should have learned the terms circumference, diameter, and radius, and also their meaning. The **circumference** is the closed curve that bounds a plane figure, and is at every point equally distant from a point within the figure called the **center.** The **diameter** is a straight line drawn from two points in the circumference and passing through the center. The **radius** is the distance in a straight line from the circumference to the center. The relationships of these parts can be approximately determined by string measurements, to verify the mathematical relationships, namely, that the circumference is approximately $3\frac{1}{7}$ (or 3.1416) times the length of the diameter, and the radius is $\frac{1}{2}$ the diameter.

When the triangular sections of the circle are stretched out, as in Fig. 21, the line *ab* represents what *was* the circumference.* If we

* Guide pupils to identify the circle measurements in this form and to propose methods for finding the area.

multiply the circumference *ab* of this circle (22 in.) by the altitude *op* of the triangles ($3\frac{1}{2}$ in., the radius of the circle), we obtain the area of a rectangle whose base is this circumference, and whose altitude is the radius of this circle; however, we must cut off half of the first triangle and place it beside the last triangle. It is obvious that the area of the rectangle *dexb* is twice as much as that of the circle represented by the row of triangles. Further proof of this can be obtained by cutting the row of triangles apart at point *c* and fitting the points of half the row

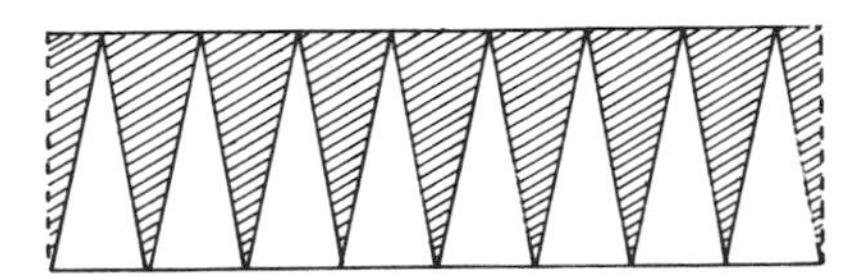

**Fig. 22.** Triangles in Fig. 21 fitted to form a rectangle.

into the other half, as in Fig. 22.

The shaded portion of Fig. 22 represents the right-hand half of Fig. 21, the unshaded portion the left-hand half; the triangles are fitted together to form a rectangle whose area is equal to the area of the circle. This figure embodies the general principle of cutting a circle into smaller and smaller triangles, thus making the curvature of the circumference increasingly negligible. From the figure we see that half the circumference multiplied by the radius is the area of the circle. For this circle, $\frac{C \times r}{2} = 22 \times \frac{7}{2} \times \frac{1}{2} = \frac{77}{2} = 38\frac{1}{2}$; therefore the area of the circle is $38\frac{1}{2}$ sq. in.

After using this diagram, most pupils will probably choose to remember $\frac{C \times r}{2}$ as the formula for finding the area of a circle. However, the more alert pupils should be encouraged to figure out how the usual formula, $\pi r^2 = A$, is derived. The symbol $\pi$, the sixteenth letter of the Greek alphabet, denotes the ratio of the circumference of a circle to its diameter. That ratio ($\frac{22}{7}$ in our circle) is the same for every circle and is approximately $3\frac{1}{7}$ or 3.1416. The circumference is $2\pi r$, or $\pi \times$ the diameter; $\frac{1}{2}$ the circumference $= \pi r$; $\pi r \times r = \pi r^2$. This formula, $\pi r^2 = A$, is more convenient when the circumference must be computed.

One way of understanding the reasonableness of using the formula

$\pi r^2$ to find the area of a circle is by looking at a diagram like that in Fig. 23.* The radius squared gives the area of one-quarter of the large square. Three times the area of this small square is not enough for the

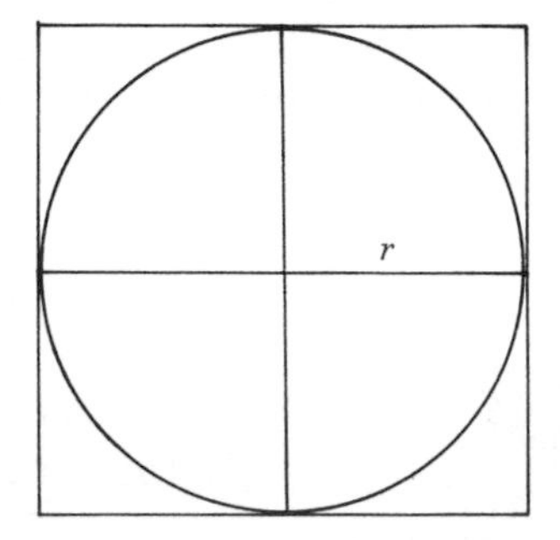


**Fig. 23.** Estimation of area of circle.

area of the circle, and four times the area of this square is too much; therefore, $3\frac{1}{7}$ ($\pi$) times it is apparently a reasonable answer.

## 7. Experience with Cubic Measures

Although children have had experience in primary school and also at home with measures of capacity in liquid measures, such as pints and quarts, using three-dimension measurement is new for middle-grade pupils and needs careful development.

Pupils may be more baffled than we realize when we say that an empty chalk box, perhaps 6 in. by 4 in. by 4 in., contains 96 cu. in., and then show a solid piece of wood 6 in. by 4 in. by 4 in., and say that it also contains 96 cu. in.

Cubic measures are probably best introduced by having on hand at least 144 cubic-inch blocks (preferably 1728 of them), showing the pupils one of them, and discussing the characteristics of a *cube*. No doubt this will be a pupil's first acquaintance with the word "cube," except for ice cubes in the refrigerator at home; these are not usually true cubes. He sees why it is called a 1-inch cube and why it is also commonly referred to as a cubic inch. (This is the place to show the class that a square inch has two dimensions and a cubic inch three.)

* Challenge alert pupils to work this out for themselves.

A cubic foot may be introduced by means of a model, which appears to be a solid, and its characteristics discussed.

Visual and manipulative experiences should be continued by using inch cubes to build models of different dimensions and counting the cubic-inch blocks used in them. Pupils can be guided so they will see that, just as was true of square measure, it is not necessary to count

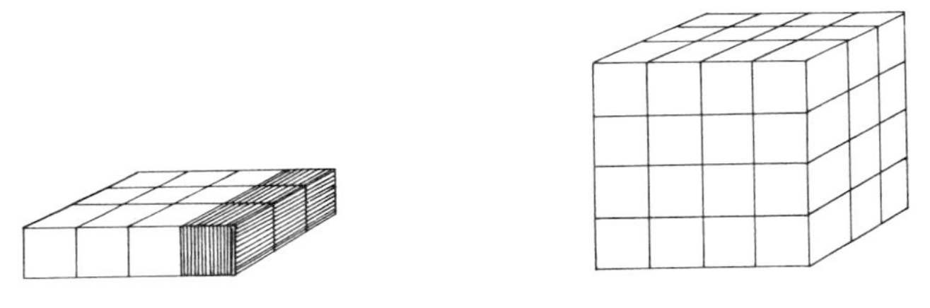

**Fig. 24.** Cubic units.

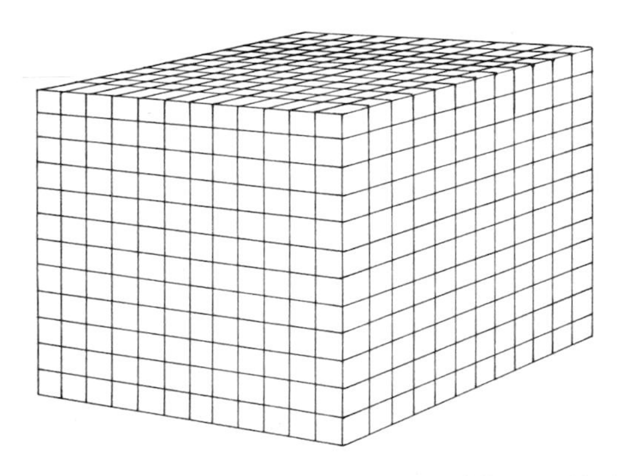

**Fig. 25.** Diagram of a cubic foot constructed from cubic inches.

the individual cubes if they count the rows on the first layer and multiply this by the number of layers.* Thus they will derive the $l \times w \times h = V$ formula.

Using hollow cubes, the teacher can explain that although solids are measured in cubic feet, as when a mason builds a stone wall and charges so much a cubic foot for it, sometimes we want to know how many one-foot cubes will be needed to fill a grain bin, for example, or a swimming pool. Here we use the three dimensions and find the number of cubic

* An opportunity for pupil discovery.

feet it *could* contain. The **volume** of a solid—or hollow—indicates the number of cubic units of a given size into which it can be cut or which it contains, as shown in Fig. 24.

Pupils should construct a cubic foot with inch cubes, as shown in Fig. 25, and *see* that 1728 cubic inches actually make a cubic foot. To increase comprehension it is very helpful for them also to construct a

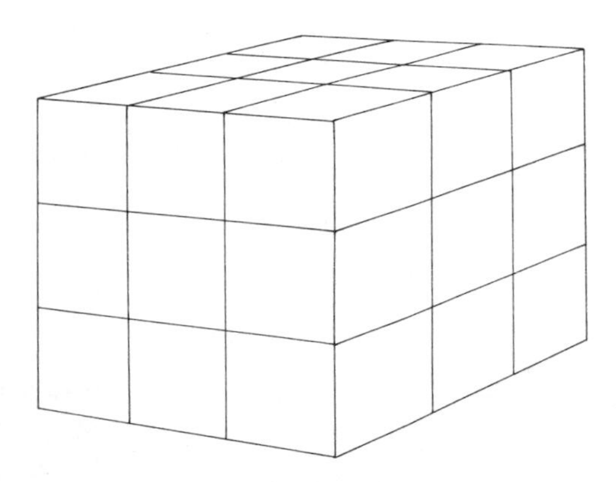

**Fig. 26.** Diagram of a cubic yard constructed from cubic feet.

cubic yard from foot cubes, as shown in Fig. 26. Following this experience, they can make a yard cube from a carton and mark square feet on all faces of it. Anderson (see References) explains how to illustrate a cubic yard by making a skeleton of one, using 12 ordinary yardsticks, 8 angle irons, and some bolts.

After basic understandings are established, some geometric terms should be introduced; for example:

1. Measures which use cubic units are referred to as measures of **volume.**
2. Three-dimensional objects are referred to as **solids,** even though they may be hollow.
3. A solid that has six square sides of equal size, each side perpendicular to its adjacent sides, is a **cube.**
4. A solid that has six rectangular sides, each side perpendicular to its adjacent sides, is a **rectangular solid.**
5. The term **cylinder** is used to indicate a solid in which two equal circles, parallel to each other, form its bases, or ends, the bases

being joined by a curved surface perpendicular to the circumference of the bases. Encourage more advanced pupils to interpret the more technical definition of a cylinder: If a rectangle is rotated, one of its sides being used as an axis, the geometric solid generated is a **right circular cylinder** (Fig. 27).

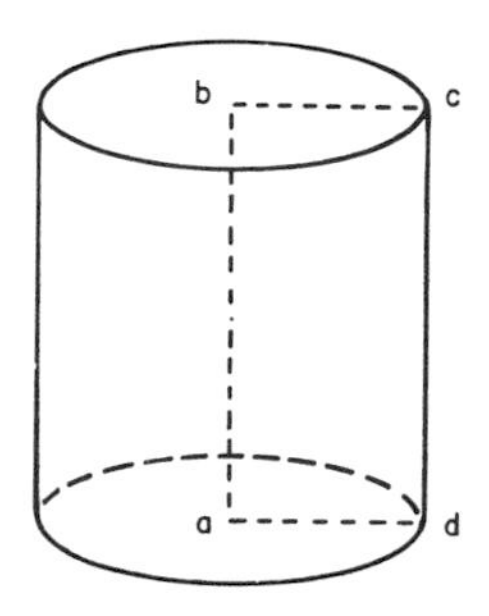


**Fig. 27.** Volume of cylinder.

Although the English system does not have the systematic relationships between units of volume and units of capacity that the metric system has, certain relationships are agreed upon; for example:

1 gallon contains 231 cubic inches.
1 cubic foot contains about $7\frac{1}{2}$ gallons.
1 bushel contains 2150.42 cubic inches.

As with other types of measurement, any problems based on social aspects will aid pupils to understand these measures.

## 8. Experience with Measures of Capacity

Measures of capacity include those we know as liquid measures and those we call dry measures. Usually a child has early experiences at home with liquid measures in buying milk and ice cream in pints and quarts and gallons. In the primary grades he should have had manipulative experiences with them, so that by the time he is in the middle grades his comprehension of units of liquid measure should be reasonably good.

He has little acquaintance with dry measures, however, unless his family is connected with farming. In that case he has heard about quarts of strawberries or blueberries, and pecks and bushels of apples, tomatoes, and potatoes; some children may be able to recognize these units of measure. However, many things formerly sold by the peck and the bushel are today sold almost entirely by the pound—for example, potatoes and tomatoes. And although the farmer talks in terms of bushels—his wheat "went 25 bushels to the acre"—he computes the number of bushels entirely by weight, the weight of a bushel of each kind of grain being standardized by state laws. Nevertheless, bushel baskets are still obtainable, and pupils should have the experience of measuring quarts, pecks, and bushels, and verifying the tables they learn and work with.

Upper-grade pupils may compute the number of bushels of grain that can be put into a bin of given dimensions, allowing $1\frac{1}{4}$ cubic feet to a bushel, or, figuring more closely, 2150.42 cubic inches to a bushel—a degree of accuracy rarely called for today.

## COMPETENCE CHECK

**1.** Do figures with the same perimeter always have the same area? Check by these figures; all have perimeters of 96 inches:

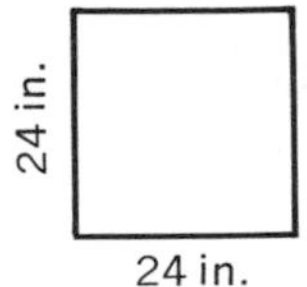


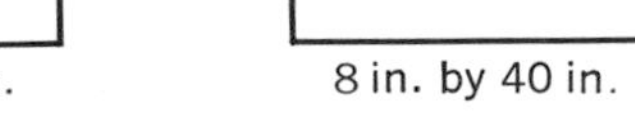


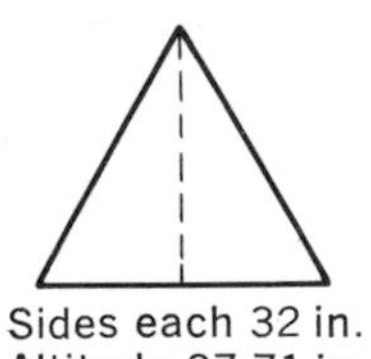


**2.** 1. An acre can be represented fairly approximately by a square 209 feet on a side. Measure off an area of ground of that size.
   2. Compute the approximate number of acres in a city block in your community; in the school yard; in other areas with which you are familiar.

**3.** Why do we not now advocate having pupils memorize each table of measurement when they begin work with it?

**4.** What procedure would you use to help pupils develop concepts of the various measuring units?

**5.** Refer to the illustrative uses of measurement in Section 4 of this chapter and list those that use linear measure, square measure, cubic measure, capacity measure.

**6.** For each of the four types of measurement listed in the preceding problem, compose and solve two problems based on the pupils' environment, such as you would expect pupils to be able to compose and solve as they work with these measurements.

7. Explain how computing areas of all other plane figures is based directly or indirectly on the computation of areas of rectangles.
8. Draw the following, and assign dimensions to each: (1) square; (2) rectangle; (3) triangle; (4) parallelogram; (5) trapezoid; (6) circle; (7) cube; (8) rectangular solid; (9) cylinder.
9. Write formulas for finding the areas of the first six figures in the preceding problem.
10. Write formulas for finding the volume of the last three of those figures.
11. What are the dimensions of a section of land?
12. What are the dimensions of a square field of 10 acres?
13. What will be the altitude of a triangular field of 10 acres, if the base of the triangle is 80 rods?
14. What is meant by tables of measurement having systematic relationships? Give illustrations.

## OPTIONAL ASSIGNMENTS

1. Construct a frame for a parallelogram from four 1-in. strips of oak-tag, two of them 9 in. long, the other two 5 in. long. Fasten them at the corners with paper fasteners as indicated in the diagram.
   1. Measure and compute the area of the enclosed rectangle when the corners are right angles.

   2. Shift the top edge of the frame somewhat toward the right. Measure and compute the area of the enclosed parallelogram.
   3. Shift the top edge farther to decrease the altitude, and measure the area.
   4. Compare the various areas and explain your findings.
   5. Does the formula for finding the area of rectangles serve for finding the area of parallelograms?
   6. Does the formula for finding the area of a parallelogram serve for finding the area of a rectangle?
2. Olander shows one way of impressing on pupils that the area of a circle *is* equal to $\pi r^2$, thus: Use a 7-in. embroidery hoop and cover the surface it rings with small marbles. With narrow strips of wood, enclose an area

$3\frac{1}{2}$ in. wide and $\pi \times 3\frac{1}{2}$ in. long; there will be three $3\frac{1}{2}$-in. squares and $\frac{1}{7}$ of another square. Try it. The same marbles also fill this area.

**3.** Explain and demonstrate the technical definition of a cylinder: If a rectangle is rotated, one of its sides being used as an axis, the geometric solid generated is a right circular cylinder. The bases of the cylinder are circles and each element of the curved surface is perpendicular to the bases.

**4.** 1. Find a satisfactory definition of a cone.
2. Construct a cone in three dimensions.
3. Demonstrate that the volume of a cone equals $\frac{1}{3}\pi r^2 \times h$, or $\frac{1}{3}$ the volume of a cylinder with the same base and altitude as the cone.

**5.** 1. Define a pyramid.
2. Construct a pyramid.
3. Give a formula for finding its volume.

**6.** 1. Define a prism.
2. Draw a prism whose bases are triangles.
3. State a formula for finding its volume.

**7.** Show how to find the area of the entire surface of a cylinder; a pyramid; a triangular prism.

## REFERENCES


Anderson, S. E., "A Simple Device for Illustrating the Size of a Cubic Yard," *Mathematics Teacher*, December, 1953, pp. 578–579.

Colvin, Fred H., "The Thousandth of an Inch in Industry," *Education*, April, 1951, pp. 511–513.

Grossnickle, Foster E., "A Laboratory of Meaningful Arithmetic," *Mathematics Teacher*, March, 1948, p. 116.

Jenkins, Jens, "Teaching the Concept of Perimeter Through the Use of Manipulative Aids," *Mathematics Teacher*, April, 1957, p. 309.

Olander, C., "A Model for Visualizing the Formula for the Area of a Circle," *Mathematics Teacher*, April, 1955, pp. 245–246.

Wheat, H. G., *How to Teach Arithmetic*, Row, Peterson, Evanston, 1951, chap. 12.

chapter 20

# Measurement (Continued)

## I. Experience with Miscellaneous Other Measures

### *Measures of Time and Temperature*

Neither temperature nor time can be measured as quantities; both can be measured only in terms of the changes they produce. Temperature changes the volume and often also the consistency of liquids and solids. The temperature at which water freezes at a certain barometric pressure is designated as 0° centigrade, and the temperature at which water boils at the same pressure, as 100° centigrade; from these points degrees of change are computed. The centigrade thermometer is used in many types of precision work, particularly in science; but the Fahrenheit thermometer is the one with which people in general are familiar. All weather reports, body temperature, cooking temperatures, and the like, are based on the Fahrenheit scale. On this scale 32° is the freezing point of water and corresponds to 0° on the centigrade thermometer; 212° is the boiling point of water and corresponds to 100° on the centigrade scale. The centigrade scale is part of the metric system of measurement.

Time may first have been recognized as indicating duration of experience from the time the sun crossed a specific meridian until it crossed it again. After much experimentation an instrument that would turn on its axis once, or perhaps twice, during that day and night might have been devised. If it worked as our modern clocks do, one indicator would go all the way around a dial 24 times during that interval.

The units by which we measure time today are standardized on astronomical happenings. A **day** is the period of time in which the earth makes a complete rotation on its axis; a **month** is the period of time in which the moon makes one revolution around the earth; a **year** is the period of time in which the earth in its orbit goes once around the sun. With the time units thus determined, there is no systematic relationship among them; all months do not even have the same number of days. However, there is continuing agitation among some people to change the calendar in order to make these relationships more systematic.

Children early become accustomed to time and to clocks, watches, and calendars as instruments for measuring units of time; they also become accustomed to temperature, and to thermometers as instruments for measuring it. Hence, as a rule they do not find these types of measurement difficult. However, children differ markedly in their ability to tell time. For this reason a teacher may group primary children for work with manipulative clock faces and provide many varieties of practice to fit the needs of each group. Some children will be learning the hour and half-hour points: others can tell the time as 2:15 or 2:30; and still others know it is 10 minutes till 2:00 or can count by 5's and say it is 2:25.

Ability to read the calendar also varies widely. Although some children cannot find the 15th of the month they are in, others know that the date is January 26, 1961, and one may say, "In 6 more days it will be February. My sister's birthday is February 4th." Here continued special practice is needed for the less advanced group.

Children need help, too, in developing time concepts in terms of its extent; for example, How far can I walk in 30 seconds? How far can I go in 1 second? Would I be very tired if I walked for 2 hours? How far could I walk in 2 hours? Young children do not have good concepts of the extent of time or space; of value here are reference standards which the teacher can help them set up.

### *Measures of Weight*

One type of measure with which children are somewhat familiar when they enter school is measures of weight. Preschool and primary children may have gone to the store for a pound of butter or a pound of coffee or two pounds of hamburger and hence are usually familiar with the word "pound;" but it remains for the school to develop the concept of how heavy a pound is. Some of this may be done in store units, in which butter cartons are filled with something that weighs a pound and the contents of a coffee can weigh a pound. Sand can be packaged to resemble sugar or flour in sacks holding 1, 2, 3, 4, 5, and 10 pounds. Pupils will become aware that a 5-pound package is "sort of heavy," and a 10-pound one is too heavy for them to carry very far.

All children are interested in their own weights, and school scales can be used in arithmetic lessons.

Middle-grade children become aware of ounces as they read amounts on bottles of flavoring extracts, perfumes, and cosmetics, and on small cans of food. They learn that on cans of food an ounce indicates $\frac{1}{16}$ of an avoirdupois pound, but that the label on drugs and extracts says fluid ounces. A fluid ounce is $\frac{1}{4}$ of a gill, a unit of liquid measure.

There are three types of weight measures: avoirdupois, troy, and apothecaries'. Most of us are almost never concerned with the last two, for troy weight is used chiefly in measuring gold and silver, and apothecaries' weights are used for drugs by doctors and pharmacists.

In addition to ounces and pounds, the avoirdupois weights include the hundredweight and ton. The hundredweight (100 pounds) is used in selling livestock and other heavy commodities. The ton (2000 pounds) is a commonly used term, as in tons of coal, tons of fish taken out of the lake, tons of freight; weak bridges may be posted for a 5-ton load limit. If children could see a ton of brick or a ton of coal, the word would have more meaning for them than they can derive from 2000 pounds. If all the children in the classroom were weighed and their weights totaled, they might discover that together they weighed a ton or almost a ton or more than a ton.

Computations involving units of weight are frequently used in problem-solving but present no particular difficulty.

### *Measures of Lumber*

The average person has few occasions on which he has to compute measurements of lumber but as a matter of information upper-grade pupils may well learn a few simple things about this. Furthermore, knowing something about business operations in his community gives a child a sense of accomplishment.

Regular wood shingles are bunched and sold by the thousand. Asphalt shingles are priced by the square (enough to cover a 10-foot square, or 100 square feet). Some materials like wallboard are sold by the square yard. Moldings (quarter-round and the like) are sold by the linear foot. But lumber in general is sold by the thousand board feet. A **board foot** is a square foot of surface not more than 1 inch thick. To compute board feet, we find the number of square feet in the surface of the board; for example, a board 6 in. wide and 10 ft. long, as in Fig. 28*a*, is $\frac{1}{2}$ ft. by 10 ft. and contains 5 sq. ft., and therefore 5 board feet, provided it is no more than 1 in. thick. However, if it is 2 inches thick, as in *b*, it contains $2 \times 5$ board feet, and if 3 inches thick, as in *c*, $3 \times 5$ board feet. When measuring lumber it is necessary, as in all area measurements, to have both length and width in the same linear units (in this case feet) before finding the square units in it. A simple formula* for computing board feet is:

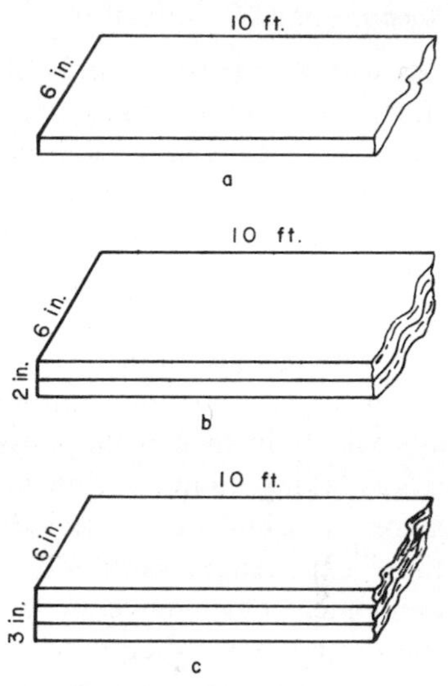


**Fig. 28.** Board measure.

Length in feet × Width in feet
× Thickness in inches = Board feet

To find the cost of 2 boards 4 in. wide, 2 in. thick, and 8 ft. long (such boards are commonly called two-by-fours) at \$150 per thousand:

$$\underset{\text{Boards}}{2} \times \underset{\text{Width in feet}}{\frac{1}{3}} \times \underset{\text{Length in feet}}{8} \times \underset{\text{Thickness in inches}}{2} = \frac{32}{3} \text{ or } \underset{\text{Board feet}}{10\frac{2}{3}}$$

At \$150 per thousand, $\frac{\$150}{1000}$ = cost of 1 ft.

$$10\frac{2}{3} \times \frac{\$150}{1000} = \frac{32}{3} \times \frac{\$150}{1000} = \$1\frac{3}{5} \text{ or } \$1.60$$

In such problems it saves time to do the entire computation in one cancellation process; thus:

$$\overset{1}{\cancel{2}} \times \frac{\overset{1}{\cancel{4}}}{\underset{\underset{1}{\cancel{3}}}{\cancel{12}}} \times 8 \times \cancel{2} \times \frac{\overset{\overset{1}{\cancel{3}}}{\cancel{\$150}}}{\underset{\underset{\underset{5}{\cancel{10}}}{\cancel{20}}}{\cancel{1000}}} = \$\frac{8}{5} = \$1\frac{3}{5} \text{ or } \$1.60$$

* Pupils should be encouraged to evolve this formula.

### *Measures of U.S. Money*

As with many other kinds of measurement concepts, when children enter school they vary widely in ability to recognize and handle money units. As a rule, all children recognize pennies. Some can go no further, but others will have had a great deal more experience with money at home. They may know all the coins and a good deal about equivalents—5 pennies make a nickel, two quarters a half-dollar, and so on.

All children are interested in money—much more so than in pints and quarts or hours and minutes—and are eager to handle it. Parents differ widely in their willingness to give children money responsibility, such as taking money to the store for groceries, taking milk money to school, or using their own judgment about spending their allowance. School experiences should be planned to suit the pupils' individual development of money concepts.

Store and post-office units that use toy money are frequently part of regular primary activities. Having the children count their own milk or lunch money each day gives them needed practice. Middle-grade pupils should be encouraged to keep records of their milk and lunch expenditures. Before they leave the third grade they should be able to add dollars and cents:

```
$ .35 Monday
   .25 Tuesday
   .25 Wednesday
   .40 Thursday
   .30 Friday
 -----
$1.55 total for the week
```

and to subtract:

```
$  .75          $ 1.00
  −.50            −.65
 -----           -----
$  .25          $  .35
```

Making change as it is usually done is one of the few occasions for subtracting by the additive method. This procedure is not easy for children to learn and should be introduced gradually. Before introducing it, the children should be thoroughly familiar with real coins. A coin chart, like that in Fig. 29, is an excellent aid; it is made by fastening coins securely to heavy cardboard in the arrangement shown. Such a chart should be placed where pupils can consult it, but be out of temptation's reach and well taken care of.

In addition to working with real coins, children should have play store experience that starts with small computations. As an illustration, the customer makes a 3-cent purchase and lays down a nickel. The clerk must know that a nickel is 5 cents in value. He says 3 cents—this is what he gave the customer in goods—then hands him a penny, saying "4 cents," and another penny, saying "5 cents." He has added

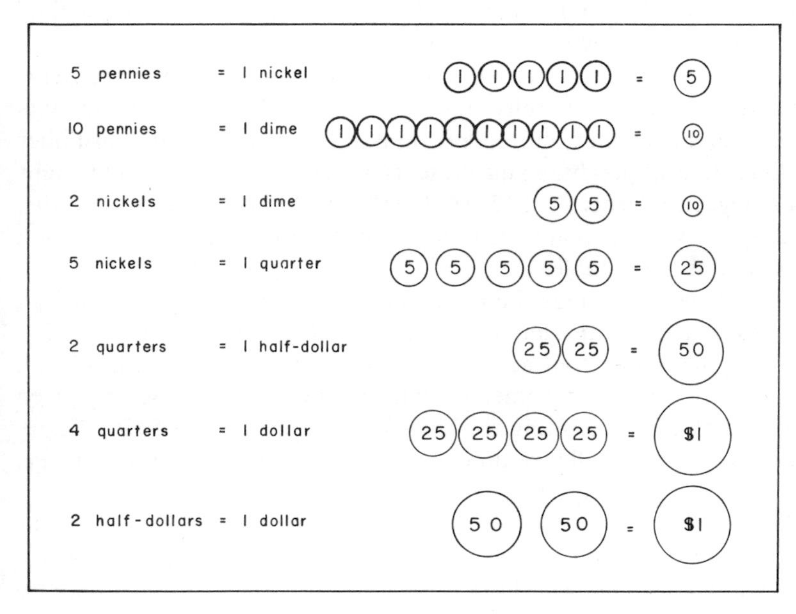


**Fig. 29.** Coin chart.

onto the purchase price the amount by which the money he received from the customer exceeded the cost of the purchase. He could have subtracted 3 cents from 5 cents and handed the customer the difference, but when purchases involve larger costs, perhaps $8.14, with change to be made from $10, a pupil could not with assurance do the subtraction without using paper and pencil. Even then he might make an error in subtraction; furthermore, unless the customer also did the subtraction, or checked what the clerk wrote, he would be doubtful as to whether he received the correct change. Obviously, every transaction would be slowed down. But when the clerk adds orally as he hands out the change, the customer can follow the addition and see that the change is correct.

Some business places—supermarkets and the like—machine-add the purchases and machine-subtract their cost from the amount given the checker; all the computing the checker has to do is to see that the change he hands the customer is what the machine indicates is due him. But the great majority of our purchases still require counting out change—bus fares, theater or movie tickets, groceries at the neighborhood store, and so on. (If the trend toward credit cards continues, perhaps the time will come when we won't carry any money.)

In the 3-cent purchase above, no judgment was required of the clerk. He had no alternative in selecting coins for change. But when amounts become more complex, more alert thinking is called for. If a customer makes a 13-cent purchase and presents a quarter, the clerk could count his change as 13 cents—14, 15, 16, 17, 18, 19, 20, 21, 22, 23, 24, 25 cents, and lay down that many pennies, a procedure which children soon recognize as undesirable.

One of the first things the clerk should learn is to use only enough pennies to get the amount to a multiple of 5, and then add by 5's. Thus in the above transaction he would say, 13 cents—14, 15, 20, 25 cents. But if the customer has made a 13-cent purchase and given the clerk 50 cents, counting the change as 13 cents—14, 15, 20, 25, 30, 35, 40, 45, 50 cents will take time, give the customer a lot of little change, and perhaps deplete the register of nickels.

Hence the clerk learns to use the highest denomination of coins possible. With a purchase of 17¢ out of a dollar, he will say 17 cents—18, 19, 20, 25, 50, $1 (17 + 3 + 5 + 25 + 50). All this requires individual practice, for pupils cannot learn it simply by watching and listening. Furthermore, it is probably the most difficult money measurement experience elementary pupils have, but the ability thus developed is extremely valuable.

### *Measures of Counting*

Some things are measured by counting; hence the word "dozen" comes into a child's vocabulary rather early. He buys a dozen eggs, a dozen rolls, a dozen cookies. Pupils in the upper grades should know that some small articles—for example, pencils—are sold in large quantities by the gross (12 dozen), and that some articles are sold in wholesale quantities by the great gross (12 gross).

Our word "score" for 20 is used as a literary term more often than for the counting of specific objects. "Four score and seven years ago," said Lincoln, instead of "Eighty-seven years ago." "The days of our years are threescore years and ten," says the Bible, instead of "seventy years."

Stationers and printers have measures of counting for paper; the general public is little acquainted with them except for the term "ream." A ream consists of 500 sheets of any size or weight. Thus we may buy a ream of $8\frac{1}{2}$-inch by 11-inch onionskin typewriter paper, or a ream of 9-inch by 12-inch white drawing paper of various weights. All schools and offices and many individuals, buy paper by the ream.

### *Measures of Angles and Arcs*

Angles are introduced in the upper grades, and for most pupils they constitute a wholly new area of learning. Angles are closely related to

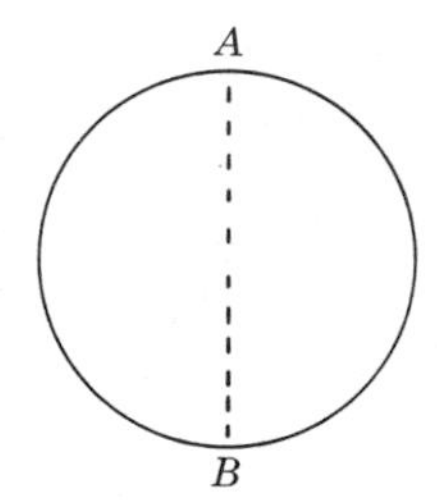


**Fig. 30.** 180-Degree segment of circle.

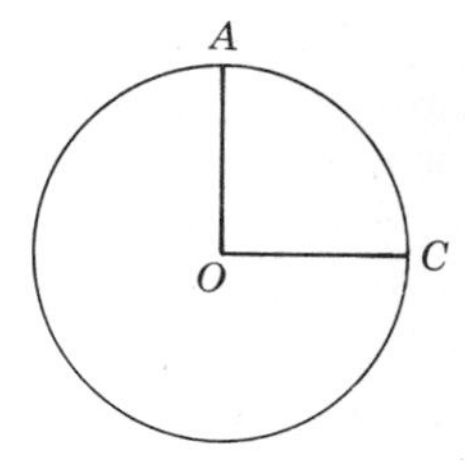


**Fig. 31.** 90-Degree segment of circle.

circles and should follow some work with circles. An essential foundation concept is that circles are measured in degrees, a degree being $\frac{1}{360}$ of the circumference of the circle, regardless of the size of the circle. This being true, half the circumference—*A* to *B* in Fig. 30—contains 180°; one-fourth of it—*A* to *C* in Fig. 31—contains 90°. The segment of the circumference, or arc, cut off by the sides of an angle formed by lines that meet in the center of the circle indicates the size of the angle. For example, lines *OA* and *OC* in Fig. 31 form the sides of angle *AOC*, and extended to the circumference cut off the arc *AC*. If this arc is one-fourth of the circle, it is an arc of 90°, and the angle *AOC* is a 90-degree angle.

The term **angle** is defined as the figure formed at the intersection of two straight lines. The lines that form the angle—*AO* and *OC* above—are called its **sides.** The length of the sides has nothing to do with the size of the angle. Thus angles $AOB$, $A'O'B'$, and $A''O''B''$ in Fig. 32 are equal; all are 90-degree angles. The point $O$ where the sides meet is called the **vertex** of the angle.

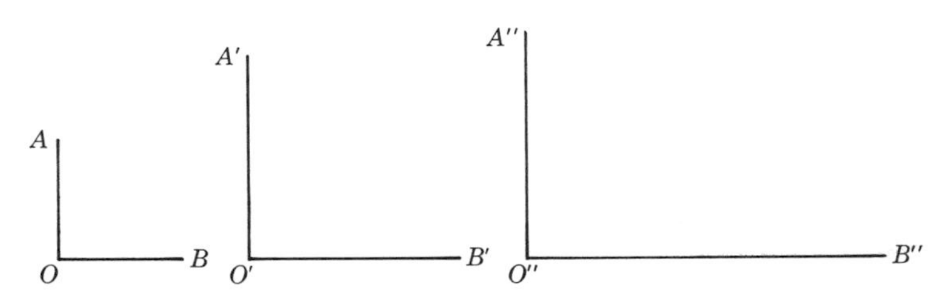


**Fig. 32.** Vertex of angles.

A disk of cardboard or oak-tag with a movable strip like a clock hand, but extending to the circumference as in Fig. 33, is helpful in learning about angles. Since we should think of the size of an angle as the extent to which a line is moved from its original position, this visual aid is especially valuable. On such a disk we mark a line $OA$, and from it move the strip $OB$ like a clock hand (Fig. 33*a*). When the strip is one-fourth of the way around the circle, as in *b*, the angle formed between it and the line $OA$ is 90°.

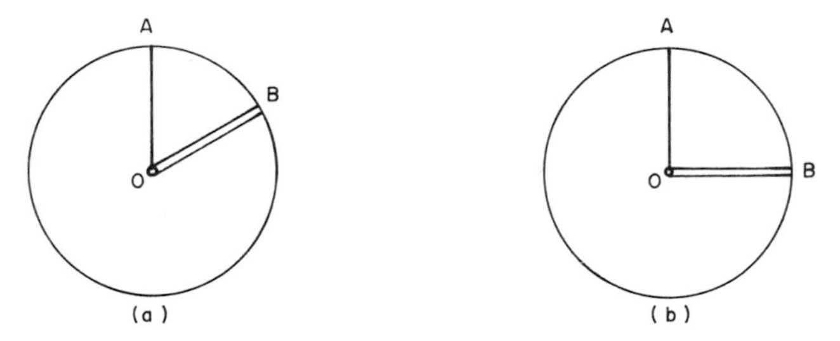


**Fig. 33.** Angle marker.

It is difficult, except on a very large circle, to label all the 360 degrees in the circumference of a circle, but intervals can be labeled as in Fig. 34, from which to compute the size of angles. A circle 2 or 3 feet in diameter, made of wallboard covered with newsprint, and with all 360-degree points indicated, is of real value in visualizing work with circles and angles.

Here again, manipulation is important. The pupils should learn to use a protractor and draw angles of different sizes and measure other angles. As they solve problems that involve angles and do practice

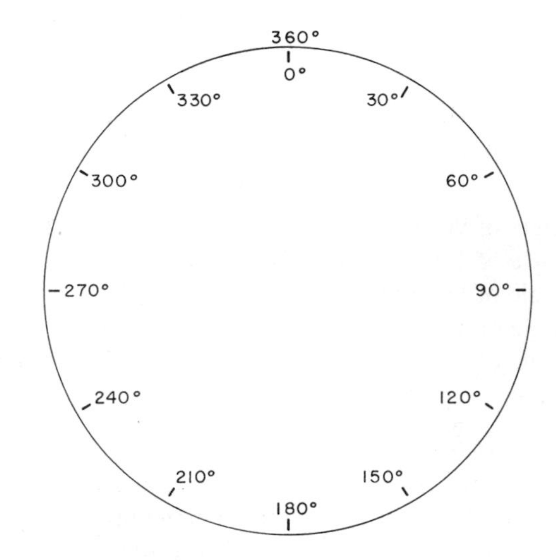


**Fig. 34.** Angle measurement.

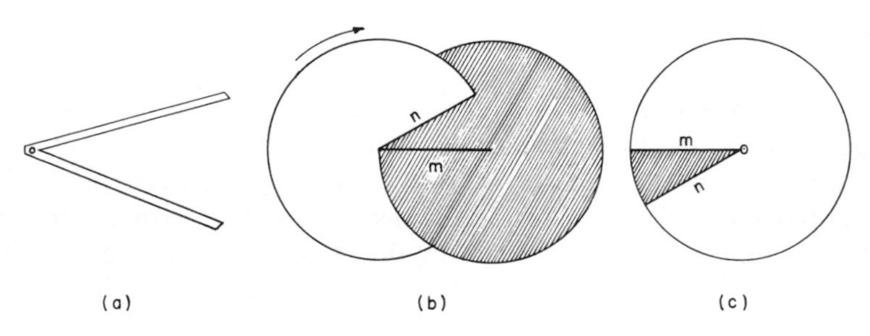


**Fig. 35.** Angle aids.

exercises, they will enjoy making and using angle aids like those in Fig. 35. In *a*, two yardsticks are joined with a very small stove-bolt for use in drawing angles on the chalkboard. In *b*, each of two cardboard or oak-tag disks of the same size but of different colors is cut along one radius, *m* and *n* respectively, interlocked, and moved into a position with centers together. In *c*, edge *n* of the open disk can be rotated from slit *m* to form larger and smaller angles. Many practice problems should be provided, such as the following:

1. Approximately what angle is formed by the clock hands when it is 4 o'clock?
2. What size angle is formed when the sides of the angle set off one-quarter of a circle?
3. Draw a sketch of a 20-degree highway grade.

For slow learners, work with angles may be kept at a minimum, but for more advanced pupils it provides an excellent foundation for geometry. It is desirable that these pupils understand the following terms:

1. An angle of 90° is a **right angle.**
2. An angle of 180° is a **straight angle.**
3. An angle of less than 90° is an **acute angle.**
4. An angle of more than 90° but less than 180° is an **obtuse angle.**
5. An angle of more than 180° but less than 360° is a **reflex angle.**
6. An **arc** is a segment of a circle.

*Measures of Electricity*

Electricity is so much a part of modern living that some information about how it is measured should be included in upper-grade arithmetic.* The unit for measuring electric power is the **watt** (W). The power of light bulbs is indicated on the bulb as 60 watt, 150 watt, etc. Because watts are very small units and their use would quickly involve very large numbers, electricity is computed in 1000-watt units called **kilowatts.** Meters are based on kilowatts and users of electricity are charged by the **kilowatt-hour,** the amount of electricity used when 1000 watts of current are in use for one hour. Thus a 150-watt light that burns for 10 hours will use 1500 watts or 1.5 kilowatt-hours of electricity.

Pupils should have guided experience in reading electric meters, and in examining bills for electricity for the recordings, the rates, and the total bill. Fig. 36 is a diagram of an electric meter. Recordings on the meter are based on the decimal system. When the hand is between two numbers, as on the ones dial, the smaller figure is used. Some knowledge of how the decimal system is used in automobile speedometers will enable pupils to read electric and gas meters; for example, they will see that when 10 kilowatts are registered, the ones dial goes back to 0 and the tens dial records 1. The reading on the diagram in the figure

* Have pupils investigate the measures involved in the use of electricity in their homes.

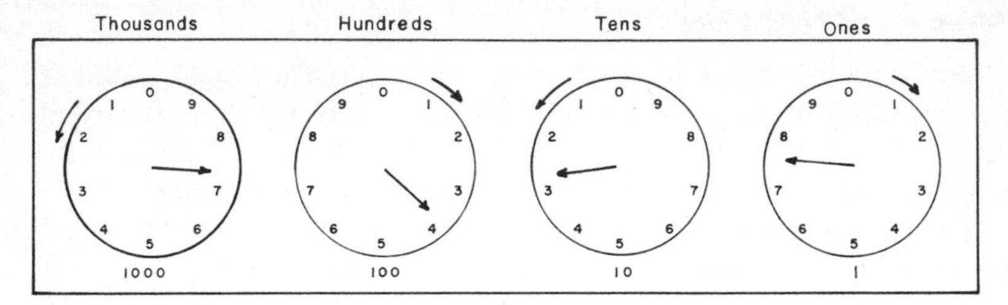


**Fig. 36.** Diagram of electric meter.

is 7327 kilowatts. The meter reader records the current reading; the previous month's reading is subtracted from it to determine the power used during the current month. Electrical appliances use varying amounts of power. Heat-producing appliances such as irons and toasters use more electricity than lights and motion appliances—such as sweepers and fans—require.

### *Measures of Gas*

Both natural and manufactured gas is used widely in homes and industries.* Gas use is also measured by dialed meters, but the units

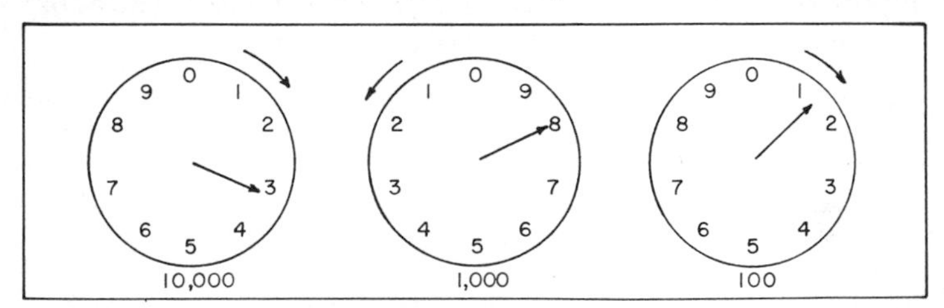


**Fig. 37.** Diagram of gas meter.

of measurement are cubic feet of gas, recorded in units of 100 cubic feet. These meters record in terms of the decimal system, as shown in Fig. 37. Here also pupils should have guided experience in reading gas meters and examining gas bills. Fig. 37 shows a recording of 38,100 cu. ft., as follows:

$$\begin{array}{ccccc} 3 \times 10{,}000 & & 8 \times 1000 & & 1 \times 100 \\ 30{,}000 & + & 8000 & + & 100 \end{array}$$

Gas is charged for at a given rate per 100 cubic feet.

---

* Ask pupils to investigate the use of gas in their homes.

*Measures of Food Value*

Foods supply three vital needs of the body. (1) They build, maintain, and repair body tissues; (2) they supply fuel which furnishes the energy required for bodily activities; and (3) they provide materials that regulate body processes and keep the body healthy and strong.

The fuel type of foods, chiefly carbohydrates and fats, are the energy providers. If these foods are not used up in energy (activity), they are stored in the body as fat. The energy value of foods is measured in calories. A **calorie** is the amount of heat required to raise the temperature of 1 gram of water 1 degree centigrade. Nutritionists have set up recommended daily calorie allowances to provide for the various needs in balanced meals.* The recommended calorie intake varies with age and weight of individuals, about as follows:

| | | |
|---|---|---|
| Man | (154 pounds), moderately active | 3000 calories per day |
| | very active | 4500 calories per day |
| Woman | (123 pounds), moderately active | 2500 calories per day |
| | very active | 3000 calories per day |
| Children | 1–3 years | 1200 calories per day |
| | 10–12 years | 2500 calories per day |

Tables listing the calorie value of foods are available in books on nutrition and in many cookbooks. Here is a partial list.

| | |
|---|---|
| Apple, raw—1 large, $3\frac{1}{4}$ in. diameter | 100 calories |
| Apple, baked—1 large | 200 calories |
| Asparagus, fresh—6 large stalks | 12 calories |
| Bacon, crisp—4 to 5 small pieces | 100 calories |
| Banana—1 medium | 100 calories |
| Beef steak—3 to 5 ounces | 242 calories |
| Butter—1 tablespoon | 100 calories |
| Apple pie—average serving | 300 calories |
| Sundae made with chocolate ice cream and chocolate walnut sauce | 425 calories |
| Peach, fresh—medium size | 50 calories |

People who watch their weight keep careful count of their calorie intake to avoid a surplus of food which will become fat. Obviously, a person who is trying to keep his weight down will eat a fresh peach for dessert instead of apple pie or a chocolate-nut sundae. Home economics courses teach the planning of meals that are well-balanced and adequate in food value.

* Encourage pupils to bring some of these lists to school.

## 2. The Metric System of Measurement

Thomas Jefferson, as Secretary of State under Washington, recommended, without success, that our measurements be brought into a decimal ratio. The weights and measures used in the American colonies at the time of the Declaration of Independence had been brought from England and were not well-standardized. In an earlier chapter we saw that they developed in a very unsystematic manner, with no uniform relationships among them.

In the early 1800's, following Jefferson's proposal, a committee of scientists in France formulated a metric system of measures, a decimal system that is in harmony with our number system. In the metric system not only is there uniform relationship within given tables of measurement—of distance, weight, and so on—but there is also a readily understandable specific relationship between the measures of length and of weight and capacity. This is evident in the following table of metric equivalents:

| | |
|---|---|
| 1000 cubic centimeters | = 1 liter |
| Weight of 1 cubic centimeter of water | = 1 gram |

The system was based on the principle that if an exact and definite standard of length is established, all the other standards can be derived from it. Quite appropriately, they called this standard measure of length a **meter.** With what seems to us a strange idea in mind, they decided to establish the length of the meter as one ten-millionth of the distance from the earth's equator to the pole, presumably an enduring and unchanging distance. Because of errors in calculation, however, the length arbitrarily adopted for the meter was not thus derived.

Other measures were then developed from the carefully constructed meter bar. Decimal divisions of the meter bar—tenths, hundredths, thousandths—were respectively named decimeters, centimeters, and millimeters, the Latin prefixes indicating the decimal part of a meter which each represented. Multiples of the meter—tens, hundreds, and thousands—were named dekameters, hectometers, and kilometers, in this case the Greek prefixes indicating the decimal multiples.

The units used for measuring areas and volumes are the length measures squared and cubed, respectively—square centimeter, cubic centimeter, square meter, cubic meter, and so on—like our square feet, cubic feet, etc. Land is measured in terms of the **are** (a square with sides 10 meters long) and the **hectare** (a square with sides 100 meters, or

1 hectometer, long). The tables of metric measures in the Appendix show these relationships and the decimal nature of the system.

The most commonly used equivalents for metric and English units are:

| | |
|---|---|
| 1 meter | = 39.37 inches |
| 1 liter | = 1.0567 liquid quarts or .908 dry quart |
| 1 gram | = .002205 pound |
| 1 millimeter | = .04 inch |
| 1 kilogram | = 2.20 pounds |
| 1.609 kilometers | = 1 mile |
| 1 kilometer | = .62 mile |
| 1 gallon | = 3.7853 liters |

Today the United States and Great Britain are the only world powers that have not adopted the metric system of measurement as their national system. Countries that include 75 per cent of the world's population use it, and it is legal for measurements throughout the world. So well adapted is it to the precise measurement of both large and small units, and so convenient in computation, that it is used almost exclusively in scientific work in our country as well as elsewhere. Since Jefferson's time many people in the United States have advocated the adoption of the metric system, but many others have opposed it. Perhaps such a change will never be made. In the meantime, however, our own system has been meticulously standardized.

## 3. Computation with Denominate Numbers

Several types of computation are involved in working with denominate numbers.* Units of one size may be changed to units of another size—for example, 24 inches to 2 feet, 32 ounces to 2 pounds. In these cases a large number of small units are changed to a smaller number of large units. Large units may be changed to small ones—for example, $6\frac{1}{2}$ feet to 78 inches. In both cases the changing of units is referred to as **reduction** of denominate numbers.

Besides reduction, all four of the fundamental processes—addition, subtraction, multiplication, and division—may be done with compound as well as simple denominate numbers, as the following illustrations show:

*Addition*

| | | | |
|---|---|---|---|
| 2 yd. | 1 ft. | 8 in. | 249 |
| +1 yd. | 2 ft. | 6 in. | +163 |
| 3 yd. | 3 ft. | 14 in. | 412 |

* Let pupils reason out these reduction procedures by exploration.

In the first problem the procedure is like that used in adding three denominations—hundreds, tens, and units—as in the second problem. There, instead of putting down 12 units, we reduce them to tens, put 1 ten over to add with the tens column, and put 2 down in the units place. So also we reduce the 11 tens to hundreds. Although the addition and reduction procedure is the same in both problems, our English system of linear measure requires 12 units of inches for reduction to the next higher unit (feet). But only 3 units in the feet column are necessary for reduction to yards. In this problem, then, the reduction is accomplished thus:

$$\begin{array}{rrrl}
2\text{ yd.} & 1\text{ ft.} & 8\text{ in.} & \\
+1\text{ yd.} & 2\text{ ft.} & 6\text{ in.} & \\
\hline
3\text{ yd.} & 3\text{ ft.} & 14\text{ in.} & \quad 14\text{ in.} = 1\text{ ft. } 2\text{ in.} \\
 & 1\text{ ft.} & (2\text{ in.}) & \\
\hline
3\text{ yd.} & 4\text{ ft.} & 2\text{ in.} & \quad 4\text{ ft.} = 1\text{ yd. } 1\text{ ft.} \\
1\text{ yd.} & (1\text{ ft.}) & (2\text{ in.}) & \\
\hline
4\text{ yd.} & 1\text{ ft.} & 2\text{ in.} &
\end{array}$$

*Subtraction*

$$\begin{array}{rrr}
4\text{ yd.} & 2\text{ ft.} & 3\text{ in.} \\
-1\text{ yd.} & 2\text{ ft.} & 8\text{ in.} \\
\hline
\end{array}
\qquad\qquad
\begin{array}{r}
214 \\
-\ 69 \\
\hline
145
\end{array}$$

Here reduction is necessary in both problems; but as was pointed out in connection with addition, the units in the first problem do not increase in multiples of 10 as they do in the second.

$$\begin{array}{rrr}
3\phantom{\text{ yd.}} & 4\phantom{\text{ ft.}} & 15\phantom{\text{ in.}} \\
\cancel{4}\text{ yd.} & \cancel{2}\text{ ft.} & \cancel{3}\text{ in.} \\
-1\text{ yd.} & 2\text{ ft.} & 8\text{ in.} \\
\hline
2\text{ yd.} & 2\text{ ft.} & 7\text{ in.}
\end{array}$$

Since we cannot subtract 8 in. from 3 in., we reduce 1 ft. of the minuend to inches. Adding this 12 in. to 3 in. gives 15 in. from which to subtract 8 in. Next we reduce 1 yd. to 3 ft. and add this to the remaining 1 ft. in the minuend; this gives us 4 ft. from which to subtract 2 ft. We then have a difference of 2 yd. 2 ft. 7 in.

*Multiplication*

The meaning of 4 yd. 2 ft. 3 in. is actually 4 yd. + 2 ft. + 3 in. Hence multiplying that compound denominate number by any multiplier is like multiplying 241 (2 hundreds + 4 tens + 1 unit) by any multiplier, thus:

$$\begin{array}{r} 2 \text{ hundreds} + 4 \text{ tens} + 1 \text{ unit} \\ \times 4 \\ \hline 8 \text{ hundreds} + 16 \text{ tens} + 4 \text{ units} \end{array}$$

We reduce the 16 tens to 1 hundred and to 6 tens, and add the 1 hundred to the hundreds product:

$$\begin{array}{r} 241. \\ \times 4 \\ \hline 964 \end{array}$$

So also, in the following:

$$\begin{array}{r} 4 \text{ yd.} + 2 \text{ ft.} + 3 \text{ in.} \\ \times 4 \\ \hline 16 \text{ yd.} + 8 \text{ ft.} + 12 \text{ in.} \end{array}$$

the product when reduced will be 19 yd.

***Division***

$$\begin{array}{r|l} & 2 \text{ yd.} + 1 \text{ ft.} + 1\tfrac{1}{2} \text{ in.} \\ \hline 2 & 4 \text{ yd.} + 2 \text{ ft.} + 3 \text{ in.} \end{array}$$

$$\begin{array}{r|rrr} & 1 \text{ yd.} & 1 \text{ ft.} & 5 \text{ in.} \\ \hline 4 & 5 \text{ yd.} + & 2 \text{ ft.} + & 8 \text{ in.} \\ & & 3 \text{ ft.} & 12 \text{ in.} \\ \cline{3-4} & & 5 \text{ ft.} & 20 \text{ in.} \end{array}$$

The division in the first problem is quite simple, but much less so in the second. Thus $\frac{1}{4}$ of 5 yd. is 1 yd., with an undivided 1 yd. as remainder. This undivided 1 yd. is reduced to feet and added to 2 ft. for a dividend of 5 ft. This divided by 4 gives 1 ft. and 1 undivided foot to put with 8 in., making 20 in. in the dividend. $\frac{1}{4}$ of 20 in. is 5 in. The complete quotient is 1 yd. 1 ft. 5 in.

In this problem the division might be accomplished without reduction, thus:

$$\begin{array}{r|rrr} & 1\tfrac{1}{4} \text{ yd.} & \tfrac{1}{2} \text{ ft.} & 2 \text{ in.} \\ \hline 4 & 5 \text{ yd.} & 2 \text{ ft.} & 8 \text{ in.} \end{array}$$

But it would be obvious to pupils that stating a measurement as $1\frac{1}{4}$ yd. $\frac{1}{2}$ ft. 2 in. is much less desirable than stating it as 1 yd. 1 ft. 5 in.

Checking with denominate numbers is done just as were the fundamental processes in abstract numbers. Thus the first division problem is checked as follows:

$$\begin{array}{rrr} 2 \text{ yd.} & 1 \text{ ft.} & 1\tfrac{1}{2} \text{ in.} \\ & \times 2 & \\ \hline 4 \text{ yd.} & 2 \text{ ft.} & 3 \text{ in.} \end{array}$$

And the second:

$$\begin{array}{lll} 1 \text{ yd.} & 1 \text{ ft.} & 5 \text{ in.} \\ & & \times 4 \\ \hline 4 \text{ yd.} & 4 \text{ ft.} & 20 \text{ in., or reduced:} \\ 5 \text{ yd.} & 2 \text{ ft.} & 8 \text{ in.} \end{array}$$

Checking could also be done thus:

5 yd. 2 ft. 8 in. = 212 in. 1 by. 1 ft. 5 in. = 53 in. 4 × 53 in. = 212 in.

The division might be done by reducing 5 yd. 2 ft. 8 in. to 212 in. and dividing that by 4, getting 53 in., and then reducing 53 in. to higher denominations:

$$\begin{array}{r|l} & 1 \text{ yd.} \\ 36 & \overline{53} \text{ in.} \\ & 36 \\ 12 & \overline{17} \text{ in. (1 ft.)} \\ & 12 \\ & \overline{\ 5} \text{ in.} \quad \text{or 1 yd. 1 ft. 5 in.} \end{array}$$

Pupils should develop ability to recognize the most advantageous form for denominate numbers, and also the form in which they are customarily used. For example, we usually say 1 hour and 20 minutes before train time, not $1\frac{1}{3}$ hours. So also we say a man is 5 feet 10 inches tall, not 70 inches. We can find $\frac{1}{4}$ of 36 inches more readily than we can find $\frac{1}{4}$ of 3 feet.

Slow pupils should not be expected to go beyond the simplest computations with denominate numbers, but the more capable students should understand these computations and develop reasonable facility in doing them without confusion. Apparently the day is past when no pupils in an arithmetic class were expected to do more than the average could do.

## 4. Scale Drawings

A **scale drawing** may be defined as a drawing in which large units of measure are represented by small units. For example, 1 inch on a map of a park may represent 1 mile, or $\frac{1}{2}$ inch on a map may represent 100 miles, or the scale may be 1 inch to 200 miles, depending upon the size of the area being mapped and the size of map desired.

All maps are based on scale drawings, as are all building plans, including those for road building and bridges. Most design plans must also be scaled. Probably the most common use of scale drawings is in road maps; but laying out a tennis court or a baseball diamond or a football field, involves scale drawing if a plan is made first.

Children in the middle grades will have experience in drawing representative areas, such as making a diagram of a floor 12 ft. by 14 ft. and finding out how many square feet or square yards of linoleum will be needed to cover it. Or they may have been asked to make a diagram of a garden plot 25 ft. by 50 ft. and find out how many rods of fence will be needed to enclose it. Although drawing diagrams usually does not require the same accuracy of measurement as scale drawings do, an alert pupil will see that the garden 25 ft. by 50 ft. is twice as long as it is wide, and will try to proportion his diagram to show this. An efficient teacher will call his pupils' attention to making their diagrams representative, and will aid them to see that a square is not a proper way to show a rectangular garden plot.

In the upper grades pupils will do more accurate representations by means of scale drawings. Some map study showing how scales are applied is good introductory work. Then may follow such questions as, "Using the scale of miles, find how far it is across your state from north to south," or "How far is it from the capital to your city?" When it is time for greater precision, textbooks should provide house plans or plans for school buildings in which one room, for example, measures $1\frac{1}{4}$ in. by $2\frac{1}{2}$ in., the scale being perhaps 1 in. to 12 ft. The pupils are to find the size of this room.

After sufficient practice of this kind to establish confidence, the pupils are introduced to the other type of problem in scale drawing, in which the actual dimensions are given and they are to draw a plan to scale. This type is more difficult than the problem in which the pupils have the plan and use a scale to determine the actual size. Simple problems are needed to begin with, as for example, "Draw a plan of a garden that is 40 ft. by 60 ft. using a scale of 1 in. to 20 ft." This probem can be made increasingly difficult by using for these dimensions: $\frac{1}{2}$ in. for 10 ft.; 1 in. for 15 ft.; 1 in. for 8 ft. and so on.

Finally the pupils are asked to set up a suitable scale for drawings. For example, "If you are to use 9 in. by 12 in. paper, what scale will be good for making a plan of (1) Your classroom? (2) The school yard? (3) The city block you live on? (4) Your state? Draw those plans according to the scales you have proposed."

As with all other types of problem, experience in real situations is a definite aid to understanding. For example, the pupils might make a scale drawing of a baseball diamond or a tennis court and then measure it off in the school yard.

## 5. Graphs

When pupils have developed some ability in drawing to a scale, as just described, they are ready to construct graphs. Both scale drawings

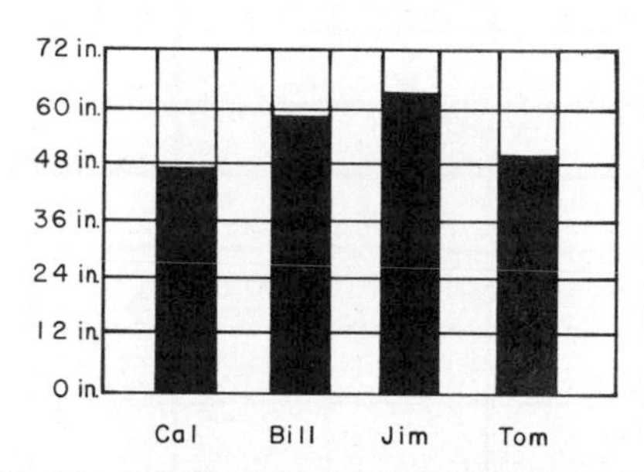


**Fig. 38.** Bar graph: Comparative heights of the Jones boys.

and graphs are based on the concept of using small units to represent large ones, and both represent numbers graphically since they indicate relative sizes.

Graphs generally have eye appeal and often provide summarizing information at a glance. Thus, the fact that Jim is the tallest of the four Jones boys is ascertained much more readily from the graph in Fig. 38 than from the data presented in tabular form in Table 1.

TABLE 1. Heights of the Four Jones Boys

| Name | Height | Height in Inches |
|---|---|---|
| Cal | 3 ft. 11 in. | 47 in. |
| Bill | 4 ft. 10 in. | 58 in. |
| Jim | 5 ft. 4 in. | 64 in. |
| Tom | 4 ft. 1 in. | 49 in. |

Most pupils have an early acquaintance with graphs (though the term graph may not yet be in their vocabulary) when their third- or fourth-grade workbooks provide a grid on which they are to record each day's grade, for example, in spelling. When a pupil has marked the points and joined them, as in Fig. 39, he has constructed a graph on which grade intervals are marked on the vertical axis and time intervals on the horizontal axis.

Fig. 38 is known as a **bar graph;** Fig. 39 as a **line graph.** Two other commonly used graphs are the **circle** or **pie graph** and the **picture graph,**

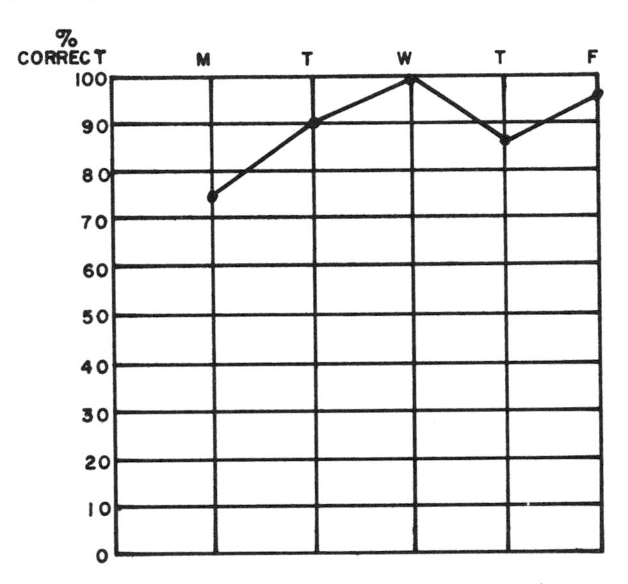


**Fig. 39.** Line graph: Spelling grades for one week.

the latter usually written as pictograph. Textbooks, particularly in science and social science, frequently use these four forms, beginning with simple forms in the middle grades and proceeding to a more complex form and more advanced informational data in the upper grades.

Reference books and newspapers, as well as textbooks, also use graphic and tabular materials widely; hence if the pupil is to be a competent reader, he must develop some ability in interpreting them. Development of this ability is considered a responsibility of the elementary reading teacher; but since these skills involve quantitative material the arithmetic teacher is responsible for developing the ability to think quantitatively in interpreting sizes and amounts. Part of this learning pupils acquire in direct teaching situations; part of it, incidentally in classroom experiences.

Graphic material is always based on tabular material; that is, data must be tabulated before they can be depicted in the form of a graph. For example, the average maximum July temperature in Duluth, Minnesota; Phoenix, Arizona; Bakersfield, Los Angeles, and San

TABLE 2. Comparative Maximum July Temperatures
(Average Maximum July Temperature)

| | |
|---|---|
| Bakersfield | 101 |
| Chicago | 85 |
| Duluth | 76 |
| Los Angeles | 83 |
| Miami | 87 |
| New York | 82 |
| Phoenix | 105 |
| San Francisco | 64 |

Francisco, California; Chicago, Illinois; New York, New York; and Miami, Florida, may be tabulated as in Table 2 and incorporated into the text. The information is there, but the reader cannot interpret it as readily as he could if it were shown on a bar graph as in Fig. 40.

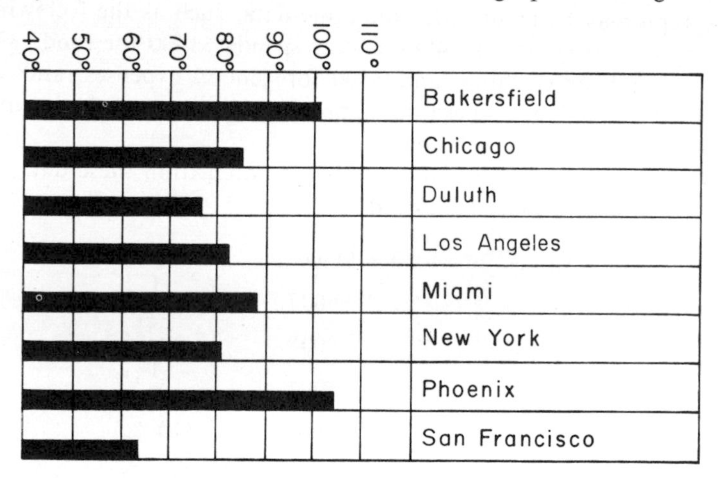


**Fig. 40.** Bar graph: Comparative maximum July temperatures.

Of the four commonly used types of graph, the line graph as a rule is best for depicting *dynamic* comparisons (increase, decrease, fluctuation), as in Fig. 39. The bar graph is good for *static* material; it may have two variables, as in Fig. 40, or more than two, as we shall see later.

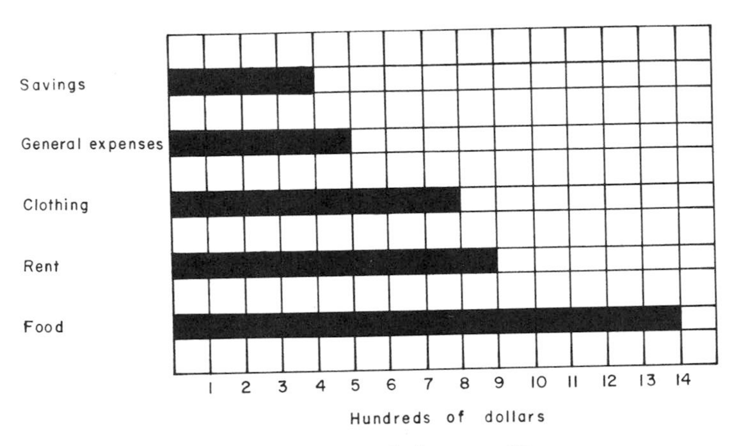


**Fig. 41.** Bar graph: Relative expenditures.

The circle graph shows proportionate amounts of a whole or a total. Like the bar graph, it is used for static information; hence either it or a bar graph may be made from the same data, such as the following: A family whose income is \$4000 a year spends \$1400 for food, \$900 for rent, \$800 for clothing, and \$500 for general expenses, and sets aside \$400 for savings. These data appear on the bar graph shown in Fig. 41.

Before a circle graph (Fig. 42) can be prepared from these data, the following problems must be solved:

| | | |
|---|---|---|
| 1. | What per cent of \$4000 is \$1400? | 35 % |
| 2. | " " " " " " 900? | $22\frac{1}{2}$% |
| 3. | " " " " " " 800? | 20 % |
| 4. | " " " " " " 500? | $12\frac{1}{2}$% |
| 5. | " " " " " " 400? | 10 % |
| | | 100 % |

Obviously the two kinds of graphs use the same data but summarize them in different ways. Whereas the bar graph (Fig. 41) shows comparative amounts spent for the various items in the budget, the circle graph (Fig. 42) shows the apportionment of the total—for example, the proportion of the budget that is spent for food. However, both the bar

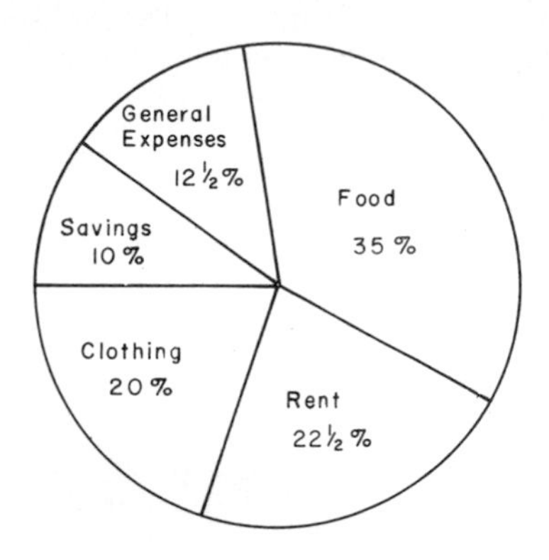


**Fig. 42.** Circle graph: Proportionate expenditures.

and the circle graph show at a glance that food is the biggest item on this family's budget.

In making any kind of graph it is customary to round off numbers to facilitate their presentation. Table 3 shows the cotton ginned in 1946,

TABLE 3. Cotton Ginned, 1946
(Thousands of bales, 500 pounds gross)

| | |
|---|---|
| United States | 13,200 |
| U.S.S.R. | (no data) |
| India | 4,200 |
| China | 3,100 |
| Mexico | 1,800 |
| Brazil | 1,700 |
| Egypt | 1,500 |
| Pakistan | 1,400 |

in thousands of 500-pound bales. These figures are rounded to thousands to begin with, and further rounded in the table to the nearest hundred thousand. The figures in Fig. 41 are rounded to the nearest hundred.

In making a pictograph, each picture unit stands for a given unit of measurement. In Fig. 43, for example, each symbol represents $100 million spent for construction of school buildings in the indicated years. These data are tabulated in Table 4, the figures being rounded to the nearest hundred million dollars.

TABLE 4. School Building Expenditures
(Rounded to hundred million dollars)

| | | |
|---|---|---|
| 1930 | $ 389,000,000 | 4 hundred million |
| 1935 | 52,000,000 | 1 ” ” |
| 1940 | 156,000,000 | 2 ” ” |
| 1945 | 59,000,000 | 1 ” ” |
| 1950 | 934,000,000 | 9 ” ” |
| 1955 | 2,442,000,000 | 24 ” ” |

As was said earlier, graphs attract attention and clarify meaning. They also aid retention and, if properly presented, not only give information at a glance—for example, only a glance at Fig. 43 is needed

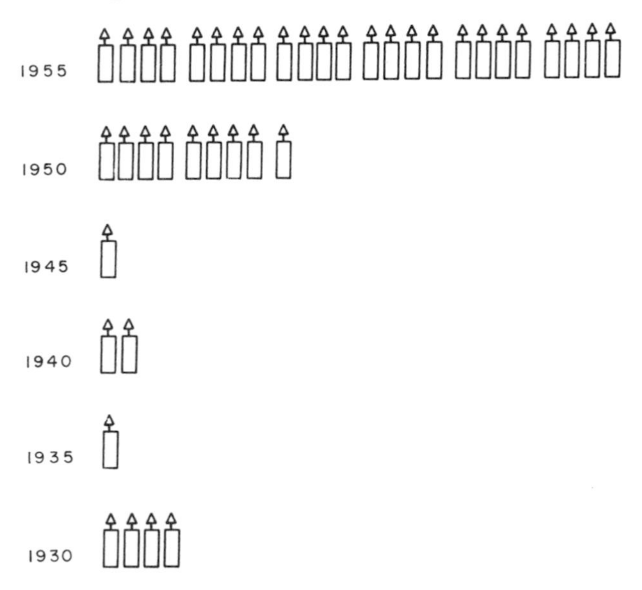


**Fig. 43.** Pictograph: Expenditures for school building construction.

to see that far more money was spent in 1955 than in any other year included on the graph—but also lend themselves to study. Why, for example, was this expenditure comparatively low in 1935 and 1945? What are some of the reasons for the rapidly increasing expenditure since 1945?

In making graphs it is important to consider the nature and amount of data, the use to be made of the graph, and its size. Constructing some graphs involves more problems than most elementary pupils are ready for; for example, the scale—the number of units to be represented by one space on the graph—must be chosen so that the graph will be of the desired size and so that reducing the data to this scale will not be too difficult.

Pupils will best understand graphs by making them. Because it is a respite from other types of arithmetic computation, most pupils welcome some work with graphs if it is kept at the level of their interest and ability. For this reason it is generally recommended that pupils be given squared paper for line and bar graphs, and prepared circles with circumferences marked off in multiples of 10° for circle graphs. Until they have acquired reasonable ability in judging scale intervals,

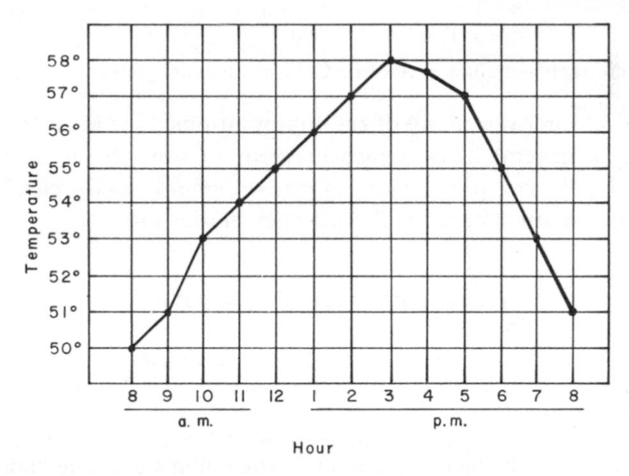


**Fig. 44.** Line graph with two variables: Hourly temperatures.

the scales should also be given them.

Here is a place for the very bright pupils to work independently in finding suitable data for the various forms of graphs and setting up appropriate scales. Furthermore, the line graph that shows more than two quantities that change together probably is suitable only for these bright pupils. Fig. 44, with two variables, is far simpler than Fig. 45, with three variables.

As this and the preceding chapter have shown, measurement is involved in a large part of computation and problem-solving in

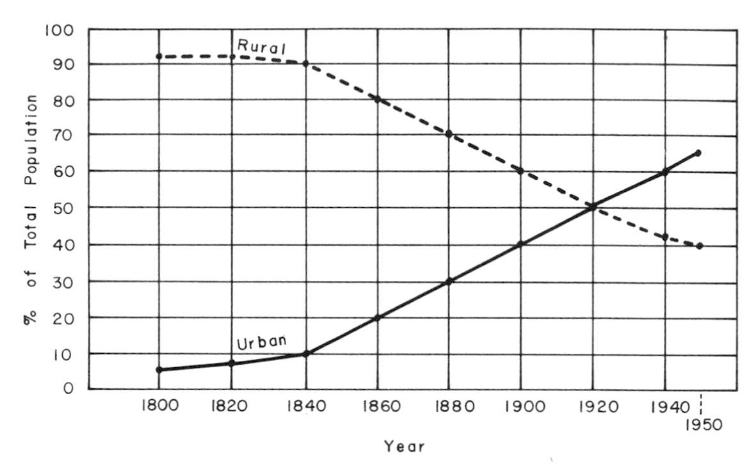


**Fig. 45.** Line graph with three variables: Comparative rural and urban population.

arithmetic. Moreover, many of the computations done most frequently by people in general involve measurement in some form. For these reasons, pupils' comprehension of measurement needs careful and systematic development from the primary grades on.

## COMPETENCE CHECK

**1.** Secure rulers marked for both inches and centimeters and draw lines of the following lengths: 6 inches, 6 centimeters; 10 inches, 10 centimeters; 1 inch, 1 centimeter.

**2.** 1. If you are traveling in Europe, what would you expect to be priced by the meter? The liter? The gram? The millimeter? The kilogram?
2. What use would you expect to make of the kilometer-mile equivalents?

**3.** Compare the reduction process in adding and subtracting compound denominate numbers with the process in adding and subtracting abstract numbers.

**4.** How do the characteristics of time and temperature measurement differ from those of length and area measurement?

**5.** Explain the additive method of subtraction in making change.

**6.** Why is the additive procedure more difficult than "take-away" subtraction in computing the amount of change?

**7.** What is the relationship between angles and arcs?

**8.** Define and draw an angle; an arc; a central angle.

**9.** Refer to Section 4 in Chapter 19. What tables of measurement are applied for age? Weight? Body temperature? Heart beat? Breathing rate? Money? Class size? Aspirin tablets? Pop? Pencils? Books? Paper?

10. 1. Draw a right angle; a 90-degree angle; a 45-degree angle; a 180-degree angle; a 270-degree angle; an acute angle; an obtuse angle.
    2. How is the size of angles determined?
11. Explain the terms: denominate numbers; simple denominate numbers; compound denominate numbers.
12. Draw a plan for a house 30 ft. by 40 ft. Divide it into rooms as you wish and give the floor area of each room.
13. Place the house in the preceding exercise on a lot 75 ft by 150 ft. Proportion the yard space as you would like it, and give measurements of the yard areas.
14. What difference is there between making a diagram of something—e.g., the stage arrangements for a play—and making a scaled drawing of it?
15. In textbooks or magazines find an illustration of each of the four kinds of graphs discussed in this chapter. Explain and evaluate each.

## OPTIONAL ASSIGNMENTS

1. 1. Reduce 84 kilometers, 565 meters to kilometers.
   2. Reduce 84 miles, 565 feet to miles.
   3. Compare the computation involved in the preceding two exercises.
2. What are some of the arguments for adopting the metric system in the United States? What are some of the arguments against it? For further discussion of these questions see the *Twentieth Yearbook* of the National Council of Teachers of Mathematics, and the papers by Read.
3. With foreign cars becoming increasingly common in this country, some of their speedometers may be calibrated in kilometers. Make a table showing the following speeds per hour in kilometers: 25 mi.; 35 mi.; 45 mi.; 50 mi.; 60 mi.; 65 mi.; 70 mi.
4. Using the following diagrams, explain the similarity of the metric system of weight to our number system:

| thousands | hundreds | tens | units | tenths | hundredths | thousandths |
|---|---|---|---|---|---|---|
| 4 | 2 | 4 | 1 . | 6 | 2 | 5 (units) |

| kg. | hg. | dg. | gram | dg. | cg. | mg. |
|---|---|---|---|---|---|---|
| 4 | 2 | 4 | 1 . | 6 | 2 | 5 (grams) |

5. Convert the following from 24-hour time to 12-hour time: 1600; 2400; 0130; 1420.
6. Acquaint yourself with the meaning and use of each of the following representative illustrations of modern measures: (1) 400 man-hours; (2) 15 denier 51 gauge hosiery; (3) 120-thread muslin; (4) 60-watt light; (5) 14-carat gold; $\frac{1}{2}$-carat diamond; (6) 16 mm. film; (7) 32-caliber gun; (8) 5 horsepower motor; (9) 110-volt current; (10) 1,000,000 passenger-miles; (11) vanilla extract, alcohol 35%; (12) 5-grain aspirin tablets; (13) 6 semester-hour credits; (14) 10 quarter-hour credits.

## REFERENCES


Achelis, Elizabeth, "The Measurement of Time," *Education*, April, 1951, pp. 507–510.

Johnson, J. T., "The Metric System," *School Science and Mathematics*, November, 1944, pp. 717–721.

Larsen, Harold D., *Arithmetic for Colleges*, Macmillan, New York, rev. ed., 1954, chap. 10.

National Council of Teachers of Mathematics, *The Metric System of Weights and Measures, Twentieth Yearbook*, 1948.

Read, Cecil B., "Arguments Against the Universal Adoption of the Metric System," *School Science and Mathematics*, April, 1950, pp. 297–306.

Spitzer, Herbert F., *The Teaching of Arithmetic*, Houghton Mifflin, Boston, 2nd ed., 1954, chap. 9.

chapter 21

# The Arithmetic of Business and Finance

## I. The Child's Early Business Experiences

As a result of good home training and appropriate school experiences, most pupils, by the time they are in the upper elementary grades, will have had some experience in handling money, making purchases, making change, and quite possibly earning money and banking savings. A few may have had some experience in budget making.

As in many other areas of learning, a teacher must start where the pupil is in these experiences and build from there. For some pupils it will be their first experience in examining and filling out bank forms—*deposit slips* (Fig. 46), *checks and stubs* (Fig. 47)—*endorsing checks*, determining the check book balance and comparing it with that on a *bank statement*. Dramatizing a bank's activities in taking in and paying out money, with pupils taking different roles at various times, is good experience for the entire class.

Next a study of *savings accounts* and how a savings account book differs from a *pass book* introduces savings deposits and withdrawals, interest being entered at stated intervals, such as each quarter. This application of percentage and interest provides a good review of these processes.

Children who have allowances can set up personal *budgets*, again applying percentage—for example, the percentage spent for clothing, for recreation, and so on. Some can study their own family's budgets, and some may make model budgets. This is a place for problems dealing with budgets and percentages that call for a thorough review of these applications of percentage.

At this stage children should learn how to read and make *sales slips*, including computing the sales tax. This provides additional good

# Farmers & Merchants Bank

In receiving items for deposit or collection, this Bank acts only as depositor's collecting agent, and assumes no responsibility beyond the exercise of due care. All items are credited subject to final payment in cash or solvent credits. This Bank will not be liable for default or negligence of its duly selected correspondents nor for losses in transit, and each correspondent so selected shall not be liable except for its own negligence. This Bank or its correspondents may send items, directly or indirectly, to any bank including the payor, and accept its draft or credit as conditional payment in lieu of cash; it may charge back any item at any time before final payment, whether returned or not, also any item drawn on this Bank not good at close of business on day deposited.

UNDER THIS AGREEMENT, ITEMS LISTED BELOW ARE TODAY DEPOSITED BY

________________________________________

Huron, S. Dak., ____________________________ 19____

**PLEASE LIST EACH CHECK SEPARATELY**

| | DOLLARS | CENTS |
|---|---|---|
| *Currency* | | |
| *Silver* | | |
| CHECKS AS FOLLOWS: | | |
| | | |
| | | |
| | | |
| | | |
| | | |
| | | |
| | | |
| | | |
| | | |
| | | |
| | | |
| | | |
| | | |
| | | |
| | | |
| | | |
| *Total $* | | |

**SEE THAT ALL CHECKS AND DRAFTS ARE ENDORSED**

KIEL BROS., INC., HURON, S. DAK.

**Fig. 46.** Deposit slip.

NO. $
DATE 196
TO
FOR

| | DOLLARS | CENTS |
|---|---|---|
| BAL. BRO'T FOR'D | | |
| AMT. DEPOSITED | | |
| " " | | |
| TOTAL | | |
| AMT. THIS CHECK | | |
| BAL. CAR'D FOR'D | | |

F&MB
HURON, S. DAK., 196 NO.
FARMERS & MERCHANTS BANK 78-43/914
MEMBER OF FEDERAL RESERVE SYSTEM
PAY TO THE ORDER OF $
DOLLARS
FOR

**Fig. 47.** Bank check and stub.

review in computing the cost of items and in adding accurately. They should also learn how to keep a simple *cash account* and how to balance it with the cash on hand. They will realize that an accurate cash account can become the basis for budget making.

## 2. Credit, Discount, and Profit and Loss

Whenever people buy, and pay later, they are using *credit.* Credit plays a tremendous part in business transactions in this country and throughout the world. The credit extended on goods purchased by individuals is known as **consumer credit.** When a dealer, for example, borrows money from a bank to buy more goods, the credit he receives is referred to as **commercial credit.**

Most stores do some business on credit; only a few sell solely for cash. The majority of employed people today receive salaries paid at a regular interval—monthly, bi-weekly, or weekly. Many of them choose to charge their purchases, paying all their bills when they get paid. *Charge accounts* are maintained by most merchants at no extra cost to the customer. Some stores have a *lay-away plan*; they advertise in July, "Buy blankets now on our dollar-saving lay-away plan." This is one form of installment buying.

Pupils will probably be somewhat familiar with *installment buying*, but may know it as "buying on time" or "buying on payments," their only concept being that a person can buy a car or a TV or a davenport by paying a little at a time. Most of them have no concept of a *carrying charge*, nor do they realize that one pays more for a TV set when he buys it "on time." However, if they have some background in computing interest, and know that interest is the money paid for the use of someone else's money, they can comprehend that if we purchase and take home a $270 refrigerator with only a small down payment, perhaps \$30, we still have \$240 that really belongs to the dealer. Furthermore, after we pay the next \$30, we still have \$210 that should be in the dealer's cash drawer. However, when the sales contract was drawn up, the total of the down payment and the installment payments exceeded the cash sale price of the refrigerator because it included the interest to be paid on the money owed the dealer. This interest is usually called a "**carrying charge.**"

Many people who make extensive use of installment buying are completely unaware of the high cost of financing their purchases. They may be shocked when they find out the rate of interest they are actually paying. For example, a record player that is priced at \$120 can be bought on the installment plan for \$25 down and five monthly payments of \$20 each (a total of \$125). The carrying charge is \$5, but what is the **actual** rate of interest? Let us see.

| | |
|---|---|
| \$120 | stated cost |
| −25 | down payment |
| \$ 95 | owed during first month |
| −20 | payment 1 |
| \$ 75 | owed during second month |
| −20 | payment 2 |
| \$ 55 | owed during third month |
| −20 | payment 3 |
| \$ 35 | owed during fourth month |
| −20 | payment 4 |
| \$ 15 | owed during fifth month |
| −20 | payment 5 |
| \$ 5 | paid for interest |

$$\$95 + \$75 + \$55 + \$35 + \$15 = \$275$$

The buyer has owed the equivalent of \$275 for one month. We turn to our interest equation: $\$275 \times ? \times \frac{1}{12} = \$5$, and find that the rate is 21%. In other words, during the period of the contract the buyer pays interest on the unpaid balance at the rate of 21%.

No one expects to pay 21% interest on borrowed money, but it is regularly paid under many credit plans as carrying charges. Most credit contracts are complicated and cannot be understood easily. Hence the average buyer accepts the contract without realizing that he may be paying exorbitant interest rates, sometimes even higher than 21%. The wise buyer reads the contract, figures the interest rate, and then decides whether he wants to make the purchase under those terms.

There are times when it is profitable to pay a considerable cost for financing in order to have immediate use of the particular item. For example, a boy's bicycle is damaged beyond repair; he uses it for delivering papers. Even though it may cost him $5 more to buy a new bicycle on the installment plan, it is worth it because it is important for him to have the use of the bicycle instead of being without it until he has saved enough money to buy one for cash.

Business houses make frequent use of *discounts.* Damaged or shopworn goods may be marked for sale at a discount; seasonal goods—galoshes, summer hats, winter coats, and so on—that are still on hand at the end of a season may be offered at a discount. The merchant wants both to get his money out of this stock and to make space for new stock. Store-wide sales are sometimes held, with nearly everything advertised at a discount. In general, a **discount** is a percentage of the marked price, the amount by which the original price is reduced. This is **simple discount.**

Wholesale dealers sometimes offer a discount series known as **commercial** or **trade discount.** This device makes it simpler for them to quote prices to merchants. Their catalogues are usually large and expensive to print, but this discount practice makes it possible for them to be used for several years. A basic price, called a **list price,** is stated for each article. Prices do not change for all articles at the same time. For example, the price listed for certain patterns of linoleum in a furniture catalogue may be reduced on a given date, but at the same time the price of certain types of mattresses increases. Discount sheets take care of these changes. The linoleum may carry one discount of 8%, and a second discount of 3%, and perhaps an additional discount of 2% for cash. These commercial discounts are taken off in a series; for example:

| | |
|---|---|
| $96.40 | list price |
| −7.71 | first discount |
| $88.69 | after first discount |
| −2.66 | second discount |
| $86.03 | after second discount |
| −1.72 | third discount |
| $84.31 | after third discount |

| | |
|---|---|
| $96.40 | |
| × .08 | |
| $7.7120 | first discount |

| | |
|---|---|
| $88.69 | |
| × .03 | |
| $2.6607 | second discount |

| | |
|---|---|
| $86.03 | |
| × .02 | |
| $1.7206 | third discount |

Few pupils will have any concern with series discounts, and probably only the most able should be asked to compute them. Salesmen, dealers, and bookkeepers usually use them. However, most pupils can understand the mathematical principles involved. They will learn that computations involving percentage occupy a large place in the work done by merchants, clerks, accountants, and salesmen; furthermore, customers should know something about discounts.

In order to run a business properly, a proprietor must keep good *business records* so he will know how much he has outstanding and hence get his collections made on time. He also needs to know how much he owes and how he is doing from month to month. His **liabilities** (what he owes) should be less than his **assets** (the value of what the business owns). The goods he sells should bring in enough to cover their cost plus his **overhead** (expenses of running the business—salaries, telephone, electricity, heat, rent, etc.) plus **a profit.** Therefore, in arriving at a selling price for his goods, he adds what is called **margin** to their cost, this includes overhead and profit.

He must thoroughly understand his business in computing his margin. For example, a man who deals in fresh fruits and vegetables and meats needs a higher margin than the dealer in canned goods and such staples as flour, sugar, and crackers, to allow for spoilage of the fresh goods.

The accompanying diagram shows that 10% of each $1 taken in is profit. In this case the merchant marks up his goods so as to have this

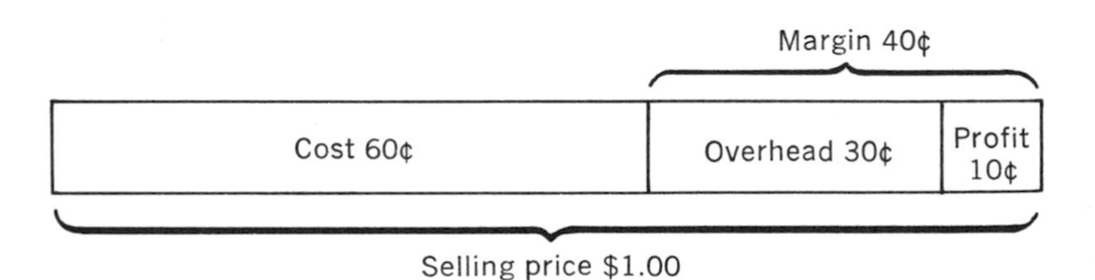


amount of profit, for out of profit have to come funds for new equipment and expansion. When a business shows a loss instead of a profit, the proprietor needs to make a change in his stock or his business practices if he is to remain in business.

Some interesting dramatizations can be provided for the class in connection with the business transactions described in this section, with pupils taking turns acting as salespeople, bookkeepers, managers, and customers. An impromptu stock might consist of books, globes, rulers, and furniture; and the pupils can have the experience of making out sales slips and deposit slips, making cashbook entries, and using discount, charge accounts, and installment buying.

## 3. Borrowing Money

An elementary-school child may borrow money from his parents or brothers and sisters, promise to pay it back when he gets his next allowance, and keep his promise and pay it. But he needs to learn that the procedure by which adults borrow money is more businesslike.

Borrowing and financing procedures are of various kinds. One of the simplest is a **promissory note** (Fig. 48). This is a means of deferred

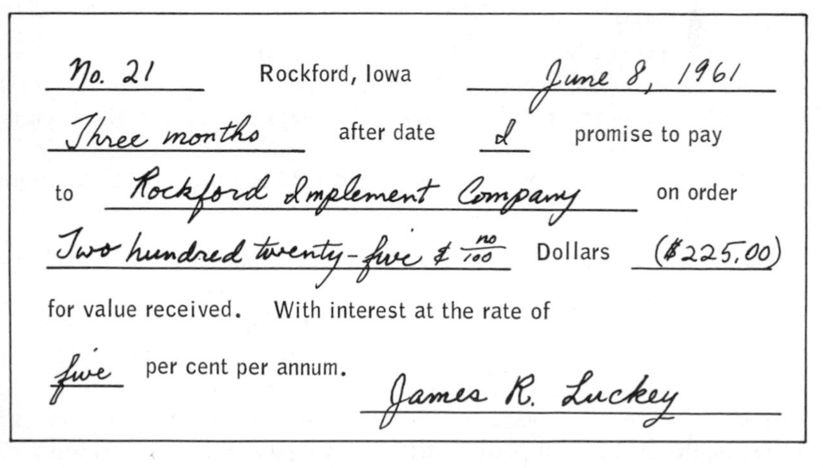
No. 21 Rockford, Iowa June 8, 1961

Three months after date I promise to pay

to Rockford Implement Company on order

Two hundred twenty-five & no/100 Dollars ($225.00)

for value received. With interest at the rate of

five per cent per annum.

James R. Luckey

**Fig. 48.** A promissory note.

payment. It may be used, for example, by a farmer who must have an expensive piece of machinery, perhaps a haystacker, for the haying season. Not having the ready cash, he makes a down payment and gives the implement dealer a promissory note for the balance, perhaps $225. The note is his written promise to pay; it states when he expects to pay and the interest rate he will be charged.

Promissory notes are frequently used by businessmen who wish to borrow a sum of money for a stated period—perhaps 30 to 90 days—by which time they will have the amount required. College students sometimes use them to borrow money from a student loan fund maintained by the college. Such notes may run for two or three years, or for the time when the student will be out of college and earning money. A series of such notes may be used; for example, one for $150 may be due a year from the date of the loan, another for $150 due two years from that date, and another for $150 due three years from that date. Whenever the time is more than a year, the note states: "with interest payable annually."

Pupils should become acquainted with the terms used on promissory notes. Thus, in Fig. 48, the terms are as follows:

1. The **maker** of the note is the borrower. (James R. Luckey)
2. The **payee** is the lender. (Rockford Implement Company)
3. The **face** of the note is the amount for which it is written. ($225.00)
4. The **rate of interest** is the stated per cent (5%)
5. The **date of the note** is the date in the heading. (June 8, 1961)
6. The **maturity date** is the date on which the note is to be paid. (September 8, 1961)
7. The **time** of the note is the period between the date of the note and the maturity date. (Three months)

People with a good credit rating may make promissory notes without any security except the borrower's word that he will pay. But many firms and banks ask for additional security besides the borrower's word. For this purpose a mortgage is customary. The implement dealer may take a mortgage on the new haystacker; the furniture dealer may take a mortgage on the bedroom suite that is being bought either on the installment plan, or with a down payment and a promissory note covering the balance.

A **mortgage** is a legal paper by which the borrower (the mortgagor) pledges to give the lender (the mortgagee) the designated property (the haystacker or the bedroom suite) in the event that he does not pay the note. Such property is called **personal property;** a mortgage covering this type of property is called a **chattel mortgage.** In general, chattel mortgages cover movable property—machinery, livestock, furniture, cars, etc.—and it is unlawful for anyone to sell or to move from the state any mortgaged property without the consent of the mortgagee. Propery taken by the dealer in the event of nonpayment is usually said to be **repossessed.**

Land and buildings constitute **real estate.** They, too, may be mortgaged. A man may need to borrow money to buy a farm or a building. He makes a down payment on his purchase, and he and the seller draw up a contract stating the terms of sale—how and when the rest of the money is to be paid, the rate of interest, etc. The buyer will be required to give a mortgage as security. The mortgage may be on the property he is buying, or on some other property he owns which is estimated to be worth more than the amount of money he is borrowing.

Both chattel and real-estate mortgages are *recorded* at the office of the register of deeds in the county courthouse. When all the debt secured by the mortgage is paid, the mortgage is *canceled* and the *release* is recorded at the courthouse.

Instead of the farmer giving the dealer a note for the balance due on the haystacker, he may borrow money at the bank and pay the dealer cash. In this case he gives the bank his note and probably a chattel mortgage on some of his property, perhaps some cows. There is one difference, however, between giving a promissory note to an individual or business firm, and a bank. When the farmer pays the implement company the $225 at the time it is due, he also pays three months' interest at 5% computed thus:

$$\frac{5}{100} \times \$225 \times \frac{1}{4} = \frac{45}{16} = \$2.81$$

This total is called the **amount** of the note; it is equivalent to $225 + $2.81, principal plus interest, or $227.81.

If the farmer borrows the money from a bank on the same terms, he must pay the bank the interest in advance. The bank computes his interest as $2.81, deducts it from $225, and gives him $222.19 in cash. At the end of the three months he pays the $225 with no interest being due. Or the implement dealer may take the farmer's note and sell it to the bank. The bank will *discount* the note, deducting the interest and giving the dealer the *proceeds*, $222.19. This enables the dealer to have the use of this money right away, and for this he is willing to pay the discount. In these bank transactions interest paid in advance is known as **bank discount.** The exact number of days from the day of discount to the day of maturity is called the **discount period.**

These financial procedures will be more realistic to pupils and better understood if they are dramatized, as was suggested earlier in the chapter in another connection.

## 4. Investments

People invest their money in many ways; hence pupils should become familiar with the terminology of investments, including stocks and bonds. The simplest, and the one elementary pupils themselves are most likely to use, is a savings account. Such accounts generally pay interest ranging from 3 to $4\frac{1}{2}\%$ that is compounded quarterly or semiannually.* That is, if on January 1 \$100 is put into a savings account, with interest compounded twice a year, the interest is computed July 1 for the six-month period; $\frac{1}{2}$ of $\frac{3}{100} \times \$100 = \$1.50$. This interest is added to the principal, \$100. For the next six months the investor has \$101.50 principal on which the interest the next January 1 will be computed as $\frac{1}{2}$ of $\frac{3}{100} \times \$101.50 = \$1.52$. For the next six months his principal will be \$101.50 + \$1.52, or \$103.02. All additional deposits he makes are added to his principal.

Most bank deposits are guaranteed, i.e., insured, by the federal government against loss by theft or embezzlement up to a certain amount; hence the depositor risks no loss and his money just keeps on earning. Investments like this which subject the investor to no risk always pay a comparatively low rate of interest. The bank uses its depositors' money for loans that bring a higher rate of interest than they pay the depositors, probably at 5 to 7 per cent. In this way they pay their overhead and make a profit.

Instead of a savings account, an investor may deposit his money and take certificates of deposit. These are certificates given the depositor as evidence of his deposits, instead of the deposits being entered in a savings account book. Interest is paid annually, and may be at a slightly higher rate than savings accounts offer; but in order to draw interest the money must be left on deposit for a full year. This type of investment is also guaranteed.

In most areas of the country there are building and loan associations, in which investors buy shares with a specified maturity value, and make monthly payments. In general these associations pay interest at a rate comparable to that paid by savings banks; interest is compounded either semiannually or quarterly. Here also, provided they are federal associations, depositors' money is secured by the federal government.

Another kind of investment, United States savings bonds, is handled

* Encourage pupils to inquire about this at several banks.

by banks as a service to the government. Many people buy these bonds as an investment; in other words, they lend money to the federal government at approximately 3% interest. The bonds are issued in denominations of \$25, \$50, \$100, \$200, \$500, and \$1000; this is called the **face value** or **maturity value** of the bond. The bonds *mature* in from eight to ten years and can then be cashed at their face value. These bonds are really a type of promissory note issued by the government to individuals. To buy a \$50 bond, we must pay an amount of money which at the given interest rate over the given time will amount to \$50. When the bond pays $3\frac{1}{3}\%$ and matures in ten years, this loaned principal is \$37.50: $3\frac{1}{3}\%$ of $\$37.50 \times 10 = \$12.50$; $\$37.50 + \$12.50 = \$50.00$, value at maturity. Bonds may be cashed before they mature but pay a much lower rate of interest.

Other government units besides the federal government sell bonds as a means of borrowing money. School districts may issue bonds to build new schools, cities may sell bonds to cover municipal improvements, such as a water system. Usually banks and other financial agencies buy these bonds as long-term investments.

Business enterprises constitute another form of investment. Of the various forms of organization,* the three most common are the proprietorship, the partnership, and the corporation.

A **proprietorship** is formed when one individual establishes a business. He himself has enough money, plus securities against which he can borrow, to furnish the capital he needs to go into business.

When two or more individuals provide the capital among themselves and establish a business, they form what is known as a **partnership.** The partners do not necessarily invest equal amounts of capital; if they do, they share the profits equally. But if two-thirds of the capital is supplied by one partner, and one-third of it by the other partner, the profits are divided on this 2 to 1 ratio.

Some business enterprises—for example, establishing a bank or an investment company or a large motel—require a considerable amount of capital. In such cases the capital may be supplied by several people, who form a **corporation.** Corporations are regulated by state law under a charter known as **the articles of incorporation,** and can issue both shares of stock and bonds. Each person who supplied capital to establish the

* Pupils may visit several business places and ask about their particular form of organization.

corporation receives a certain number of shares, depending on the amount of capital he provided.

Corporations generally issue two kinds of stock, **preferred stock** and **common stock;** both may be sold to the public. Both usually have a stated **par value** that is determined at the time the corporation is established; the par value may be set at any figure. Investors who believe that the particular enterprise will be profitable buy these shares and thus become **stockholders** in the corporation. Profits from the business are known as **dividends;** they are distributed to the stockholders, usually quarterly, on the basis of the number of shares each stockholder owns.

The dividends paid on preferred stock are usually a percentage of the par value of the shares, and holders of this type of stock have first claim on any dividends. Dividends on the common stock depend on the earnings of the business and are paid only after the dividends on the preferred stock have been paid.

Like governments, corporations may issue **long-term bonds** as a means of borrowing money for expansion or other stated purposes. These bonds are less speculative than shares of stock, because interest must be paid on the bonds regardless of whether any funds are available for dividends for the stockholders.

Shares of stock are usually bought and sold through **stockbrokers** who are connected with brokerage houses. The transactions take place in a **stock exchange,** such as one of those in New York City the brokers collecting a **commission** from both parties to the transaction. The market price of stock varies in accordance with changing political and economic conditions and the international situation. Many daily newspapers throughout the country carry a long list of stock quotations which enable anyone interested to tell whether the particular stock is rising or falling in value. The following is a stock quotation for one day:

| 1960–61 | | | Sales | | | | |
|---|---|---|---|---|---|---|---|
| High | Low | Stock | in 100's | High | Low | Close | Net ch. |
| $157\frac{1}{4}$ | 144 | U.S. Rub pf 8 | 13 | $156\frac{1}{2}$ | $155\frac{1}{2}$ | $156\frac{1}{2}$ | $+1\frac{1}{2}$ |

This is interpreted as follows: The highest market value, for U.S. Rubber preferred, in 1960 to the current day, is $157\frac{1}{4}$; the lowest is \$144. Dividends paid last year were \$8 per share. Today 1300 shares were traded, some selling as high as $\$156\frac{1}{2}$ and some as low as $\$155\frac{1}{2}$.

At the close of trading, the stock sold at $\$156\frac{1}{2}$, a gain of $\$1\frac{1}{2}$ from its price at the close of the last business day.

## 5. Insurance and Annuities

Insurance is, in general, a form of protection against loss—of property, because of fire, storm, or theft; of money, because of hospital and medical expense or unemployment; of work time, because of illness or accident; of life, by the person insured. Thus there are innumerable types of insurance coverage: life, accident, health and hospital, automobile, fire, hail, liability, endowment, unemployment and so on.

All insurance is based on the general principle that for payment of a small percentage of the amount of the insurance at regular intervals, the insurance company will pay the insured the stated amount of insurance on proof of loss, accident, damage, etc., as specified. The contract between the insurance company and the insured person is called a **policy.** The amount of insurance is called the **face** of the policy. The payment made by the insured is the **premium;** interest on it accrues. In life and accident insurance the person who will receive the money on the death of the insured is called the **beneficiary.**

**Premium rates** depend on various factors. The chief factor in life insurance is the age of the insured when he takes out the insurance. In fire insurance, the rates depend on such factors as the number of families occupying a dwelling, the type of construction, and its location in relation to a source of water supply.

An **annuity** is a form of insurance that is actually savings. Premiums are paid at regular intervals by the insured for a stated number of years. At the end of this time, he ceases to pay premiums and instead receives from the annuity specified amounts each month for the rest of his life. Similar to an annuity is an **endowment policy;** it matures in a given number of years, commonly twenty, at which time the premiums paid by the insured plus accrued interest equal its face value, which is paid the insured in cash. This type of insurance is of great help to parents who want to provide a college education for their children.

**Social Security** is a form of insurance issued by the federal government for employed people. The employee and his employer each pay a specified percentage of the employee's salary as a premium during the years he works. When he reaches retirement age—at present 65 for men, and 62 or 65 for women—he is paid monthly benefits.

## 6. Taxation

**Taxation** is a matter in which everyone is involved—even elementary pupils if they live in a city or state that has a **sales tax** whereby they must pay a certain percentage on practically everything they buy.

There are many types of taxes, and they may be levied by various government units—federal, state, and city—school districts, and other intermediate governmental units.

The federal government levies taxes as a means of obtaining money for national defense, the salaries of the numerous federal officers, the maintenance of federal institutions, and so on. The **income tax,** both personal and corporate, is an important source of these funds. Although the federal government does not levy a sales tax as such, it collects a considerable amount of money by means of two taxes: **luxury taxes** paid on such articles as furs, leather goods and purses, cosmetics, and so on; and **excise taxes** which are levied on the manufacture and consumption of certain articles and the right to carry on certain businesses within the country.

Some states levy their own income tax and many states and cities collect sales taxes, usually 1 to 3% of the purchase price of goods taxed.

**Property taxes** are a prevalent type of taxation throughout this country; they include taxes on both **personal property** and **real estate.** In most states property taxes provide the major part of the money needed to operate local government and schools; for usually all units of government except the federal government, but including school districts, share the proceeds from these taxes.

Although most of the financial transactions discussed in this chapter involve percentage, some of them—for example, installment buying, insurance, and income tax—are more complicated to compute than the property tax. The simple equation for computing a property tax was presented in an earlier chapter as rate × valuation = tax.

When **tax rates** are to be established, all the government units, including the school district, that derive income from property taxes, make out their annual budget, deduct anticipated income from other sources (tuition, state aid, licenses, etc.) and thus arrive at the amount to be obtained from property taxes. The assessor's office determines the **property valuation,** both real estate and in some cases personal, for the area, and then determines the tax by the above equation. The tax money to be raised is thus divided by the total valuation to determine the rate to be used in a given area—city, school district, township, etc.*

The tax rate may be expressed as a per cent of the assessed valuation, as so many mills on a dollar, or as so many dollars per hundred dollars of valuation. For example, $4\frac{1}{2}\%$, 45 mills on the dollar, and $4.50 per hundred are equivalent tax rates.

Many other types of tax are levied—estate taxes, inheritance taxes, poll taxes, and so on. However, lack of space makes a discussion of them impossible.

## 7. Transmitting Money

In business and finance it is frequently necessary to transmit money to distant places. There are several ways this can be done.

People who have a checking account can use **personal checks.** However, a small fee, called **exchange**—possibly 10 cents on checks of $100 or less—is sometimes charged by an out-of-town bank that cashes the check.

A common means of transmitting any amount of money is a **bank draft.** This is really a check, drawn by a local bank on a large city bank in which it has deposits, that is payable to the person or firm to whom the money is sent. A small fee is charged for a bank draft.

**Postal money orders** are also a convenient means of transmitting money. A postal money order is an order by the local postmaster to the postmaster in the town where the payee lives to pay that person the specified sum of money. Fees charged for postal money orders are prorated according to the size of the amount. **Express money orders** and **telegraph money orders** are also available at about the same cost as postal money orders. In all these cases, including bank drafts, the sender is given a receipt for the money by the issuing office. In the case of a personal check, the canceled check is the receipt.

**Credit cards** are being used increasingly. They are a special convenience in traveling, because by showing them the traveler can supply many of his needs on credit, thus making it unnecessary for him to carry large amounts of cash. Many hotels, motels, restaurants, and gasoline stations honor these cards and charge him with expenses thus

* Have pupils ask about current tax rates at home and bring some figures to school.

incurred. He is billed at the end of each month just as he is for charge accounts in his home town.

Even the many people who prefer to pay as they go do not need to carry more than small amounts of cash, for they can obtain **traveler's checks** from banks for a small fee. These are checks, payable to an individual, drawn by a local bank on a large city bank, where it has deposits. The checks are issued in several denominations from $10 up, and are easily cashed, on identification, in any bank or business place. If cash in the form of currency is lost, its recovery is almost hopeless; but if traveler's checks are lost, their holder needs only to notify his bank to stop payment on them, thus preventing anyone else from cashing them.

No new mathematical processes are involved in the business and financial topics discussed in this chapter, earlier chapters on decimals and percentage provide all the computational background required. However, as has been said earlier, in addition to being extensively concerned with computation, arithmetic should also be concerned with the use of computation in everyday life. This is the reason for including this chapter, which covers in some detail several of the social aspects of arithmetic.

## COMPETENCE CHECK

1. Explain how to open a savings account at a bank, and also a checking account. Compare their purpose.
2. What will you pay for a chair priced at $69.50 if there is a discount of 15%?
3. Make out a sales slip for the chair.
4. Draw a picture of a page in a savings account book showing deposits, withdrawals, interest, and the balance.
5. Set up a model budget for yourself.
6. Define debit column and credit column in a cashbook.
7. Draw up a balanced cashbook page.
8. Define the term "credit."
9. What are the values and dangers in installment buying?
10. Define the following words: Mark-up. Margin. Overhead. Selling price. Cost. Profit. Loss. Discount.
11. What is another name for "series discount," and why and when is it used?
12. If you were taking a trip, how might you use credit cards? Traveler's checks?
13. Explain bank discount.
14. How many of the following terms refer to both checks and notes: date, rate, maker, payee, time, face, maturity date?

15. Name and describe the two kinds of mortgage that are in common use.
16. Define mortgagor. Mortgagee.
17. When and how is there a release of a mortgage?
18. What is exact interest? Name one occasion for its use.
19. Name three types of investment in which the risk is low.
20. List four means of transmitting money. Explain and evaluate each one.
21. Name and discuss several types of taxation.
22. Write two other forms in which tax rates may be expressed that are equivalent to $3.50 per hundred.
23. What tax will be due on a piece of property valued at $8500 if the rate is $3.50 per hundred?

## OPTIONAL ASSIGNMENTS

1. Consult various local stores about their plans for selling a home appliance, a piece of furniture, an automobile on credit. How does this price of these various goods compare with their cash price?
2. Define inflation. How does it affect us as individuals?
3. What is meant by the purchasing power of money? The changing value of a dollar? Soft money?
4. Define compound interest. Give an example of it.
5. Why are properties not mortgaged for their full value?
6. Compare the risk involved in each of the following types of investment: (1) a promissory note with no security; (2) a mortgage on a new dry-cleaning shop; (3) a United States government bond; (4) stock in a corporation that runs city buses; (5) a bank certificate; (6) stock bought in the New York Stock Exchange; (7) preferred stock in a local bank.
7. Bring to class and interpret market quotations listed in a daily paper.

## REFERENCES

Taylor, E. H., and Mills, C. N., *Arithmetic for Teacher Training Classes*, Holt, Rinehart & Winston, New York, 4th ed., 1955, chaps. 16–20.

## INFORMATIVE MATERIALS

(Available at little or no cost)

Better Business Bureau Booklets: "Facts You Should Know About Borrowing"; "Facts You Should Know About Saving Money"; "Facts You Should Know About the Consumer Education Study"; "Facts You Should Know About Budgeting," National Better Business Bureau, Inc., Chrysler Building, New York City 1.

*Budgeting Through School Savings*, Educational Section, United States Savings Bonds Division, Treasury Department, Washington 25, D.C.

Money Management Booklets: "Your Budget"; Children's Spending"; "The Health Dollar"; "The Food Dollar"; "The Shelter Dollar"; "Home Furnishings"; "The Recreation Dollar"; "Your Shopping Dollar"; "Time Management"; "George Clark's Cartoons on Money Management for the Family," Household Finance Corporation, 919 North Michigan Avenue, Chicago, Illinois.

*Personal Money Management*, American Bankers Association, 12 East 36 Street, New York City.

*Where Does the Money Go?* Union Dime Savings Bank, 40th St. and Avenue of the Americas, New York City 18.

*Your Money*, Federal Reserve Bank, Minneapolis, Minnesota.

chapter 22

# Mental Arithmetic, Approximation, and Rounding Off Numbers

## I. Place of Mental Arithmetic in the Elementary Grades

From the time arithmetic came into the elementary curriculum as a regular school subject, the branch of it that is commonly referred to as mental arithmetic has had its ups and downs, with pedagogical interest in it waxing and waning.

Throughout the nineteenth century, beginning with the publication of Warren Colburn's *First Lessons in Intellectual Arithmetic*, mental arithmetic held an important place in teaching arithmetic. At that time arithmetic was used chiefly in the marketplace, and rapid and accurate calculation was its principal aim. Partly for that reason and partly because the mental discipline theory was then at its height, mental arithmetic flourished. Selectmen, the forerunners of the school board, examined teachers in mental arithmetic as a criterion of teaching competence. Likewise, pupils were examined by school officials in rapid mental calculation ($4 + 6 \times 2 - 3 + 8 \div 5$) as evidence of successful learning.

In the early 1900's, psychological research began to discredit faculty psychology, mental discipline, and automatic transfer of training, and with them mental arithmetic. There was a parallel trend in American reading instruction. When it was shown that the phonetic method was failing to accomplish certain types of reading outcomes, particularly comprehension, educators formulated new reading methods, and phonics teaching disappeared from the curriculum. Not for decades did either phonics or mental arithmetic find its way back into the elementary curriculum to any extent.

Since the early 1940's the literature on the teaching of arithmetic, and arithmetic textbooks as well, have given increased attention to mental arithmetic. However, there has been considerable lack of uniformity in the use of terms; some texts avoid the term mental arithmetic, perhaps as too suggestive of difficult brain work, and others, no doubt in an attempt to use terms more readily comprehended by early elementary-grade pupils, use such expressions as "without pencils" and "Write only the answers."

## 2. Modern Interpretation of Mental Arithmetic

When the term mental arithmetic is used in textbooks today, what does it imply? Just as it always has, it means computing without using written algorisms. In fact, an algorism is merely the recording of thought processes, especially a series of them, as an aid in arriving at the final result. It is a conventional pattern of an abstract nature that is widely used to indicate a certain type of computation, as in the algorism $25\overline{)6251}$.

Mental arithmetic is included in the modern curriculum, not as an exercise for the brain, but largely because of a conviction that it makes a definite contribution to meaningful learning in arithmetic. Where there is no thinking, there is no meaning. Often there is no thinking—only automatic computation with the given figures when pupils begin work with pencil and paper as soon as they see the problem.

Mental arithmetic involves thought processes that enable the pupil to grasp the problem and comprehend the number relationships so that he will know the form of computation required before he begins to write it. It also aids in estimating results both before and after doing written computation. For example, $15 \times 298 = ?$ Since 298 is almost 300, and $15 \times 3 \times 100 = 4500$, the answer 4470 is probably correct—at least it is *reasonable*—whereas only a moment's mental computation will show that 470 is incorrect.

Mental arithmetic is also involved in interpreting quantitative statements, an ability frequently needed in reading, with understanding, the textbook and reference material for the elementary grades. Examples are: "In a given area, 80% of the population are illiterate," "The normal rainfall of a certain California city is about 4 inches a year" (as compared with approximately 36 inches in the pupil's home community).

## 3. Wide Use of Mental Computation in Daily Life

An earlier chapter mentioned some of the common uses of rapid mental computation: "I am buying twelve 4-cent stamps—that's 48 cents, so a 50-cent piece is enough and I'll have 2 cents in change." The pupil in the cafeteria line who has 30 cents for his lunch must calculate quickly what he can buy for this amount.

Some studies have been made of the use of mental arithmetic in daily life; unfortunately they have not been too thorough. Flournoy's study[1] reported that college students found 75% of the arithmetic used during a 24-hour period involved mental arithmetic and 25% involved paper and pencil, with 48% of the mental arithmetic requiring exact answers and 27% approximate answers. In another study Flournoy made of pupils in Grades 3 to 6, she reported that 83, or 71.6% of the 116 uses reported involved no paper and pencil and that 84.3% of these 116 required exact answers.

Even these limited studies make us realize that some mental calculation is called for in the daily activities of almost everyone. It is easy to conceive that far more of our daily computation activities might be of the mental type except for the fact that many people—elementary pupils, college students, and other adults as well—are frustrated when faced with the need to do a few simple computations without paper and pencil.

## 4. Mental Arithmetic Procedures at the Elementary Level

Mental arithmetic is not an activity for the upper grades only, nor is it an ability pupils acquire rapidly or suddenly. If pupils are to develop reasonable competence in using it, foundations should be laid in the primary grades and skill in applying it be developed in later grades.

At the primary level pupils should be given experience in estimating the number of objects in groups, after they have counted and *know* what 4 is, or 6 or 8. The teacher might say, "You will need sharp eyes now, for I'm going to show you a group of counters [perhaps checkers on a paper plate] and I want you to tell me whether there are about 5 or about 10 in the group. You'll have only a minute to look at them." Groups of sticks may also be used.

One of the errors of teaching in the past has been that pupils were

[1] Frances Flournoy, "Providing Mental Arithmetic Experiences," *Arithmetic Teacher*, April, 1959, pp. 133–139.

given a set of examples for which they were to write answers. Left to their own devices they dawdled and counted, exerting a minimum of mental activity. They began to compute problems without reading them carefully and with little thought about them. Bad mental habits can be forestalled by having more of the work at the primary level oral, guiding the pupils' thinking and requiring concentration from them.

As pupils become more competent as they reach the intermediate grades, many other kinds of practice in oral arithmetic can be provided, including such types as the following:

1. Encourage pupils to do computations mentally whenever possible.
2. Give them frequent opportunities to give oral interpretations of quantitative statements.
3. Provide frequent practice in selecting sensible and reasonable answers from multiple-choice lists for both abstract examples and problems.
4. Have them make a practice of estimating the reasonableness of their answers as a check on all their written work.
5. Give them frequent experiences in explaining the solution of problems without numbers.
6. Teach them how to interpret quantitative statements in terms of "reference measures"; for example, the story says, "Only about 100 yards from their cabin they discovered a den of foxes." How far is 100 yards? Knowing that it is approximately the length of a city block adds excitement and interest to the story. Many illustrations of this sort were mentioned in the chapters on measurement.

## 5. Proficiency in Mental Arithmetic at the Elementary Level

In a recent study to determine the effectiveness of instruction in mental arithmetic,[2] Flournoy used specially prepared booklets with 550 pupils in 20 intermediate-grade rooms for 52 school days. Her conclusions, in essence, were that these pupils exhibited a need for specific experience in mental arithmetic and that they showed significant gains in confidence on tests in mental computation and problem-solving. To her it seems plausible that intermediate-grade pupils can become

[2] Frances Flournoy, "The Effectiveness of Instruction in Mental Arithmetic," *Elementary School Journal*, November, 1954, pp. 148–153.

adept at handling situations involving mental arithmetic in their everyday activities, but are likely to perform much below their ability level unless the schools provide specific experiences in mental arithmetic for them.

This means that progressive proficiency in mental arithmetic will not be attained by elementary pupils by occasional incidental experiences, but rather by systematic, well-planned, direct teaching experiences for which teachers at every grade level have some responsibility.

Somewhat earlier than Flournoy's study, Hall made a survey to determine the ability of a sixth-grade group to solve certain verbal arithmetic problems without using paper and pencil.[3] His study showed a positive correlation of .74 between intelligence and this ability. This, of course, emphasizes the need for gearing experiences in mental arithmetic to the ability of pupils. Although every pupil should be given some practice in mental computation, it should be simple for pupils of low ability, but be extended to include such types as will challenge the more capable pupils. Someone has given the name "mind stretchers" to experiences that challenge on every level; every pupil needs mind stretchers.

### 6. Importance of Approximations, Estimates, and Rounding Off

Many of the computations we do mentally do not call for exact answers. We put a cake in the oven at 10:30; it is to bake for 45 minutes. We compute mentally: "I'll take it out about 11:15." Here the measurement of time need not be accurate. So also, if we want three-quarters of a pound of nuts that cost 98 cents a pound, we compute the price as about 75 cents to determine whether we have enough money for it.

Children in the primary grades are accustomed to use counting to check their computations; 3 chairs + 4 chairs gives them an exact answer, 7 chairs. But as they progress in school they should recognize that most numerical results are not exact. To be sold legally, a pound of butter must be 1 pound ± a small amount for error; a quart of milk is close to an exact quart; a bushel of apples only approximates an exact bushel.

[3] Jack V. Hall, "Solving Verbal Arithmetic Problems Without Pencil and Paper," *Elementary School Journal*, December, 1947, pp. 212–214.

This is so because the measuring instruments in common use do not permit precision of measurement. For example, scales may be slightly out of adjustment; cloth tape measures may shrink or stretch slightly. If there was a slight error in the weight of a 1-pound load of bread, the error on three loaves would be larger, but the relative error per loaf would not increase. However, a total error of half an ounce on three loaves of bread would be of much greater significance than an error of half an ounce on a 100-pound sack of sugar.

If three pupils measure the width of the schoolroom, they will not be able to agree on the *exact* length, but they probably can agree on the length to the nearest inch. One gets 20 ft. $3\frac{3}{4}$ in.; the second, 20 ft. $3\frac{7}{8}$ in.; and the third, 20 ft. $3\frac{5}{8}$ in. All find that it is 20 ft. and nearer 4 in. than 3 in., so they round off the number to the nearest inch.

Some introduction to estimating, approximating, and rounding off numbers should be provided for middle- and upper-grade pupils. When an exact answer is called for and is possible, accuracy of computation is essential. For example, if 28 pupils contribute 25 cents each to the Junior Red Cross, accurate computation will provide an exact answer ($7), since the 28 pupils and the 25 cents contributed by each are exact amounts. But $\frac{1}{3}$ yard of material priced at $1.69 a yard will cost $.56$\frac{1}{3}$; $\frac{2}{3}$ yard of the same material will cost $1.12$\frac{2}{3}$. The $\frac{1}{3}$ yard and the $\frac{2}{3}$ yard do not represent absolutely precise measurement, they are accepted, and if the computation is accurate, the price is considered correct. But since there is no way to exchange $\frac{1}{3}$ cent, this is rounded off to the nearest cent (a mental calculation) and the price is $.56. Since the fraction in $1.12$\frac{2}{3}$ is more than $\frac{1}{2}$, this cost is rounded off to $1.13.

Pupils must learn *when* rounding off is appropriate and when it is not. If we are offered a discount of $16\frac{2}{3}\%$, we cannot claim 17%, nor do we want to settle for 16%. For example, a chair is priced at $49.50 and the merchant offers $8.25 discount ($16\frac{2}{3}\%$); he will not offer $8.42 (17%). Obviously, this is not the place to round off $16\frac{2}{3}\%$ to 17%.

Theoretical quantities are often replaced by convenient estimates. Thus, $\pi$ (pi) is the symbol for the number that represents the ratio of the circumference to the diameter of a circle. This ratio is more than 3 to 1 and less than 4 to 1, but it is impossible to write a common fraction or a decimal fraction that exactly expresses the fractional part of that number. The decimal 3.1416 and the common fraction $3\frac{1}{7}$ are commonly used to indicate an approximation to the exact number represented by

$\pi$. Since $\frac{1}{7}$ is a repeating decimal, if we tried to obtain an exact value for it we would have $0.142857142857 \cdots$ in an unending series. Writing the decimal to approximate $\pi$, we would have 3.14159, also continued—but not repetitive—in an unending series. Hence this is generally rounded off to 3.1416. Obviously using $3\frac{1}{7}$ will not give an exact answer when this value is used for $\pi$, but for our purposes it is an adequate approximation.

Very large numbers also are commonly represented by round numbers. Thus the earth's mean distance from the sun is rounded to 93,000,000 miles, and the mean distance from the sun to Mercury, the planet nearest the sun, is 36,000,000 miles.

Rounding off numbers and computing with approximate numbers become increasingly complex and eventually are in the realm of higher arithmetic. Very bright upper-grade pupils will be challenged by significant digits and approximations, and with some practice can acquire considerable skill in estimating. But much can be done for the average pupil, too, if given practice in estimating answers. He should be able to look at a series of addends like $49.9 + 250 + 3.15 + 20.8$ and say the sum will be about 324, or to look at $4.3 \div .5403$ and say the quotient will be about 8.

Arithmetic teaching in the last two generations has kept pupils "pencil-bound"; and because they immediately resort to written algorisms, they have entirely neglected the possibility of making a quick mental estimate to use as a check on the result obtained by "figuring." The habit of making estimates gives confidence. Furthermore, in many cases an estimate is an adequate answer for the problem at hand, as in the following: "In 1945, 10,167 thousand tons of wood pulp was produced, and in 1955, 20,829 thousand tons. In 1945, 28,122 million board feet of lumber was produced, and in 1955, 39,108 million board feet. Estimating from these figures, which of these wood products made the greater proportionate gain in this ten-year period?"

## 7. Short Cuts as Aids to Mental Computation

A few short cuts to computation were mentioned earlier in this text; but since in a good many cases knowing a simple short-cut rule enables us to compute mentally what appears to require written computation, it is appropriate to point out some of these cases and the rules.

However, short cuts are for those who understand the full procedure; usually they are not for the slow learner.*

1. Multiplying by 10 or multiples of 10:
   a. To multiply by 10, add a zero to the multiplicand and move the decimal point one place to the right; e.g., $6.4 \times 10 = 64.0$.
   b. To multiply by any multiple of 10, add as many zeros as there are in the multiplier and move the decimal point that many places to the right; e.g., $62.4 \times 1000 = 62{,}400.0$.
2. Dividing by 10 or multiples of 10:
   a. To divide by 10, move the decimal point one place to the left; e.g., $642 \div 10 = 64.2$.
   b. To divide by any multiple of 10, move the decimal point as many places to the left as there are zeros in the divisor; e.g., $1696 \div 1000 = 1.696$.
3. Multiplying by aliquot parts of multiples of 10:
   a. To multiply a number by 25, multiply it by 100 and divide by 4; e.g., $72 \times 25 = 7200 \div 4 = 1800$; or multiply $\frac{1}{4}$ of the number by 100; e.g., $72 \times 25 = 18 \times 100 = 1800$.
   b. To multiply a number by 250, multiply it by 1000 and divide by 4; e.g., $240 \times 250 = 240{,}000 \div 4 = 60{,}000$; or multiply $\frac{1}{4}$ of the number by 1000; e.g., $240 \times 250 = 60 \times 1000 = 60{,}000$.
   c. To multiply a number by $33\frac{1}{3}$, multiply it by 100 and divide by 3; e.g., $2100 \times 33\frac{1}{3} = 210{,}000 \div 3 = 70{,}000$; or multiply $\frac{1}{3}$ of the number by 100; e.g., $2100 \times 33\frac{1}{3} = 700 \times 100 = 70{,}000$.
4. Multiplying by numbers whose digits are all 9's:
   a. To multiply a number by 9, multiply it by 10 and subtract the number; e.g., $36 \times 9 = 360 - 36 = 324$.
   b. To multiply a number by 999, multiply it by 1000 and subtract the number; e.g., $28 \times 999 = 28{,}000 - 28 = 27{,}972$.
5. Multiplying a two-digit number by 11:
   a. To multiply a two-digit number (the sum of whose digits is less than 10) by 11, write the two digits in the thousands and units places in the product, and write their sum in the hundreds place; e.g., $27 \times 11 = 297$.
   b. To multiply a two-digit number (the sum of whose digits is 10 or more) by 11, write the right-hand digit in the units place in the product, the first figure of their sum in the tens place, and the

* Guide pupils to develop these processes and formulate the rules.

other digit increased by 1 in the thousands place; e.g., $47 \times 11 = 517$.

6. Multiplying two two-digit numbers both ending in 5:
   a. If the sum of the two tens digits is an even number, to one-half the sum of the tens digits add the product of the tens digits and annex 25 to the result; e.g., $45 \times 65 = 2925$ ($\frac{1}{2}$ of 10) $+ 24 = 29$.
   b. If the sum of the two tens digits is an odd number, ignore the remainder when taking $\frac{1}{2}$ their sum, and annex 75 to the result, instead of 25; e.g., $45 \times 95 = 4275$ ($\frac{1}{2}$ of 13) $= 6 + 36 = 42$.
7. Multiplying two two-digit numbers when the tens digits are the same and the units digits add up to 10:

   Multiply the units digits and make their product the last two digits in the answer. Increase one of the tens digits by 1. Multiply this number by the other tens digit and make the product the left-hand digits in the answer:

$$
\begin{aligned}
45 \times 45 &= 2025 \\
5 \times 5 &= 25 \\
4 + 1 &= 5 \\
5 \times 4 &= 20
\end{aligned}
$$

$22 \times 28 = 616$:

$$
\begin{aligned}
8 \times 2 &= 16 \\
2 + 1 &= 3 \\
3 \times 2 &= 6
\end{aligned}
$$

8. Using the tell-tale 9's in multiplication:
   a. The product of 9 and any other number from 1 to 10 contains digits whose sum is 9; e.g., $2 \times 9 = 18$; $4 \times 9 = 36$.
   b. Any product of which 9 is a factor contains digits whose sum is 9 or a multiple of 9; e.g., $2 \times 13 \times 5 \times 9 = 1170$.
9. Using the series idea in addition:

$$
\begin{aligned}
46 + 8 &= 46 + 4 \text{ (to get to 50)} + 4 \text{ more} = 54 \\
126 + 15 &= 126 + 4\,(130) + 11 = 141
\end{aligned}
$$

10. Using the principle of compensation:

$$300 - 197 = 300 - 200 + 3 = 103$$

## 8. Integration of Mental Arithmetic in Total Arithmetic Program

As pointed out in the various sections of this chapter, mental arithmetic is not an activity apart from the regular procedures, but rather a component part of all arithmetic. It should be integrated with the regular computational and problem-solving procedures at every level, from the primary grades up.

Elementary pupils will become interested and proficient in this type of work only if their successive teachers recognize the value of providing experiences that give pupils practice in mental arithmetic.

## COMPETENCE CHECK

**1.** List for each grade level, from the first to the eighth, a mental arithmetic activity or practice that you consider appropriate for that grade.

**2.** Where might rounding off to the nearest inch be appropriate? To the nearest mile? To the nearest hundred miles? To the nearest cent? To the nearest million dollars? To the nearest ounce? To the nearest ton? Cite figures to illustrate.

**3.** Discuss your own experience with mental arithmetic and your attitude toward it.

**4.** Use short-cut procedures to solve each of the following:

1. $.0642 \times 100$
2. $7.2901 \div 1000$
3. $498 \times 33\frac{1}{3}$
4. $260 \times 99$
5. $43 \times 11$
6. $69 \times 11$
7. $85 \times 25$
8. $35 \times 65$
9. $34 \times 36$

## OPTIONAL ASSIGNMENTS

**1.** Consult Taylor and Mills, Larsen, or other sources, and find out what is meant by apparent error in measurement; by relative error; by maximum error. Give illustrations.

**2.** 1. On the basis of Taylor and Mills or other sources, report on significant figures.
   2. How are these figures involved in approximate numbers and in rounding off numbers?

## REFERENCES

Larsen, Harold D., *Arithmetic for Colleges*, Macmillan, New York, rev. ed., 1954, chap. 11.

Petty, Olan, "Lay That Pencil Down," *Grade Teacher*, May, 1957, p. 57.

Taylor, E. H., and Mills, C. N., *Arithmetic for Teacher Training Classes*, Holt, Rinehart & Winston, New York, 4th ed., 1955, chap. 21.

chapter 23

# Problem-Solving

## I. Interpretation of Terms

In general, no textbook on teaching elementary arithmetic has been considered complete without a chapter on problem-solving. Unfortunately, however, the terms "problem" and "problem-solving" have been interpreted far from definitely. Thus the word "problem" has indicated at different times an abstract computation (e.g., 64 × 765), a practice exercise (e.g., What will 3 pairs of hose cost at $1.35 a pair?), and a new arithmetical experience calling for reasoning and really reflective thinking (e.g., How many revolutions will a wheel 20 in. in diameter make in travelling a distance of 10 ft.?).

It is to the last of these that the word "problem" is applied throughout this book. Thus interpreted, an adequate discussion of problem-solving might well have been included in Chapter 4, which dealt with reflective procedures as being most conducive to successful learning in the problem-solving aspects of arithmetic.

However, since later chapters have discussed the various arithmetic processes and their meaning and use, problem-solving at the present point implies a thorough understanding of these processes and the purposes for which they are used; for without this, problem-solving cannot be efficiently handled. It is from the point of view of representing the application of cumulative learning that a chapter on problem-solving is presented at this point. This does not mean that problem-solving is to be considered an area of arithmetic entirely separate from the fundamental operations; on the contrary, their close relationship has been pointed out throughout this book.

Most of the research referred to in this chapter comes from sources that give little specific interpretation of the term "problem-solving"; nevertheless, it seems pertinent and, in general, applicable to problem-solving as it is defined in this chapter.

## 2. Steps in Arithmetical Problem-Solving

A true problem is a situation that faces an individual or a group who want to find a solution but have no ready-made method for doing so. Hence a problem in arithmetic may be defined as a situation that is described in words and involves a quantitative question to which an answer is sought, but for which no computational process is indicated. For example, "This 50 cents pays for how many days' milk at the rate of 5 cents a day?" is a problem to a primary pupil as a beginning experience in division.

Though the old procedure of formal analysis in problem-solving has proved ineffective, as will be shown later, a systematic attack on a problem is generally desirable. Useful steps in such an attack are:

1. Reading the entire problem carefully to get a mental picture of the total situation and to understand the question asked.
2. Analyzing the problem situation to determine the steps needed in solving it.
3. Applying known principles and concepts to determine the relationship of the given data.
4. Formulating the proper algorism by which to indicate those relationships.
5. Performing the computation called for by the algorism.
6. Checking the reasonableness and accuracy of the answer.
7. Deriving generalizations.

These steps may be followed by an individual in solving an unfamiliar quantitative problem, or they may be the basis of a class's cooperative exploratory experience, such as was described in Chapter 4. Both situations imply a reflective or developmental type of procedure, the steps being merely a guide to thinking.

## 3. Steps in Problem-Solving Illustrated

The following paragraphs show how the above seven steps may be applied to a simple problem for a middle-grade pupil—for example, "Lee's father agreed to take him and four other boys to the Shrine

Circus in a town 80 miles away if the boys would pay for the gasoline. He said his car made about 18 miles to a gallon of gasoline, and the gasoline he usually bought cost 34¢ a gallon."

1. Interpreting the problem situation: Here five boys are to share equally the cost of gasoline for the entire trip. The problem question is: What will each boy have to pay? It will be helpful if they draw a line to represent the 80 miles; they will then realize that their return trip will also be 80 miles.

2. Analyzing the problem situation: The following steps are involved: (a) Knowing the total distance. (b) Knowing how many gallons of gasoline will be needed to travel that distance. (c) Knowing how much this many gallons of gasoline will cost. (d) Knowing how much each boy will need to pay.

3 and 4. Determining number relations and formulating algorisms for each step: (a) $2 \times 80$ miles = total miles to go. (b) Total distance ÷ distance traveled on 1 gallon of gasoline = number of gallons of gasoline required. (c) Number of gallons × price of 1 gallon = total cost. (d) Total cost ÷ 5 = each boy's share.

5. Completing the computation to obtain an answer.

6. Judging the reasonableness of the answer and checking the accuracy of the computation. Is \$3 for the car, or 60¢ for each boy reasonable?

7. Deriving generalizations: To find each person's share when there are five people, find $\frac{1}{5}$ of the total amount.

In Step 1 some ability to visualize the situation is essential in many types of problems, particularly those involving measurement. A drawing or a diagram, whenever applicable, is a definite aid to visualization; hence pupils should be given experience at every grade level in making drawings and diagrams to illustrate problems.

Instead of drawings, dramatization is frequently used at the primary level. For example, in such a problem as "If there are 4 chairs in a row and 3 are taken away, how many chairs are left?" actually moving the chairs will aid in solving it. As was pointed out in an earlier chapter, drawing pictures as in 3 balls + 4 balls (**O O O** + **O O O O** = **O O O O O O O**) is of questionable value in illustrating action; but when used to illustrate an equation the procedure has merit, for it shows balance.

Some problem situations are not difficult to interpret, but if the numerical data are in new or unusual form, the number relationships may not be clear at once. If the pupil is taught to restate such a problem with simpler numbers, he will readily discover the appropriate algorism and can apply it to the data in the problem. With this procedure, such a problem as "How long will it take a car to travel a mile if it travels at the rate of $\frac{2}{3}$ of a mile a minute?" becomes "How long will it take a car to go 150 miles if it travels at the rate of 50 miles an hour?" So also, "How many miles are there in 12 kilometers? One kilometer equals $\frac{5}{8}$ of a mile," is like "How many inches are there in 3 feet? There are 12 inches in 1 foot." This procedure is called the method of **analogies,** and pupils should be encouraged to apply it in any problem situations that are not at once clear.

Step 2 is likely to be the most difficult. If the reflective procedure is used, several lines of attack may be formulated before each step is identified.

Step 3 calls for facility in recognizing the uses of each of the fundamental processes—for example, when to multiply, and why. It is this step that requires proficiency in the computational processes without which pupils can never develop independence and confidence in problem-solving.

Step 4 is simple after the pupil realizes that a certain process, e.g., multiplication, is the one required.

Step 5 also is simple, if the pupil knows how to perform the various fundamental processes.

Step 6 involves no new activity if the pupil, from the primary grades on up, checks the reasonableness of an answer and also accuracy in computation. With consistent guidance by the teacher, this procedure should become practically habitual.

Step 7 will be developed gradually, but it should be initiated in primary grades.

If pupils learn steps to problem-solving in the primary grades, they will develop the additional skills gradually as the problems become increasingly complex in the middle and upper grades.

## 4. Problem-Solving a Weak Spot in Arithmetic Teaching

Since arithmetic first began to be taught, one of the major objectives has been problem-solving. But standardized tests have consistently shown that pupils are weaker in this—whatever their interpretation of the problem—than in the fundamental processes. For this reason, teaching problem-solving constitutes a real challenge to elementary teachers.

Textbook material that is assumed to provide experience in problem-solving often imparts no *real* learning about problem-solving. A common procedure has been to show pupils how to use processes and then give "problems" to provide practice in performing the computations. This book classifies such exercises as "keeping-in-practice" exercises. In many texts, however, the pupils learn the procedure for subtracting unlike fractions, for example, and then are given a page of so-called problems, such as: "A live chicken weighed $6\frac{3}{4}$ lb. After dressing, it weighed $4\frac{5}{8}$ lb. How much weight was lost in dressing?" No thinking is involved here because the pupil knows he is going to subtract in every "problem" on the page. Such "problem-solving" actually serves no purpose except drill in computation, and therefore does not aid in the development of true problem-solving ability.

## 5. School Responsibility for Weakness in Problem-Solving

Because the general difficulty experienced by pupils in solving problems is recognized as a weak spot in arithmetic teaching, considerable investigation and experimentation have been carried on in an effort to determine the causes of this difficulty and devise more effective procedures. For example, there have been studies of the relationship between reading skills and problem-solving ability, the value of formal analysis as a problem-solving procedure, the use of "cue words," the ability of the elementary child to reason, the relationship between experience and problem-solving, the grade in which problem-solving should be introduced, and the relationship between intelligence and problem-solving.

Some of these studies have in fact paved the way for more effective procedures in the problem-solving aspects of arithmetic. For example, it has been shown that there *is* a relationship between reading skills and problem-solving ability, but that there is no significant difference between good and poor achievers in problem-solving so far as measurement of *general* reading skills is concerned, but there is a difference between them so far as *specific* reading skills, such as locating information, are concerned.[1] According to one study, " . . . Four of the reading skills on which good and poor achievers in problem solving differed significantly were associated in one way or another with vocabulary,"

[1] Trevor K. Serviss, "Problem Solving," *Grade Teacher*, April, 1956, p. 43.

and, furthermore, those pupils " . . . differed significantly on retention of clearly stated details."[2]

Some studies have investigated the value of formal analysis as a problem-solving procedure. Burch says that several of these investigations indicate a positive relationship between competence in formal analysis and achievement in problem-solving tests, but none provide evidence of a cause-and-effect relation.[3]

Other studies—for example, that by Washburne and Osborne[4]—revealed that pupils who did their problems in their own way had better scores than those who first had to take single specific steps: (1) What is given? (2) What is to be found? (3) What is to be done? (4) Estimate the answer. In the Washburne and Osborne study many pupils reported that they never used formal analysis unless they had to, and some said that they became confused when they tried to use it. Conclusions of this study are as follows:

1. Pupils in this test tended to score higher when not required to use the formal steps, despite the fact that most of them had had good training in formal analysis.
2. Higher mean scores for pupils using only algorisms than for those using formal steps indicated that directly responding to each step may be more difficult than solving the problem.
3. Even when strongly indoctrinated in the process, pupils were not inclined to use it.

Such a study indicates that formal analysis is probably of doubtful value in problem-solving. However, some claim that pupils profit from using the analytical procedure because using it requires them to read the problem more carefully. But it seems likely that a favorable attitude toward problem-solving will insure careful reading of problems without the drudgery of formal analysis. Dawson concludes that research indicates that analogy may be useful for the superior pupil but confuses the slower.[5] The present writer believes that superior pupils are irked by having to write the several steps—to them this is an

[2] John P. Treacy, "The Relation of Reading Skills to the Ability to Solve Problems," *Journal of Educational Research*, October, 1944, pp. 86–95.

[3] R. L. Burch, "Formal Analysis as a Problem-Solving Procedure," *Journal of Education*, November, 1953, pp. 44–47.

[4] C. W. Washburne and Raymond Osborne, "Solving Arithmetic Problems I," *Elementary School Journal*, November, 1926, pp. 219–226.

[5] M. Dawson, "Making Problem Solving Easier," *The Instructor*, January, 1951, p. 29.

unnecessary slowing-down—when they can grasp the entire problem situation quickly and proceed with the computation at once.

A few decades ago the use of "cue words" as a key to which of the four fundamental processes was called for became popular. Such words as "altogether," indicating addition; "was left," subtraction; "times as many," multiplication; and "for each," division, were drilled upon, thus increasing the already too prevalent habit of manipulating figures with little thought or reasoning. The cue method was developed along with the drill theory of psychology. In accordance with the stimulus-response idea, a pupil was expected to respond almost automatically to any of the cue words which, more often by chance than by reason, resulted in the correct answer, and the answer was the thing. Although some elementary textbooks still teach reliance on some cue words, a number of research studies—among them one by McEwen[6]—have shown that the cue method is not effective.

Perhaps advocates of the cue method considered elementary-grade pupils incapable of reasoning. In this matter Van Engen[7] says that cue words and "Read the problem carefully" do not take into account the way children think; that ". . . childish thought is devoid of logical necessity"; and, further, that those presumed aids do not provide an approach that is on the child's level of thinking. His theory is that manipulation of objects, under the teacher's guidance, eventually supplies the basic elements of the child's thought processes when the objects are no longer present but are replaced by symbols; that visualizing the manual operations suggested by the wording of the problem and ignoring irrelevant data constitute problem-solving activity. Hence it would seem that, for the child, centering his attention on the actions that imply addition, subtraction, and so on—a procedure consistently advocated in this book—is thinking in its early stages.

Here again we must remember that if pupils are to learn to solve problems with some degree of independence, they must be given time to think through the situation and visualize the action involved before beginning to "figure," and, when diagrams will aid, a chance to make them. Here is an illustrative problem: "Janet is going to select a new

[6] N. R. McEwen, *The Effect of Selected Cues in Children's Solutions of Verbal Problems*, Doctoral Dissertation, Duke University, 1941, as reported in Walter S. Monroe (ed.), *The Encyclopedia of Educational Research*, rev. ed., Macmillan, New York, 1956, p. 54.

[7] H. Van Engen, "*The Child's Introduction to Arithmetic Reasoning*," *School Science and Mathematics*, May, 1955, p. 358.

rug for her room. She finds they are made in the following sizes: 6 ft. by 8 ft., 9 ft. by 12 ft., 12 ft. by 15 ft. Her room is 10 ft. by 12 ft. What size rug should she select?" In solving the problem, Janet will think through the situation and the imagined action somewhat as follows: "The 12 ft. by 15 ft. rug is bigger than the entire floor. I need a diagram to scale to see how the 9 ft. by 12 ft. rug will fit, and another diagram to see how the 6 ft. by 8 ft. one will fit." As Janet proceeds with making the diagrams, the answer becomes clear.

Van Engen says that no other approach seems to offer so much hope for eventual progress in teaching children to solve problems, and that "here is a fertile field for research." According to him, a little-publicized study by Jean Piaget[8] in 1928 is one of the most important studies of a young child's ability to reason that has been made.

In the development of appropriate reading skills and in helping children learn to reason, the school has a major responsibility. Furthermore, if certain techniques, e.g., the use of cue words and formal analysis, are shown to be ineffective, they should be discarded. Every effort should be made to utilize the findings of research on the optimum grade level for the introduction of specific types of problem materials and procedures.

## 6. Shared Responsibilities for Weakness in Problem-Solving

That there is a relationship between experience and problem-solving ability is a generally accepted assumption, but there has been some scientific investigation in that area also. A relationship between vocabulary and ability to solve problems has been verified. Experience with measures—pint, quart, foot, yard, and so on—helps to develop a vocabulary of meaning. Experience in handling money, and shopping, banking, travel, and innumerable other sorts of experience, help to give problem situations meaning. The value of using problems related to the pupil's home and school environment, so far as possible, in presenting each new type of computation has been stressed in earlier chapters.

White[9] found a statistically reliable relationship between experience and ability to solve problems. According to Hydle and Clapp,[10] if the

[8] Jean Piaget, *Judgment and Reasoning in the Young Child* (trans. from the French by Marjorie Warden), Harcourt, Brace & World, New York, 1928.

[9] Reported in Walter S. Monroe (ed.), *op. cit.*, p. 54.

[10] Reported in *ibid.*, p. 54.

problems could be visualized (a background of experience would facilitate this), their solution was almost as easy as if the problem situation was in the child's real experience.

Problems close to the child's experience can be visualized more readily; for example, ads distributed for local sales can be used as a basis for problems. Although this provides vicarious experience, the subject matter is meaningful and the experience realistic. If a pupil is to be able to solve problems, he must be familiar with the problem situation, or be able to comprehend the situation fully, for this clarifies understanding.

The relationship between intelligence and problem-solving ability has been investigated, and there is evidence that intelligence is a major factor in this ability. Intelligence contributes to the child's being able to concentrate his thought on the relevant factors in a problem situation and to use what is called abstraction to shut out all other factors. In such a problem as: "Bill and Wayne rode their bicycles 4 miles to the lake to fish. After fishing for 2 hours, Wayne had caught 8 fish and Bill had caught only half that many. How many did both boys have?" The pupil who attacks it intelligently realizes at once that the time and distance are irrelevant as far as finding the total number of fish caught is concerned.

In the areas of pupil experience and pupil intelligence, the school must recognize the limitations and try to meet individual needs. Much remains to be done in our schools in this respect.

## 7. More Specific Causes of Difficulty

The preceding paragraphs have discussed several factors that have been found to have a significant relationship to problem-solving ability. Using a somewhat different approach, several investigators have attempted to analyze specific causes of difficulty in arithmetical problem-solving. Representative of such reports is that of Brueckner, who has made extensive diagnostic studies. He lists the following causes of difficulty:[11]

1. Failure to comprehend the problem in whole or in part as a result of inferior reading ability, inability to visualize the

[11] L. J. Brueckner, "Improving Pupils' Ability to Solve Problems," *Journal of the National Education Association*, June, 1932, pp. 175–176.

situation, lack of practice in solving problems, and similar reasons.

2. Carelessness in reading that results in the omission of essential ideas, or misreading.
3. Inability to perform the computations involved, either because of forgetting the procedure or having failed to learn it.
4. Confusion of process, resulting in the random trial of any process that may come to mind.
5. Lack of knowledge of essential facts, rules, and formulas such as how many inches there are in a yard, or how to find the perimeter of a rectangle.
6. Carelessness in arranging written work, and general lack of neatness.
7. Ignorance of quantitative relations, such as the relation between selling price, cost, profit, and margin, because of lack of vocabulary or of understanding of principles.
8. Lack of interest resulting from repeated failure, difficulty of the problem material, its unattractiveness, and the like.
9. General lack of mental ability.

Upon scanning these causes of difficulty as listed by Brueckner, we see clearly that some of them are inherent in the problems themselves. Others involve poor mathematical background, including lack of understanding of the computational processes and essential principles. Still others are due to inefficient work habits, which in reality affect other lesson areas as well as arithmetic. Here again is an area in which the school must assume full responsibility for pupil weakness and for bringing about improvement.

## 8. Improving Problem-Solving Ability in Arithmetic

Investigations of problem-solving difficulties and their apparent causes have resulted in numerous proposals for removing the difficulties and improving pupils' problem-solving ability. Four of these proposals are discussed in the following paragraphs.

### *Using suitable problems*

The problems used in the early experience with problem-solving should (1) deal with the pupils' own experiences or experiences of others they are familiar with, (2) motivate interest, (3) make use of appropriate style and vocabulary, and be well worded, and (4) apply processes and skills that the pupils understand.

That problems should deal with pupils' own experiences and come within their realm of interest, particularly in their early experience with problem-solving, was pointed out earlier in this chapter.

As far as wording problems is concerned, the pattern of wording in most textbook problems presents first the information data, and last the problem question; for example, "Dick had 20 cents. He earned 10 cents more, and then spent 15 cents for ice cream. How much did he have left?" In most cases the pupil reads the information casually because he does not know what use he will make of it. The question might have read, "Did Dick earn more than he spent?" or "Did he have more money than he started with?"

Note the difference when this problem is worded as follows: "In this problem we want to find out how much money Dick had left. He had 20 cents to start with, earned 10 cents more, and then spent 15 cents for ice cream." Here the pupil knows at once what information he is seeking, and checks the data he needs to find the answer. All of us read informational material with more interest and more comprehension if we are looking for the answer to a definite question.

As another illustration, compare the interest and thought processes in the following two: (1) "Our schoolroom is 20 ft. wide and 24 ft. long." (So what!) "What is its area?" (We need the length and width but we have to read back to find these dimensions.) (2) "We want to know the area of our schoolroom." (OK, how long and how wide is it?) "It is 24 ft. long and 20 ft. wide." (No searching for the data.)

### *Focusing attention on the process of learning rather than on the product of learning*

If the process instead of the product of learning is the center of attention, finding the correct answer will no longer be the chief aim in solving problems. Teachers who do not evaluate and give credit for effective steps in solving a problem, as well as for the right answer, discourage pupil thinking, and thereby retard the development of real problem-solving ability. How pupils learn and apply the various methods of solving different types of problems is at least as important as the answers they obtain—and in general more important. This does not mean disregarding the value of accuracy in computation; rather it puts the answer in its proper perspective.

### *Developing problem-solving readiness*

As indicated earlier, one of the hindrances to problem-solving ability is poor mathematical background. Unless the first-grade child comprehends the meaning of addition, subtraction, and multiplication, he cannot use them successfully in problem-solving. Likewise, unless the pupil in the middle and upper grades can use the four fundamental processes easily, and understands the mathematical principles, equations and numerical relationships he has acquired in cumulative learning up to his present level, he is not prepared to do satisfactory work in problem-solving. Thorough mastery of the processes gives a pupil a feeling of being at home with figures and makes him confident, thus enabling him to devote all his attention to the reasoning phases involved.

Another factor which makes for lack of readiness in problem-solving is poor and careless work habits. All teachers, not merely the arithmetic teacher, have a responsibility in this aspect of pupil development. Therefore, if pupils have not already acquired the habit of writing neat and well-organized papers, their present teacher must stress this in preparing them for successful problem-solving. Likewise, though a pupil may have reasonably good general reading ability, if he has not acquired the special reading skills which are significantly related to problem-solving ability, the arithmetic teacher will need to help him develop them. It is a generally accepted axiom that *every* teacher is a teacher of reading.

All these abilities are basic to readiness for problem-solving on each grade level. Certainly every arithmetic teacher will do well to recognize them as basic and to strive to develop them before expecting real proficiency in the reflective type of problem-solving.

### *Providing for better comprehension of problem-solving techniques*

Although the three proposals just discussed can make definite contributions to pupils' problem-solving ability, it is this fourth proposal that apparently points the way to real gains. Providing better comprehension involves the whole area of teaching procedures and has potentialities which thus far have hardly been tapped. We saw in Chapter 3 that current experimentation with methodology and materials, together with a better understanding of how learning takes place, has created new hopes for a kind of arithmetic teaching that will lead to better understanding of new processes. Proficiency in problem-solving, as well as in computation, will result from this new outlook on arithmetic teaching. Some of these possibilities are discussed in the next section.

## 9. Insightful and Independent Learning in Problem-Solving

Long fettered by bond psychology and the drill theory, arithmetic teaching has begun to acquire a changed pattern as a result of these new developments. Experimental teaching procedures have unquestionably strengthened the theory that understanding gives permanence to acquired skills and to the acquisition of learning in general. The drill method was too often devoid of understanding.

Ample research evidence shows that manipulative experiences, along with exploratory reasoning, the discovery of number relationships, and the formulation of generalizations—a combination of processes long known as inductive learning, but rarely applied to arithmetic—aid understanding and help insure permanent learning. The relation of these experiences to a reflective type of teaching was discussed in Chapter 4. The value of these learning processes in teaching problem-solving is now more widely recognized than in the past, and there is every indication that they will have an increasingly important part in elementary arithmetic learning in the immediate future.

If a reflective teaching pattern, such as is advocated in this book, is to be employed in teaching problem-solving in arithmetic, the teacher must keep several conditions in mind.

1. The atmosphere of the classroom must be conducive to a feeling of being accepted and at ease on the part of the pupils.
2. The class must have a cooperative attitude, and be receptive to the ideas and opinions of others.
3. The arithmetic period must be anticipated with pleasure.
4. Suitable problem material must be provided.
5. There must be time for unhurried thought and relaxed activity.
6. The teacher must remember that concepts usually do not come as single flashes of insight, but unfold slowly, step by step, even with guidance.
7. The teacher should recognize that there is usually more than one correct and acceptable solution to every problem (though some may be too indirect to be practicable) and should commend every correct solution.

## 10. Sequential Development Essential in Arithmetic

Although this book advocates that problems be kept within the pupils' realm of experience as far as possible, it does not advocate depending on incidental school experiences for adequate learning in problem-solving skills. Because sequential arrangement is a basic characteristic of arithmetic, some systematic instruction is essential. Certainly not to be neglected, however, is the value of using all real classroom problems of a suitable level, as for example, "How much will our Valentine party cost if we buy two dozen cookies at 35 cents a dozen, and 4 quarts of milk at 19 cents a quart?"

This book gives no attention to the ultraprogressive idea of activity units in which arithmetic is integrated somewhat incidentally, such as a unit entitled "Our City's Recreational Program." Not that the economic and financial aspects of such a program are not of value in applying arithmetic, but rather that a series of such units cannot alone provide for an organized arithmetic curriculum involving sequential development.

## 11. Brighter Prospects for Problem-Solving

That arithmetic should be taught in a way that will enable pupils to become independent, self-reliant, and confident in working with numbers, and especially in solving problems, and that it *can* be taught in this way, are basic tenets of this book. Accordingly, examples of teaching procedures directed toward these outcomes have been used frequently.

If children from the primary grades on have been encouraged to relate all types of arithmetic computation to problems in which they would be used, if they have had adequate experience with the interpretation and application levels of learning in arithmetic instead of being limited solely to the recognition and recall levels, and if they have been accustomed to seek a solution to problems by mental experimentation, they will attack new problems with confidence, employ visual and manipulative aids as needed, and later do work on an abstract level.

Furthermore, if teachers will take new interest in teaching problem-solving more proficiently, if they will devote more attention to eliminating difficulties, to selecting suitable materials, and to developing problem-solving readiness, and then use teaching techniques that encourage insightful and independent learning, marked improvement in problem-solving ability at the elementary level can be reasonably expected to result.

## COMPETENCE CHECK

**1.** 1. Explain formal analysis as a problem-solving procedure.
2. What are the general conclusions in this chapter as to its value in problem-solving?
3. What is your own feeling about it as you have experienced it?

**2.** Examine some elementary arithmetic textbooks for illustrations of emphasis on cue words. What is their value?

**3.** To what extent do you feel that first-grade children are capable of solving problems? Explain your point of view.

**4.** Evaluate the proposals in this chapter for improving problem-solving ability.

## OPTIONAL ASSIGNMENTS

**1.** Explain what Bell and others meant by "an expanded algorism."

**2.** Does Blecha interpret the term "verbal problems" as it is used in the present text?

**3.** What relationship does Erikson point out between problem-solving ability and certain other factors?

**4.** What role does attitude play in the problem-solving aspect of arithmetic according to Fedon?

**5.** Report on any of the other articles in the references that interest you.

## REFERENCES

Bell, Carmen, *Making the Concepts and Operations of Arithmetic Meaningful Through the Use of Expanded Algorisms*, Master's Thesis, Ohio State University; reported in Kenneth E. Brown, *Analysis of Research in the Teaching of Mathematics 1955 and 1956*, U.S. Department of Health, Education, and Welfare, Office of Education Bulletin No. 4, 1958.

Blecha, Milo K., "Helping Children Understand Verbal Problems," *Mathematics Teacher*, March, 1959, pp. 106–107.

Erickson, Leland H., "Certain Ability Factors and Their Effect on Arithmetic Achievement," *Arithmetic Teacher*, December, 1958, pp. 287–293.

Fedon, J. Peter, "The Role of Attitude in Learning Arithmetic," *Arithmetic Teacher*, December, 1958, pp. 304–310.

Keliher, Alice V., "Creative Teaching of Arithmetic," *Grade Teacher*, February, 1958, p. 121.

Pierro, Peter S., "Using the Problem-Solving Methods," *Arithmetic Teacher*, April, 1959, p. 160.
Thorpe, Cleata B., "The Equation: Neglected Ally of Arithmetic Processes," *Elementary School Journal*, March, 1960, pp. 320–324.
Van Engen, H., "Twentieth Century Mathematics for the Elementary School," *Arithmetic Teacher*, March, 1959, pp. 71–76.

chapter 24

# Visual, Manipulative, and Other Types of Aids

## 1. Importance of Sensory Aids to Learning

Multisensory aids are of many kinds; their use has been emphasized throughout this book. Manipulation of objects and of counters, and dramatization—the putting together and taking apart of groups—are provided for beginning pupils. Thus these children have the experience of touching, seeing, telling, and finally writing, along with hearing.

As pupils move into the intermediate grades, manipulation continues to be used when new types of fractional parts and measurement are introduced. The pupils will also be given visual experiences, as in making diagrams for problems, and seeing the equivalence of certain common fractions, decimal fractions, and per cents.

Upper-grade pupils need the experience of measuring off an acre of land, of discovering for themselves that the circumference of a circle is about $3\frac{1}{7}$ times its diameter, that the volume of a cone is $\frac{1}{3}$ the volume of a cylinder having the same base and altitude, and so on.

## 2. Aids Closely Related to Individual Needs

As was pointed out in Chapter 5, the slow learner needs more sensory aids, and needs them for a longer period, than the very bright pupil does. However, some of the aids and devices discussed in that chapter serve other purposes than to facilitate the understanding of simple quantitative meaning. For both the slow and the bright, motivation of interest is essential to progress and in many cases manipulation and other devices help to supply this.

Some pupils are interested in challenges of an individual type—tricks, puzzles, and the like, but group competition, such as various games, motivates interest in almost all students. The very bright need activities that challenge them beyond the class requirements. These may include making and demonstrating various types of aids—for example, showing how the Romans computed with their system of notation, or making an abacus and showing how it is used. Enrichment of the arithmetic program, as we saw in Chapter 5, uses many of these materials and activities to supplement the essentials.

## 3. Games and Other Devices as Motivation for Practice in Arithmetic

Whatever the grade level, no pupil learns and *knows* the combinations, algorism forms, and principles in arithmetic after one lesson. Practice is essential for fixing new combinations and patterns of computation in mind, and the lower the pupil's intellectual level, the more practice is required for retention of learning. In modern educational parlance the long-popular term "drill" has largely given way to the term "practice." No doubt practice has more meaning for elementary-grade children than drill does. At any rate, regardless of the terminology, there remains the need for extended work to acquire new learnings and achieve facility in recall or performance.

Simple repetition is very tiresome, particularly to a disinterested child; actually it yields no returns. To be effective, practice must be accompanied by interest and attention, and the will to learn; and here games and other devices may make an important contribution. When practice takes the form of a game, it becomes more acceptable; interest and attention increase, and pupils "bone up on" certain combinations that help them to be on the winning side. The most alert discover schemes and clues that aid recall—the result of insight. But even when competition is less exciting, the pupil finds adding his scores in a bean-bag game much more interesting than adding the same figures in an arithmetic example.

When drill in arithmetic was the order of the day, and meaning and understanding were less emphasized than they are today, many teachers used games as "frosting for the drill cake." But at length arithmetic games fell into disrepute. When a teacher wrote Grossnickle asking where to secure devices and materials for making arithmetic more enjoyable, he replied that if she meant games, she should consult books on the teaching of arithmetic "about twenty years ago" (1928); he added, "I do not approve of using games to teach arithmetic."[1]

That number games were popular in the 1920's is evident from the books published around that time—for example, Harris and Waldo's *Number Games for Primary Grades* (1917), and Stone's *The Teaching of Arithmetic* (1922); in the latter, pages 70–94 are devoted to a collection of games. That they were later frowned upon is shown by Grossnickle's response just quoted, and by their omission from the professional books[2] published in the 1940's and early 1950's—another example, as in the case of phonics and mental arithmetic, of overdoing the purging.

Today, again as in phonics and mental arithmetic, games for arithmetic practice have experienced a revival; as witness such publications as Dumas' *Arithmetic Games*;[3] Spitzer's *Practical Classroom Procedures for Enriching Arithmetic*[4] (includes games); Marks, Purdy, and Kinney's *Teaching Arithmetic for Understanding*[5] (a "games" item appears in the index and pages 411–418 concern "Games for Fixing Skills"); and Ginn and Company's booklet, *Ginn Games for Arithmetic Grades* 3–8, for use with their *Arithmetic We Need* series. Even further indication of the interest in and approval of the use of games is the number of unpublished graduate studies recently done on this subject.[6]

[1] Foster E. Grossnickle, "Counselor Service" a column in *The Instructor*, May, 1948, p. 60.

[2] For example, L. J. Brueckner and Foster E. Grossnickle, *How to Make Arithmetic Meaningful*, Holt, Rinehart & Winston, New York, 1947; and H. G. Wheat, *How to Teach Arithmetic*, Row, Peterson, Evanston, 1951.

[3] Enoch Dumas, *Arithmetic Games*, Fearon, San Francisco, 1956.

[4] Herbert F. Spitzer, *Practical Classroom Procedures for Enriching Arithmetic*, Webster, St. Louis, 1956.

[5] John L. Marks, C. Richard Purdy, and Lucien B. Kinney, *Teaching Arithmetic for Understanding*, McGraw-Hill, New York, 1958.

[6] Billie Rosson Burk, *Sources, Descriptions and Suggested Uses of Stories, Poems, and Games Involving Number in Grade One*, Master's Thesis, University of Texas, Austin, 1956. Here the problem was to compile enrichment materials for first-grade arithmetic and suggest procedures for using them. A wide variety of materials were available, including 30 books, 50 songs, 40 jingles, and 40 games.

Bernice Clark Brunskill, *A Critical Compilation of Arithmetic Games for the Elementary School*, Master's Thesis, Ohio State University, Columbus, 1955. This study finds that drill is needed in arithmetic after understanding is established. Arithmetic games, carefully chosen as far as certain criteria and number concepts in each grade are concerned, provide practice. The greater part of the thesis is concerned

Unless arithmetic games are judiciously used, they can of course be a detriment to a classroom; but when wisely used, they are a valuable asset. They not only help fix arithmetic facts and processes in mind for ready use, but give life and interest to an arithmetic period. They also help a child to develop socially and emotionally. Waiting his turn, being a good loser, applauding the winner, acquiring a spirit of fair play, and developing self-control are all factors in character and personality development to which games contribute.

Whether games or class exercises are used as practice, certain guiding principles should be recognized.

1. Meaning and understanding should be established before giving practice for speed and accuracy.
2. After a high degree of accuracy has been attained, speed should be developed.
3. Practice must be accompanied by attention and be motivated by feeling a need to know.
4. Known and easy facts should not receive as much practice as those not yet mastered.
5. Practice should be organized so that the pupils have the opportunity to experience the satisfaction that results from accomplishment.
6. Practice should be distributed; it should continue only as long as interest can be maintained.
7. Practice should be an activity which pupils anticipate with enthusiasm.
8. Variety increases the effectiveness of practice.
9. Knowledge of progress helps to motivate practice and thereby induces learning.

## 4. Knowledge of Progress and Encouragement as Motivation

In all types of learning, but particularly in practicing for proficiency, whether it is in arithmetic computations or in golf, the question "How

---

with a compilation of games, organized according to the concepts to be developed.

Miriam Myers Wise, *An Investigation of the Feasibility of the Use of Teaching Aids, Games, and Devices in the Teaching of Arithmetic*, Master's Thesis, Ohio, State University, Columbus, 1955. Here the purpose was to explore whether the use of such materials is feasible, to determine criteria for their use, and to classify and catalogue them for other teachers.

am I doing?" should be answered in some way—by a progress chart, by earned scores, by the number of "I know" cards in the pile, or by verbal encouragement from the teacher. The method of answering the question apparently is not of great importance.

If teacher response is used, teachers should realize that, according to research in all subjects, commendation is most effective and reproof is effective to some extent, but that either is more effective than no response at all. Perhaps part of the value when games are used for practice is that the group serves somewhat as a cheering section: "You're doing fine—go on!"

## 5. Visual Aids as Learning Devices

It is not easy to separate visual aids from manipulative devices, nor is it necessary to do so. What the pupil does—for example, putting 4 blocks with 3 blocks for $4 + 3 = 7$—he also *sees*, thus obtaining the value of both kinesthetic and visual aids.

Modern arithmetic series that are profusely illustrated provide a great number of visual aids that vary in effectiveness. Although many other visual aids, such as diagrams, number lines, and so on, have been mentioned at various places in this text, slides, filmstrips, and movie films have as yet been given no attention. Many of them rank high in value; however, a teacher should always preview them and use only those that contribute definitely to his pupils' needs, or at least to the needs of certain groups.

Regardless of the subject for which a filmstrip or movie film is used for supplementary learning, its purpose and what to look for should be explained to the pupils beforehand; there should also be a follow-up discussion, and in most cases a second showing. Although hundreds of teaching films and filmstrips in arithmetic are available, no list is presented here because it is much better for each teacher to secure current catalogues from the sources at the end of this chapter and select those suited to his grade level and special needs.

Although an **opaque projector** is used less commonly than projectors for slides, filmstrips, and movies, it offers unique, and often very valuable advantages. Since it *reflects* the material shown, pictures or illustrations from other books, oral practice exercises, and the like can be thrown on the screen. For example, a teacher can show a previously made diagram for explanation or class discussion. So also, pupils' arithmetic papers can be shown, without names, for commendation, criticism, or correction; and good pupil-made diagrams can be shown and the work praised. A resourceful teacher will find hundreds of uses for an opaque projector.

### 6. Need for Teacher Efficiency and Good Judgment

Although the various aids and devices can make a definite and very effective contribution to arithmetic learning throughout the elementary grades, they will do so only when used by a competent teacher. A teacher should have a definite purpose in using them. Too often, however, they are used merely to entertain pupils, keep them busy, or fill up the time.

As is true with any other materials of instruction, a teacher should select these aids and devices, having in mind the purposes to be achieved, the stage of development of his pupils, and the individual differences in their needs and interests.

Unfortunately in many schools these materials do not perform the service they should, not because of any fault on the part of the teacher, but because the supervisory program does not enable teachers to obtain films and other aids at the time they are needed. This situation should be corrected whenever present.

### 7. Illustrative Riddles, Puzzles, and Brain Teasers

1. A teacher brings to class a box that contains 25 apples for 24 pupils and himself. How can each of them receive an apple and have one apple left in the box?
2. Arrange 9 pennies in 10 rows so there will be 3 pennies in each row.
3. Ask a friend to write any number, then multiply it by 2, add 10 to the product, divide the result by 2, and subtract the original number. Tell him you know his answer is 5. Suppose he writes 4; the special and general solutions follow.

| | *Special Solution* | *General Solution* |
|---|---|---|
| | 4 | $x$ |
| Multiply by 2 (4 × 2) | 8 | $2x$ |
| Add 10 (8 + 10) | 18 | $2x + 10$ |
| Divide by 2 (18 ÷ 2) | 9 | $x + 5$ |
| Subtract original number (9 − 4) | 5 | $x + 1$ |

4. Write your house number, double it, add 5, multiply by 50, add your age, subtract the number of days in a year, add 115, and point the result off into dollars and cents. The number of dollars is your house number; the number of cents is your age.
5. Choose any two numbers. Find $\frac{1}{2}$ their sum and $\frac{1}{2}$ their difference, and add these two numbers. The answer is always the larger of the original numbers.[7]

## 8. Games for Practice in Mental Arithmetic

1. *Number Bingo.* Use cards containing combinations for all four fundamental processes. Make bingo cards that have answers to the combinations; use separate cards for each of the processes. The leader calls out a combination, e.g., $3 \times 4$, and the pupils cover the answer, 12. The pupil with the first completed row of answers makes a score. This can be used as an individual or group game.
2. *Fishing.* Use fish-shaped oak-tag cards, each with two paper clips (to attract the magnet) and a short pole with a string and a magnet attached to the end of the string. Write number combinations on one side of the cards and scatter them in a "pool" on the floor, with the number side down. If a pupil knows the answer to the combination on the fish he catches, he keeps the card; if not, he hands the pole on to the next pupil. If he knows the answers, he may continue fishing until he has 5 fish; but then he must pass the pole on. The number of fish each child has may be the score, or the cards may have numbers on them that are added for scores; this depends on the ability of the group.
3. *Telephone Game.* The teacher or leader holds one toy telephone, another one is located so that individual pupils, when called on, can use it. The teacher calls a pupil on the telephone, then says, "Hello, I am calling 9 take away 5;" depending on the group's ability, he may or may not hold up a flash card, showing the combination. The child at the other phone says, "Hello, this is 4." The teacher says, "Thank you," or if the answer is incorrect he says "I'm sorry, I have the wrong number," and calls someone else to the phone.

[7] For other material of this type, see David Sullivan, "Magic Number," *The Instructor*, June, 1948, p. 31; Ethel Hulslander, "Magic Number," *The Instructor*, October, 1948, p. 56; for Roman puzzle problems, see Harold D. Larsen, *Arithmetic for Colleges*, Macmillan, New York, rev. ed., 1954, p. 11.

4. *Buzz.* There are many ways to adapt this old game. As you count, have the class say "*Buzz,*" or any other agreed-upon word, at every multiple of 3, or 5, or 7, or 11, etc., depending upon the ability of the group.

## COMPETENCE CHECK

1. Make any four of the easily made aids described in the Appendix, for any grade level you choose and tell which grade you chose.
2. Construct an aid that is not described in the Appendix; use the same grade level.
3. Write a lesson plan that includes use of at least one special aid or device described in this chapter. Use the following as a lesson plan outline:
   I. General aims
   II. Specific aims
   III. Materials
   IV. Procedure
   V. Evaluation
4. Cite psychological justification for using arithmetic games in the classroom.

## OPTIONAL ASSIGNMENTS

1. Using the references at the end of this chapter and any others you choose, make a resource file for use with primary, intermediate, or upper grades (according to your own interest) that will enable you to find exactly what you want when you want it. Have the file include sections on (1) films and filmstrips; (2) pictures, diagrams, graphs, and the like, for use on the bulletin board or with the opaque projector; (3) puzzles and tricks with numbers; (4) catchy problems; (5) games for small groups; (6) games for large groups; and (7) others you wish to include.
2. Make an index for your file.
3. With either Grossnickle or Brueckner and Grossnickle as a guide, evaluate the illustrations in some elementary arithmetic textbooks; add items you choose yourself.

## REFERENCES

Brueckner, L. J., and Grossnickle, Foster E. *How to Make Arithmetic Meaningful*, Holt, Rinehart & Winston, New York, 1947, chap. 23.

Dumas, Enoch, *Arithmetic Games*, Fearon, San Francisco, 1956.

Gregory, M. Cattell, "A Mathematics Exhibit," *Mathematics Teacher*, October, 1930, pp. 382–384.

Grossnickle, Foster E., "Illustrations in Arithmetic Textbooks," *Elementary School Journal*, October, 1946, pp. 84–92.
Larsen, Harold D., *Enrichment Program for Arithmetic*, Row, Peterson, Evanston, 1956. (Eight booklets for Grades 3 through 6.)
Marks, John L., Purdy, C. Richard, and Kinney, Lucien B., *Teaching Arithmetic for Understanding*, McGraw-Hill, New York, 1958, pp. 411–418.
National Council of Teachers of Mathematics, *Multisensory Aids in the Teaching of Mathematics, Eighteenth Yearbook*, 1945.
Spitzer, Herbert F., *Practical Classroom Procedures for Enriching Arithmetic*, Webster, St. Louis, 1956.
Stone, John C. *The Teaching of Arithmetic*, L. W. Singer, Syracuse, 1922, pp. 70–94.
Willerding, Margaret F., "Review of the Fundamental Processes—the Cross-Number Puzzle," *School Science and Mathematics*, January, 1954, pp. 51–52.
*The Instructor*, Visual Aids Supplement with each January issue.

## SOURCES OF GENERAL ARITHMETIC TEACHING AIDS

Beckley-Cardy Company, Chicago, Ill.
Milton Bradley Company, Springfield 2, Mass.
Bremner Multiplication Records, Dept. K-23, Wilmette, Ill.
Creative Playthings, Inc., 316 North Michigan Ave., Chicago 1, Ill.
Cuisenaire Company of America, Inc., 235 East 50th St., New York 22, N.Y.
The Garrard Press, 510 North Hickory St., Champaign, Ill.
Holt, Rinehart & Winston, 383 Madison Ave., New York 17, N.Y.
Ideal School Supply Company, 8324 South Birkhoff Avenue, Chicago 20, Ill.
The Judy Company, 310 North Second Street, Minneapolis 1, Minn.
F. A. Owen Publishing Company, Dansville, N.Y.
The Strathmore Company, Dept. 197, Aurora, Ill.
J. Weston Walch, Box 1075, Portland, Maine.

## SOURCES OF PROJECTION MATERIALS

Bailey Films, 6509 De Longpre Ave., Hollywood 28, Calif.
Charles Beseler Co., 217 South 18th St., East Orange, N.J. (Vu-Lyte opaque projector.)
Coronet Films, 65 East South Water St., Chicago 1, Ill.
Curriculum Films, Curriculum Materials Corporation, 17 East 48th St., New York 16, N.Y.
Dukane Corporation, St. Charles, Ill.
Encyclopædia Britannica Films, 1150 Wilmette Ave., Wilmette, Ill.

The Educational Film Guide, H. W. Wilson Company, 950 University Ave., New York 52, N.Y.
Eye Gate House, Inc., 2716, 41st Avenue, Long Island City 1, N.Y.
The Filmstrip House, 347 Madison Ave., New York 17, N.Y.
Jam Handy Organization, 2821 East Grand Blvd., Detroit 11, Mich.
Johnson-Hunt Productions, 6509 De Longpre Ave., Hollywood 28, Calif.
Knowledge Builders, Visual Education Building, Floral Park, N.Y.
Popular Science Film Strips, McGraw-Hill Book Company, 330 West 42nd St., New York 36, N.Y.
Society for Visual Education, Inc., 1345 West Diversey Parkway, Chicago 14, Ill.
University of Illinois, Division of Extension, Visual Aids Service, Champaign, Ill.
Visual Education Consultants, Inc., 2066 Helena St., Madison 4, Wis.
Young America Films, McGraw-Hill Book Company, 330 West 42nd St., New York 36, N.Y.

chapter 25

# Evaluation of Arithmetic Learning

## I. Four Steps Involved in Teaching

Four steps are involved in teaching on any level, if we include the formulation of a philosophy in preparation for the three steps mentioned in Chapter 6: (1) formulating a philosophy of basic principles and ideas in a given subject area; (2) setting up objectives in harmony with that philosophy; (3) providing for suitable activities and procedures for attaining these objectives; and (4) evaluating accomplishment to obtain knowledge of progress toward the objectives. These four steps are closely interrelated.

Objectives should not be haphazard, incidental, or short range; they should be an organized part of the over-all pattern for a certain grade level, which in turn fits the purposes of teaching elementary arithmetic. If the objectives are well-planned, a year's work in arithmetic acquires a wholeness and a relatedness which contribute to understanding and to learning.

Some educators, leaning perilously in the direction of progressivism, maintain that definite goals circumscribe teaching and learning activities and put all the emphasis on the end product, giving little or none to the process; to them, the process is more important than the product. However, others—the present writer among them—maintain that working toward definite outcomes serves as a necessary guide in planning teaching, particularly teaching a sequentially organized subject like arithmetic, and that well-planned procedures make the process highly important. Neither the process nor the product should be considered unimportant in the teaching of arithmetic; both need emphasis.

## 2. Need for Expansion in the Four Steps in Teaching

As was said in Chapter 6, in the past too many teaching plans employed these four steps in a very limited way. The underlying philosophy emphasized chiefly the computational aspects of arithmetic; there was one main objective, rapid and accurate computation; one procedure, drill; and one evaluation technique, testing for speed and accuracy, but including incidental work with problems for its contribution to skill in computing.

Modern arithmetic teaching has come a long way in expanding this philosophy. The present use of several additional types of objectives, mentioned in Chapter 6, in turn calls for greatly expanded procedural techniques and for a corresponding expansion of evaluation procedures.

Schools today have, in general, expanded their procedural techniques and in this respect have more or less kept pace with new objectives. However, in the opinion of many arithmetic authorities,[1] evaluation techniques have not kept abreast of the new objectives and procedures. It is chiefly to this need that the remainder of this chapter is devoted.

## 3. Development and Use of Standardized Tests

The earliest commercially produced tests in arithmetic were problem scales devised by Stone in 1908, and by 1913 some Standard Research Tests had been compiled by Courtis. From then on, standard arithmetic tests developed rapidly.

A **standardized test** is one for which norms have been established; a **norm** is the average performance attained by a given group taking a test. Norms are sometimes set up in terms of grade in school, and sometimes as percentile rank. In order to establish reliable norms, a

[1] Herbert F. Spitzer, "Techniques for Evaluating Outcomes of Instruction in Arithmetic," *Elementary School Journal*, September, 1948, pp. 21–31; Maurice L. Hartung, "A Forward Look at Evaluation," *Mathematics Teacher*, January, 1949, pp. 29–33; Calhoun C. Collier, *The Development of a Noncomputational Mathematics Test for Grades 5 and 6*, Doctoral Dissertation, Ohio State University, Columbus, 1956; R. L. Morton, "What Research Says About Teaching Arithmetic," *Journal of the National Education Association*, January, 1954, p. 20; David Rappaport, "Testing for Meanings in Arithmetic," *Arithmetic Teacher*, April, 1959, pp. 140–143.

test must be given to a large population, usually several thousand. Hence if a test is given to three or four thousand children in the fifth and sixth grades, and the fifth-grade pupils have an average score of 168, this sets the fifth-grade norm. Thereafter pupils who take the test and make a score of 168 are said to be at the fifth-grade level in arithmetic. Many tests are scaled to averages for the month in the grade; thus end of first month in fifth grade (5.1), end of second month (5.2), and so on.

In establishing percentile norms, the scores of all the population taking the test, perhaps 3000 fifth-grade pupils, are arranged in rank order and organized in percentiles by means of a statistical procedure. In this scheme a 99th percentile rank indicates that the pupils whose scores are in that group did as well as or better than 99% of the 3000 who took the test. A 25th percentile rank indicates a score as good as or better than that made by 25% of the 3000.

Standardized tests are prepared by experts who scientifically weed out worthless questions and determine the reliability and validity of the test as a part of preparing it. A test is **reliable** if it consistently measures what it *does* measure; this means that if pupils took the test a second time, their rank order on the basis of scores would be the same as it was the first time.

A test is **valid** if it measures what it is intended to measure. Suppose that a test claims to measure ability to compute with decimals. If a pupil whose class performance indicates that he understands decimals and can compute with them easily, makes a score on the test that ranks him about where his class grades do, the test is said to have **statistical validity.** Standardized tests should also have **curricular validity.** As we shall see later, this is too often not considered when standardized tests are used.

Standardized tests have certain definite uses and purposes. Most of them are of the survey type. They may be used as the basis for remedial work in areas where certain pupils are weak, or as a basis for grouping pupils for instruction. A few specially designed diagnostic, and readiness tests in arithmetic are on the market, but neither is extensively used.

Standardized tests may also provide a basis of comparison, and indicate progress. If a test is given to fourth-grade pupils one year, and an alternate test form is given the same pupils a year later, the group may show less than a year's progress, or more than a year's progress.

Thus the relative progress of the pupils as well as their relative ability can be measured.

But these tests have some disadvantages. Unfortunately, the relative progress indicated by the tests may reflect unfairly on teachers. In comparing two fourth-grade classes as far as progress is concerned, the many factors that may influence the results should not be overlooked; for example, the groups may not be equal in learning ability, though both have had the same curriculum and materials.

Administrators are sometimes disturbed by the showing certain classes make on standardized arithmetic tests. Some criticize the teacher for not having taught arithmetic well; others insist on more time being spent on the subject. But probably only a few investigate the curricular validity of the test. This can be done only by comparing the test, item by item, with the arithmetic curriculum for that grade. All standardized tests are based on national norms. The fifth-grade arithmetic curriculum for the children in Maine, Georgia, or New Mexico, for example, on whom the test was standardized, may differ considerably from the curriculum in South Dakota; as a result, the South Dakota scores may be lowered because these pupils have had no work on some of the material covered by the test.

Hickerson points out what he, and probably many others, consider another undesirable characteristic of standardized tests.[2] This is the fact that both the test makers and teachers know that some parts of the test are beyond the ability of everyone in the group. Pupils are usually told not to worry if they cannot do all the problems because they are not expected to do so. Even when people are experienced in taking these tests, such a statement introduces an element of uncertainty about how they are doing, and may easily induce psychological anxiety, which is no doubt more disturbing to some pupils than to others.

Another deficiency of standardized tests that must not be overlooked is their inadequate coverage of certain desirable outcomes that should be evaluated. They test mainly speed and accuracy of computation, problem-solving ability, to a limited degree, and occasionally some vocabulary comprehension.

Standardized tests then must be used with understanding and discrimination. Furthermore, they should be selected only after the teacher has studied their characteristics, curricular content, and specific

[2] J. Allen Hickerson, *Guiding Children's Arithmetic Experiences*, Prentice-Hall, New York, 1952, p. 41.

uses, always keeping in mind the purposes they are to serve. The *Mental Measurements Yearbooks*,[3] usually available in college libraries, describe such tests well, as do also test catalogues such as those listed at the end of this chapter.

## 4. Tests Published with Textbooks

Many of the modern arithmetic textbook series are accompanied by published tests. These are generally designed as survey tests to be used at the beginning of the year, or in some cases at the beginning or end of a unit or chapter. To some extent, they are diagnostic in purpose, in that weakness in certain types of work previously covered can be discovered. And by the same token they are readiness tests that help determine whether pupils are prepared to undertake the new work. Many of these tests have a broader scope of evaluative techniques than standardized tests have. Of necessity standardized tests must be completely objective; that is, the questions must have one and only one correct answer. Many of the textbook tests have some subjective questions whose grading requires the teacher's judgment, such as: "Make a diagram to show how many $\frac{1}{8}$ inches there are in $\frac{3}{4}$ inch."

## 5. Teacher-Made Tests

Although these various types of published tests are available, most of the tests given to elementary pupils are made by their teachers; these are frequently referred to as **informal tests.**

Essay-type tests—that is, tests with subjective questions—fell into disrepute about 1930, when research studies indicated apparently grossly erratic judgment on the part of the teacher in marking this type of test. Objective questions were held to be the only fair solution to the question of judgment in marking tests. This movement, however, had little effect on arithmetic testing, for up to that time it had been mainly objective since accuracy was practically the sole basis for evaluating computation, and correctness of answer the only criterion for evaluating problem-solving. This was true of teacher-made tests as well as of standardized tests and those accompanying textbooks.

[3] O. K. Buros (ed.), *Fifth Mental Measurements Yearbook*, 1959. Also consult earlier editions.

Although there are more than a few weaknesses in the average teacher-made tests, these tests are more likely to have curricular validity than are the other types.

## 6. Need for New Evaluation Techniques

As has been said, the expansion of outcomes sought in the teaching of arithmetic has made necessary a change in procedures. And if the extent to which these outcomes are attained is to be evaluated effectively, new techniques of evaluation are also needed.

Up to the present, the development of these new techniques has barely begun. The task is not easy. Skill is necessary to formulate questions that test such learnings as (1) the social applications of arithmetic; (2) its rationale, involving meanings and understandings; (3) its contributions to the higher mental processes (analysis, discrimination, comparison, etc.); (4) the ability to estimate and to use approximations; and (5) the ability to generalize and to apply generalizations. All of these are considered desired outcomes in arithmetic teaching today.

As a matter of fact, objective paper-and-pencil tests, for so long the only method of testing, cannot be used to test some of the outcomes now sought in teaching arithmetic. Such tests must be supplemented by subjective questions and by the teacher's observations.

Though it was long assumed that testing for learning in any area should be done at the end of a given learning period, the term "evaluation" today implies the continuous use of all the means of gathering evidence of pupil learning. It accompanies the learning experiences themselves and involves much more than paper-and-pencil testing. Some of it depends on the teacher's observation and judgment, as for example:

1. Listening to a pupil "think out loud" as he does an example or problem.
2. Noting attitudes and interests as shown by pupils' news reports, the aids they make, etc.
3. Noting significant creative tendencies and abilities in quantitative situations.
4. Noting pupils' ingenuity in discovering alternate processes, short cuts, number relationships, generalizations, etc.
5. Noting their ability to rationalize the reasonableness of an answer.

6. Noting a pupil's ability to explain his own and other pupils' solutions.
7. Noting his ability to detect errors in his own and other pupils' solutions.

Obviously a teacher who has from 25 to 40 pupils cannot keep in mind each individual's progress in this many types of learning. Having a folder for each pupil aids in collecting evaluatory data during the year, such as samples of work at various intervals, check lists and anecdotal records indicating abilities and needs, and test results. Such data give a much truer evaluation of pupils' abilities and accomplishments in arithmetic than a "final" paper-and-pencil test given the class at the end of the year. Work for the teacher? Yes, plenty of it. Satisfaction for the teacher, the pupil, and his parents? Yes, again. Instead of a rather vague report that John seems to have trouble with arithmetic, such data make possible a more definite report: "This is where John has trouble in arithmetic."

## 7. Improving Teacher-Made Tests

Though a number of evaluation procedures other than paper-and-pencil tests were suggested in the preceding section, that test will continue to be a valuable instrument of appraisal, provided it is revised to fit more of the newer types of objectives. This revision requires test-making skill, but interested and competent teachers can readily acquire that skill if they make a conscious effort to do so.

A college course in tests and measurements will give teachers substantial help regarding types of questions to include, their effective wording, and the specific purposes for which each type is best suited. However, teachers will find texts on measurement[4] valuable, as well as the many illustrations in the references at the end of this chapter.

A limited number of illustrative questions are presented here. They are organized on the basis of their purpose, not grade level. Most of the purposes included here can be used as expanding concepts from the

[4] H. H. Remmers and N. L. Gage, *Educational Measurement and Evaluation*, Harper, New York, rev. ed., 1955; C. C. Ross and Julian C. Stanley, *Measurement in Today's Schools*, Prentice-Hall, Englewood Cliffs, 3rd ed., 1954; James M. Bradfield and H. Steward Moredock, *Measurement and Evaluation in Education*, Macmillan, New York, 1957.

first grade up. The questions vary markedly in level of difficulty; for example, 1b is on the first-grade level, 1a, c, and d on the intermediate-grade level.

ILLUSTRATIVE TEST QUESTIONS

1. Comprehension of meaning of numbers:
   a. Match the equivalent fractions

| | |
|---|---|
| _____ $\frac{1}{4}$ | (a) $\frac{3}{12}$ |
| _____ $\frac{2}{3}$ | (b) $\frac{8}{10}$ |
| _____ $\frac{5}{8}$ | (c) $\frac{15}{24}$ |
| _____ $\frac{4}{5}$ | (d) $\frac{3}{4}$ |
| _____ $\frac{6}{8}$ | (e) $\frac{4}{6}$ |

   b. Put a mark on the fifth ball. O O O O O
   c. Explain the value of each digit in 26,420.
   d. (Underline the words that make the sentence correct.) One trillion is (larger than; smaller than) one billion.
2. Comprehension of social uses of number:
   a. (Fill in blanks with words that make the sentence correct.) Father drove into a gas station and asked for 10 __________ of gas and 1 __________ of oil.
   b. (Underline the figure that makes the sentence correct.) If I borrow money at the bank, I am most likely to pay interest at the rate of (1%; 5%; 25%; 80%).
   c. Write a verbal problem that will call for this computation: 20 × 36 inches.
3. Computational ability:
   a. $49\overline{)32146}$ b. $4\frac{2}{3} \times \frac{7}{8} \div 1\frac{8}{9} = ?$
4. Comprehension of vocabulary and meanings:
   a. (Match the descriptive words with the numbers that illustrate them.)

| | |
|---|---|
| _____ $2\frac{1}{4}$ | (a) denominate number |
| _____ 16 | (b) prime number |
| _____ 6 miles | (c) improper fraction |
| _____ $\frac{21}{4}$ | (d) mixed number |
| _____ 13 | (e) multiple of 4 |

b. Which group of fractions has a common denominator? _____

(a) $\frac{1}{2}, \frac{1}{3}, \frac{1}{6}, \frac{1}{8}$

(b) $\frac{2}{5}, \frac{1}{5}, \frac{4}{5}, \frac{3}{5}$

(c) $\frac{2}{3}, \frac{1}{2}, \frac{2}{5}, \frac{2}{2}$

c. Match the letters indicating a figure or part of a figure with each term at the left:

_____ circumference
_____ radius
_____ altitude
_____ right angle
_____ base

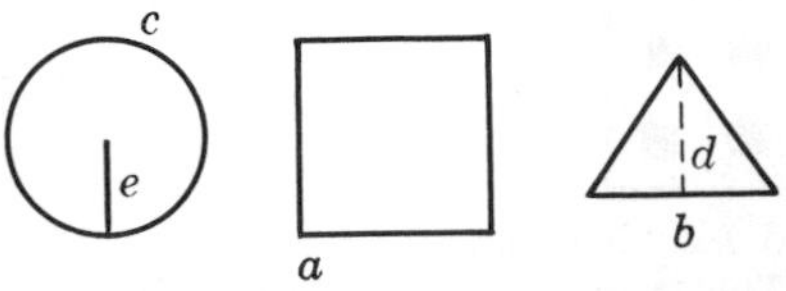

c e a d b

5. Comprehension of principles or generalizations:

a. Which of the following examples are in a form that can be added? Show by adding them.

(a) $\frac{1}{8}$ $\frac{3}{8}$ $+\frac{6}{8}$

(b) $2\frac{1}{4}$ $+4\frac{4}{5}$

(c) 2. bu. +6 pk.

(d) 4 sq. in. +1 in.

b. (Write in the blank the word or words that make each statement correct.)

(a) If both terms of a fraction are multiplied by the same number, the resulting fraction is (larger than; smaller than; of the same value as) the original fraction. ________

(b) If the same number is added to both terms of a fraction, the resulting fraction is (the same as; not the same as) the original one in value. ________

6. Knowledge of essential mathematical information:

a. (Fill in the blanks with the correct number.)

(a) 1 yard = _____ inches
(b) 1 pound = _____ ounces
(c) 1 square foot = _____ square inches

b. Write the formula for finding the area of a triangle.

c. If Betty saves a dime a day, how much will she save in a year?

7. Ability to apply rationalization:

a. Using the figures (.6; 6.) for illustration, explain why moving the decimal point one place to the right multiplies a number by 10.

b. Explain why multiplying a number by $\frac{1}{3}$ gives the same answer as dividing it by 3.

8. Ability to analyze a problem situation:
   a. A box is 3 in. wide and 4 in. long and contains 36 cu. in. What is its height? Make a diagram and explain your solution.
   b. What is the *next step* in solving the following problem? A tank 6 ft. long, 3 ft. 8 in. wide, and 2 ft. 6 in. deep will hold how many gallons of water? (1 cu. ft. holds $7\frac{1}{2}$ gal.) Its dimensions are found to be 6 ft. by $3\frac{2}{3}$ ft. by $2\frac{1}{2}$ ft.
9. Ability to transfer comprehension from a concrete object concept to a visual image concept, to a graphic representation:
   a. The teacher holds up a card with four large black dots, like this:

, shows it for a moment, covers it, and asks the pupils to draw what they saw.
   b. The teacher holds up an outline picture of a cube or a rectangular solid, hides it, and asks the pupils to draw what they saw.
10. Ability to visualize a problem situation without concrete aids:
   a. We have two balls, one of them 22 in. in circumference, and the other 42 in. How many revolutions will each of them make in rolling a distance of 10 ft?
   b. I have 24 cents to spend for 4-cent candy-bars. To solve this problem I would ____ add; ____ subtract; ____ multiply; ____ divide.
11. Ability to grasp the essentials of a problem situation and to discover either necessary information that is lacking, or irrelevant data that are included:
   a. Indicate in the blanks after each problem any necessary information that is not given, or any figures that are not needed for solving the problem.
      (a) During vacation Jim earned $60 a month. He used 8% of it for recreation, 75% of it for clothes, and spent some for snacks, lunches, and other incidentals. The rest he saved. What per cent of his earnings did he save?
      Figures not needed ____________
      Figures needed but not given ____________
      (b) Four boys decided to pool some of their vacation earnings and buy some basketball equipment. Brian had earned $16, John $21, Mike $19, and Bill $23. They found the equipment they wanted cost $36. If they shared the cost equally, how much did each one put in?
      Figures not needed ____________
      Figures needed but not given ____________

A series of questions such as the above cannot be all-inclusive, but it indicates the types of outcomes desired and appropriate questions for evaluating them. Such questions should be supplemented by tests of mental computation, like the following: At $4.85 each, the 6 pieces of wallboard we want would cost about ($12.50; $18.75; $30.00; $36.50).___________

## 8. Testing and Learning Complementary

Pupils should be helped to understand the purpose of tests; they should become interested in evaluating their own progress. Research has shown that, when rightly used, testing can be a valuable learning experience. For example, (1) when teachers grade tests and hand them back to the pupils without any discussion of errors, a later test usually indicates that the pupils have gained little from their errors the first time; in other words, the testing procedure did not motivate them to learn what they did not know. (2) When, as he gives back the papers, the teacher discusses with each pupil the errors he made, and the pupil corrects them, more progress in learning will occur than in the first case. (3) The degree of learning is greatest when pupils, with teacher supervision, evaluate their own answers. Here the teacher has an opportunity to observe the pupil's working procedures and help him discover a better attack on the problem, or a more direct solution, and also to help him see he is being handicapped by not knowing certain mathematical facts.

Obviously, this last test procedure is time-consuming. However, probably no time is lost in the long run because the procedure has a remedial purpose, the pupil responds to sympathetic assistance, and there will be less need for repetition of explanation and practice later.

Testing can provide excellent motivation, not of the threatening negative type—"You'd better learn this now because we're going to have a test and you don't want to flunk it, do you?"—but rather of the type described above in which a pupil sees what he had wrong and why it was wrong so that the next time he meets a situation like it he will recognize it.

Pupils should realize that the purpose of testing is learning; that they do not learn for the purpose of passing tests. Both teachers and pupils should be interested in measurement in terms of its contributions to learning, which will be made if tests are planned to complement learning. However, there is no point in writing tests that evaluate the broader outcomes in arithmetic, like those in the preceding section, unless pupils have the same type of experiences in their daily classwork in arithmetic.

The teacher should be careful to see that the classwork problems are not stereotyped—always stated in the same way—with the same wording used again on tests. Part of a pupil's learning results from his knowing more than one way of stating an example or problem. Thus "How many pints in 2 quarts?" may appear another time as "How many pint-jars will be needed to hold as much as 2 quart-jars hold?" So also, $\begin{array}{r} 2649 \\ \times 42 \\ \hline \end{array}$ may appear as $42 \times 2649 = ?$ another time.

Teacher-made tests also give pupils an opportunity to apply what they are being taught in their classwork—for example, estimating the reasonableness of an answer—for which standardized tests provide little opportunity. Most teacher-made tests are mastery tests. A pupil knows he should be able to do everything in the test and he expects to have time to finish it. This may not be true of practice exercises in computing.

### 9. Effective Evaluation the Culmination of Effective Teaching

Evaluation of necessity follows teaching. If a good evaluation program is set up, a criticism that was often true in the past—that there is more testing than teaching in some schools—will no longer be valid.

Teachers who are interested in improving evaluation techniques will find many ways to do so. They can learn how to make tests that complement and motivate learning and give an adequate picture of pupil accomplishment, yet do not cause their pupils periodic fear and anxiety, or require excessive time and energy on the part of the teacher in scoring.

The fact remains, however, that there is no substitute for a day-by-day high teaching level in the classroom.

## COMPETENCE CHECK

**1.** Write a summarizing paragraph of this chapter that tells how evaluation of arithmetic can be made more effective.

**2.** What four steps are involved in teaching on any level? How are they interrelated?

**3.** List the six types of objectives presented in Chapter 6.

**4.** List and explain four characteristics of standardized tests.

**5.** 1. What useful purposes can standardized tests serve?
   2. Name some of the ways they are improperly used.

**6.** Describe the table of norms for one of the standard tests.

7. Why are teacher-made tests more likely to have curricular validity than standardized tests?
8. 1. Write an objective-type question for an arithmetic test.
   2. Write a subjective type of question.
   3. Does a problem always involve an objective question? A subjective question? May it be either? Explain your answer.
9. Do you favor giving some credit for a test problem when the right procedure was used but the answer is wrong? Why or why not?
10. List several of the evaluation techniques discussed in this chapter, in addition to paper-and-pencil tests.
11. Write an additional question for each of the eleven Illustrative Test Questions in this chapter.

## OPTIONAL ASSIGNMENTS

1. Report on Mason's "Take-Home Tests." What is your reaction to the plan?
2. Report on your reaction to Brueckner's "Evaluation in Arithmetic."
3. Name four standardized arithmetic tests that you think would be good. Discuss their merits and tell where they can be purchased.
4. Examine an up-to-date elementary arithmetic textbook series and describe how it provides for evaluating learning.
5. Using a textbook for any grade level you choose (indicate text and grade), make what you consider a good paper-and-pencil test that covers the year's work.

## REFERENCES

Brueckner, L. J., "Evaluation in Arithmetic," *Education*, January, 1959, pp. 291–294.

Mason, H. L., " 'Take-Home Tests' for the Eighth Grade Arithmetic Class," *Mathematics Teacher*, March, 1954, pp. 213–214.

Spitzer, Herbert F., "Testing Instruments and Practices in Relation to Present Concepts of Teaching Arithmetic," National Society for the Study of Education, *Fiftieth Yearbook*, 1951.

Sueltz, Ben A., "The Measurement of Understanding and Judgments in Elementary School Mathematics," *Mathematics Teacher*, October, 1947, p. 279.

## TEST CATALOGUES

The following publishers are representative of the many from whom test catalogues may be secured:

California Test Bureau, 5916 Hollywood Boulevard, Los Angeles, Calif.

Educational Test Bureau, 720 Washington Ave. S.E., Minneapolis, Minn.
Educational Testing Service, 20 Nassau St. Princeton, N.J.
Harcourt, Brace & World, Inc., 750 Third Ave., New York, 17, N.Y.
Houghton Mifflin Company, 2 Park St., Boston, 7, Mass.
Public School Publishing Company, 509–513 Northeast St., Bloomington, Ill.
Science Research Associates, 259 East Erie St., Chicago 11, Ill.

# *part* TWO

## REVIEW OF COMPUTATION AND APPLICATION OF ARITHMETIC PROCESSES

section **A**

# Computation

## Set I. Addition and Subtraction of All Forms of Numbers

1. a. $\begin{array}{r} 9509 \\ 638 \\ 2084 \\ 7251 \\ 76 \\ +2145 \\ \hline \end{array}$ b. $\begin{array}{r} 8756 \\ 429 \\ 1002 \\ 79 \\ 9045 \\ +\ 124 \\ \hline \end{array}$ c. $\begin{array}{r} 109{,}200 \\ -\ 13{,}762 \\ \hline \end{array}$ d. $\begin{array}{r} 70{,}000 \\ -45{,}682 \\ \hline \end{array}$

2. Subtract 60,401 from 492,742.

3. $\begin{array}{r} 4\frac{7}{12} \\ 3\frac{1}{6} \\ \frac{1}{2} \\ 8\frac{7}{8} \\ +2\frac{2}{3} \\ \hline \end{array}$

4. a. $\begin{array}{r} 36\frac{1}{4} \\ -29\frac{5}{6} \\ \hline \end{array}$ b. $\begin{array}{r} 28 \\ -13\frac{9}{16} \\ \hline \end{array}$ c. $\begin{array}{r} 100\frac{1}{3} \\ -\ 50\frac{5}{8} \\ \hline \end{array}$

5. Place in column form and add: 12.165 + 3.5 + 6.04 + 9 + .5.

6. Subtract 7.035 from 10.7.

7. What must be added to $4\frac{7}{8}$ to make $6\frac{3}{4}$?

8. Change to similar decimals and add: 2.05; 316.001; 4.2061; 3.000125; .6.

9. a. $67\frac{1}{4} + 8\frac{7}{9} = ?$

b. $178\frac{4}{5} - ? = 65\frac{2}{3}$

c. $? + 172\frac{19}{20} = 200$

10. a. $50.701 - 2.004 = ?$
b. $927.65 + ? = 1000.35$
c. $? - 41.0809 = 16.203$

11. Add and check by casting out 9's:

| a. | b. | c. |
|---|---|---|
| 3449 | 6592 | 2348 |
| 1265 | 4359 | 2165 |
| 8749 | 1259 | 6148 |
| 5840 | 2007 | 9803 |
| 3750 | 5483 | 6217 |
| 4289 | 2817 | 1438 |
| 2109 | 1427 | 1836 |
| +2001 | +9030 | +5190 |

## Set 2. Multiplication of All Forms of Numbers, Including Cancellation and Equations

1. $\begin{array}{r} 8795 \\ \times\ 678 \\ \hline \end{array}$

2. $11\frac{2}{3} \times 13\frac{4}{5}$

3. a. $102.90 \times .0675$ b. $132.00625 \times 9.1$

4. What short cut can be used to multiply each of the following:

a. $872 \times .25$
b. $423 \times .33\frac{1}{3}$
c. $6.512 \times 10{,}000$
d. $48 \times .5$
e. $1280 \times 1.25$
f. $99 \times 29$
g. $66\frac{2}{3} \times 4500$

5. $\frac{3}{4} \div \frac{7}{8} \times \frac{4}{5} \times 3\frac{1}{2} \div 6$

6. Find the product and check by casting out 9's: $3471 \times 149$.

7. Which of these multiplication and addition associations will never occur in multiplying by the underlined multiplier?

a. $\underline{2} \times 8 + 6$
b. $\underline{3} \times 9 + 5$
c. $\underline{6} \times 2 + 9$
d. $\underline{4} \times 2 + 1$
e. $\underline{9} \times 1 + 8$
f. $\underline{3} \times 1 + 7$

8. $\dfrac{25 \times 14 \times 72 \times 120}{15 \times 6 \times 9 \times 10}$

9. Divide $4 \times 7 \times 21 \times 15$ by $3 \times 8 \times 42 \times 6$.

10. 47 is 3 times what number?

11. a. $3000 \times .000\frac{1}{3}$

b. $2.75 \times 3.1416$

c. $4.56 \times .00\frac{1}{2}$

## Set 3. Division and Ratio

1. $16\frac{1}{2} \div 5\frac{7}{8}$
2. $247.566 \div 3.41$
3. $120 \div .625$
4. $8\frac{4}{5} \div 16$
5. $.54 \div 45$
6. $247{,}566 \div 341$
7. In $3\overline{)296}$ with quotient $98\frac{2}{3}$, 3 is called the __________ ; $98\frac{2}{3}$ is the __________ ; and 296 is the __________ .
8. a. $\frac{8}{20} = \frac{?}{15}$ b. $\frac{?}{16} = \frac{15}{60}$
9. Is $3 : 17 = 9 : 45$ a true proportion? Why or why not?
10. $6 : 21 = 4 : ?$
11. $2\frac{1}{4} : 9 = ? : 16$
12. $4 : \frac{1}{4} = 24 : ?$
13. Express the ratio 1 to 5 as a per cent.
14. $225 \div 25 = 72 \div ?$
15. $\frac{2 \times 5}{3 \times 10} = \frac{4}{6 \times ?}$
16. $8\frac{2}{5} \div 2\frac{4}{5} = 42 \div ?$
17. Divide and check by casting out nines: $279\overline{)36{,}042}$.
18. What multiple of the divisor must be recalled for each number in the columns when the respective divisors are used?

| 6 | 5 | 8 |
|---|---|---|
| 28 | 41 | 38 |
| 17 | 16 | 97 |
| 57 | 39 | 59 |
| 32 | 23 | 73 |

19. Divide and check both, by two methods:

a. $4.5 \overline{)16{,}004}$ b. $270 \overline{)219{,}672}$

20. Supply the numbers needed to balance the following equations:

a. $6 \div 2 = 120 \div ?$
b. $.0042 \div 7 = 42 \div ?$
c. $2.26 \div .8 = ? \div 8$
d. $16.25 \div 2 = ? \div 200$
e. $7.2 \div 6 = 72 \div ?$

21. Divide each by 100 decimally:

a. 65 c. $\frac{4}{5}$ e. 42.67

b. 4.002 d. $5\frac{1}{8}$ f. 100.69

22. What is the ratio of $\frac{5}{8}$ to $\frac{4}{6}$?

23. What is the ratio of 9 hr. to 1 day?

24. What is the ratio of 1 gal. to 1 cu. ft.?

25. What is the ratio of .08 to .002?

26. What is the ratio of the circumference of a circle to its radius?

27. The ratio of $n$ to 6 is as 5 to 1. What is the numerical value of $n$?

28. The ratio of 12 to $n$ is $\frac{1}{2}$. What is the value of $n$?

29. $3 : ? = .01 : .001$

30. $? : \frac{1}{3} = \frac{3}{4} : 4$

## Set 4. Relating Common Fractions, Decimals, and Per Cents

1. Write each of the following as common fractions, decimals, and per cents:

a. $\frac{3}{4}$ f. $6\frac{1}{2}\%$ j. 2.50

b. $16\frac{2}{3}\%$ g. .0425 k. 4.5%

c. 1.32 h. $\frac{1}{7}$ l. $\frac{5}{6}$

d. .06 i. 250 m. .0025

e. $66\frac{2}{3}\%$

2. 43 is what per cent of 179?

3. $6\frac{1}{2}\%$ of what number $= 97\frac{1}{2}$?

4. What is $112\frac{1}{2}\%$ of 160?
5. $4\frac{1}{2}\%$ of $N$ = what decimal part of $N$?
6. .06 of $N$ = what per cent of $N$?
7. .0425 of $N$ = what per cent of $N$?
8. 150% of 72 = ?
9. What is $N$ if 83% of $N$ = \$146.08?
10. \$469 is 140% of what amount?
11. Express \$18.75 per \$1000 as mills per dollar.
12. If 1400 = 100% of a number, 112 is what per cent of it?
13. What is 100% of an amount of money if \$24.75 is $12\frac{1}{2}\%$ of it?
14. 475 is what per cent of 95?
15. 95 is what per cent of 475?
16. 1650 is 20% of what number?
17. 1.01 times a number equals what per cent of the number?
18. 3.3% of a number equals what decimal part of the number?
19. What is $137\frac{1}{2}\%$ of 270?
20. Write $6\frac{9}{3}$ in the best form for an answer.
21. Express each of the following indicated divisions as a fraction in lowest terms, a decimal, a per cent and a ratio:
    a. $18 \div 72$
    b. $14 \div 64$
    c. $32 \div 8$
    d. $15 \div 20$
22. Which is the greater in value, $\frac{5}{12}$ or $\frac{4}{7}$? Explain your answer.
23. A ribbon 6 ft. long can be cut into how many ties each $\frac{2}{3}$ ft. long?
24. Illustrate with drawings:
    a. $3 \div \frac{3}{8}$
    b. $12 \div 1\frac{1}{2}$
    c. $32 \div 12$
25. Simplify:
    a. $\dfrac{4\frac{7}{8}}{3\frac{1}{10}}$
    b. $\dfrac{2\frac{1}{2} \times \frac{3}{8}}{4\frac{1}{5} \div 2}$
    c. $\dfrac{66\frac{2}{3}}{1000}$
26. Change to thousandths (decimal form):
    a. $\frac{1}{16}$
    b. $\frac{16}{54}$
    c. $\frac{8}{9}$
    d. $\frac{16}{150}$

27. $\frac{7}{10}$ is $\frac{4}{5}$ of what number?

28. $\frac{1}{2}$ is what per cent of $\frac{2}{3}$?

29. Find the number of which 75 is .3%.

30. What number increased by $16\frac{2}{3}\%$ of itself is 28?

31. What number is 10% more than 70?

32. Find the number of which 81 is 300%.

33. Change each of the following to a common fraction in the lowest terms:

a. .1875 c. .0236 e. $.333\frac{1}{3}$

b. .000075 d. .003 f. $.006\frac{2}{3}$

### Set 5. Denominate Numbers

1. 6 ft. 5 in. + 5 ft. 6 in. + 1 ft. 2 in.
2. 3 hr. 15 min. + 4 hr. 25 min.
3. 5 lb. − 2 lb. 8 oz.
4. 10 yd. 4 in. − 8 yd. 7 in.
5. Multiply 2 gal. 1 qt. by 5.
6. Divide 9 hr. 24 min. by 4.
7. 6257 cu. in. = ______ cu. yd. ______ cu. ft. ______ cu. in.
8. 157 sq. in. = ______ sq. ft. ______ sq. in.
9. 640 acres = ______ sq. mi.
10. Divide 12 hr. 15 min. by 8.
11. Divide 7 lb. 10 oz. by 3.
12. Divide 6 hr. 45 min. by 2 hr. 30 min.
13. $4\frac{2}{3}$ yd. = ______ ft. or ______ in.
14. Add: 2 pk. 4 qt.; 1 pk. 6 qt.; and 2 pk. 1 qt.
15. 4 yd. 1 ft. 3 in. is how much short of 5 yd.?

### Set 6. Factors, Multiples, and Divisors

1. Find the prime factors of 126; 241; 165; 732; 110; 316.
2. Find the common factors of each group:

a. 21; 76; 42 b. 72; 65; 51 c. 12; 27; 39; 78

3. Find the lowest common denominator for each group of fractions:

   a. $\frac{1}{64}$; $\frac{7}{12}$; $\frac{1}{32}$

   b. $\frac{2}{15}$; $\frac{8}{9}$; $\frac{4}{55}$

   c. $\frac{1}{6}$; $\frac{7}{20}$; $\frac{11}{36}$

4. Find the least common multiple for each group:

   a. 16; 27; 49; 3
   b. 25; 4; 35; 7
   c. 124; 16; 72; 14

5. Find the greatest common divisor for each group:

   a. 16; 144; 36; 48
   b. 75; 60; 120; 90
   c. 96; 24; 18; 120

## Set 7. Roots and Powers

1. What is the square root of each of the following numbers: 81; 64; 49; 100; 400?

2. Find the square root of each to not more than one decimal place, and check each answer: 256; 1764; 1200.

3. Write these numbers as powers of 10, using negative exponents:

   a. .01
   b. .001
   c. .0001
   d. .000001
   e. .000000001

4. Write the following numbers with exponents to indicate powers of 10:

   a. 100
   b. 1,000,000
   c. 1000
   d. 1,000,000,000,000
   e. 100,000
   f. 10,000,000

5. Place after each 10 (used as multiplier) the proper exponent to make the equation correct:

   a. $425{,}000 = 4.25 \times 10$
   b. $80{,}000 = 8 \times 10$
   c. $281{,}000{,}000 = 2.81 \times 10$
   d. $45{,}000{,}000 = .45 \times 10$

6. Replace exponents with zeros, and multiply:

   a. $2.91 \times 10^4$
   b. $.65 \times 10^6$

7. Multiply, keeping the exponents:

   a. $6.72 \times 10^5$
   b. $1.465 \times 10^3$

8. a. $1.5 \times ? = 150$
   b. $1.5 \times ? = 1500$
   c. $1.5 \times ? = .0015$
9. What is the square root of each of the following numbers:

| a. 49 | b. 81 | c. 169 |
|---|---|---|
| 324 | 121 | 144 |
| 16 | 225 | 625 |

10. What is the square of each of the following:

| a. 18 | b. 100 | c. 40 |
|---|---|---|
| 12 | 50 | 72 |
| 6 | 21 | 1000 |

11. Find the square root of each of the following numbers by factoring:

| a. 1296 | b. 1521 |
|---|---|
| 900 | 5184 |
| 676 | 2500 |

12. Find the square root of each of the following:
    a. 41,616
    b. 625,000,000
    c. 7396
    d. 998,001
13. Find the square root of $\frac{49}{144}$; $\frac{16}{81}$; $\frac{400}{625}$.
14. Find the square root of each of the following to two decimal places:
    a. 264.0625
    b. 83.7225
15. Each of the digits in the number 642,126 has two values, intrinsic value and place value. Show what is meant.
16. Multiply the intrinsic value of each digit in 6,124,221 by its positional value and add them for the total value of the number.
17. Show what power of 10 each of the first 12 orders has.
18. Show what power of 12 each of the first 6 orders has in the duodecimal system.
19. How many units does 50,126 in the duodecimal system represent? Explain your answer.

### Set 8. Miscellaneous Processes

1. Which of the five estimates is nearest the correct answer when 59.245 is divided by .77: 740; 7400; 74; 7.4; .74?
2. Write the following numbers in words:
   a. 42,639,407,000,061
   b. 200,002,200,002,020
3. Write in figures:
   a. fifty trillion, sixteen million, four hundred twenty thousand, sixty-three.
   b. one septillion, sixteen quintillion, four hundred eighty quadrillion, three hundred.
   c. nine decillion, nine octillion, nine billion, nine.

**4.** Write in words:

a. 65.24009 b. 1000.0024 c. 50000.050

**5.** Write in decimal figures:

a. seventy-five and four thousand two hundred forty-one millionths.
b. eight thousand one and eight thousand one hundred-thousandths.

**6.** What is the reciprocal of $\frac{3}{8}$? Of 4? Of $2\frac{1}{2}$?

**7.** Solve the formula $V = \frac{1}{3}Bh$ for $h$.

**8.** In the number 269,142 how many thousands are there? How many ten thousands? How many hundred thousands?

**9.** In the number 42,214 how does the value of the 4 at the left compare with the 4 at the right?

## Set 9. Miscellaneous Mental Computations

**1.** Practice in adding by endings: To each number in the rows add 6, then 7, then 8, then 9:

| | | | | | | | |
|---|---|---|---|---|---|---|---|
| 5 | 15 | 35 | 85 | 65 | 45 | 95 | 75 |
| 16 | 86 | 26 | 76 | 56 | 96 | 46 | 66 |
| 7 | 27 | 87 | 67 | 17 | 47 | 57 | 37 |
| 28 | 98 | 68 | 38 | 88 | 58 | 78 | 48 |
| 9 | 59 | 29 | 89 | 69 | 29 | 49 | 99 |

**2.** Count by 2's to 100 beginning with 1 (1, 3, 5, etc.).

**3.** Count by 3's to 100.

**4.** Count by 4's to 100.

**5.** Count by 9's to 100.

**6.** Count down from 100 by 9's (100, 91, etc.).

**7.**

| | | | | | | |
|---|---|---|---|---|---|---|
| 33<br>+64 | 35<br>+61 | 37<br>+42 | 39<br>+50 | 32<br>+67 | 36<br>+43 | 34<br>+62 |
| 92<br>+16 | 86<br>+13 | 75<br>+44 | 80<br>+33 | 96<br>+32 | 21<br>+88 | 94<br>+32 |
| 76<br>+73 | 65<br>+72 | 50<br>+86 | 60<br>+57 | 83<br>+63 | 84<br>+91 | 92<br>+85 |
| 83<br>+54 | 90<br>+55 | 99<br>+40 | 62<br>+85 | 31<br>+76 | 51<br>+72 | 90<br>+18 |
| 75<br>+40 | 59<br>+90 | 20<br>+93 | 71<br>+96 | 88<br>+71 | 93<br>+74 | 66<br>+92 |

**8.** $\begin{array}{r} 1000 \\ -\ 241 \\ \hline \end{array}$ $\quad \begin{array}{r} 10{,}000 \\ -\ 3{,}621 \\ \hline \end{array}$ $\quad \begin{array}{r} 10{,}000 \\ -\ 6{,}249 \\ \hline \end{array}$ $\quad \begin{array}{r} 2000 \\ -\ 496 \\ \hline \end{array}$

$\begin{array}{r} 5000 \\ -1475 \\ \hline \end{array}$ $\quad \begin{array}{r} 2.000 \\ -1.628 \\ \hline \end{array}$ $\quad \begin{array}{r} 40.002 \\ -16.999 \\ \hline \end{array}$ $\quad \begin{array}{r} 6000 \\ -\ 725 \\ \hline \end{array}$

**9.** $\frac{1}{6}$ of 96 $\qquad$ $\frac{3}{4}$ of 160 $\qquad$ $\frac{2}{3}$ of 189

$\frac{1}{4}$ of 128 $\qquad$ $\frac{7}{8}$ of 240 $\qquad$ $\frac{4}{5}$ of 125

$\frac{1}{3}$ of 720 $\qquad$ $\frac{1}{2}$ of 8490 $\qquad$ $\frac{1}{6}$ of 186

$\frac{1}{7}$ of 497 $\qquad$ $\frac{3}{7}$ of 140 $\qquad$ $\frac{1}{8}$ of 404

$\frac{5}{6}$ of 240 $\qquad$ $\frac{3}{5}$ of 600 $\qquad$ $\frac{1}{2}$ of 5006

**10.** $45 \div 15 = \ ? \div 5$ $\qquad$ $6 \times 3 = \ ? \times 2$

$21 \div 3 = 49 \div \ ?$ $\qquad$ $? \times 4 = 3 \times 8$

$100 \div 20 = \ ? \div 1$ $\qquad$ $7 \times \ ? = 21 \times 2$

$? \div 12 = 15 \div 5$ $\qquad$ $9 \times 0 = \ ? \times 15$

**11.** $4\overline{)624}$ $\quad 2\overline{)302}$ $\quad 8\overline{)728}$ $\quad 7\overline{)770}$ $\quad 9\overline{)810}$

$3\overline{)456}$ $\quad 9\overline{)657}$ $\quad 6\overline{)864}$ $\quad 11\overline{)341}$ $\quad 12\overline{)600}$

$11\overline{)781}$ $\quad 4\overline{)428}$ $\quad 7\overline{)413}$ $\quad 9\overline{)963}$ $\quad 12\overline{)492}$

**12.** The first step in division is to think what multiple of the divisor is needed. What multiple of 7 is needed to divide each number by 7?

16 $\quad$ 45 $\quad$ 83 $\quad$ 66 $\quad$ 29 $\quad$ 54

What multiple of 6 is needed?

49 $\quad$ 16 $\quad$ 32 $\quad$ 52 $\quad$ 28 $\quad$ 43

What multiple of 9 is needed?

38 $\quad$ 84 $\quad$ 77 $\quad$ 56 $\quad$ 66 $\quad$ 45

**13.** Estimate the first quotient figure in each:

$29\overline{)3972}$ $\quad 72\overline{)6745}$ $\quad 97\overline{)8061}$ $\quad 45\overline{)7218}$

$96\overline{)8621}$ $\quad 328\overline{)20{,}413}$ $\quad 125\overline{)72{,}641}$ $\quad 99\overline{)8729}$

**14.** Find the least common multiple:

a. 6, 18, 9, 4 $\qquad$ c. 8, 7, 4, 5

b. 5, 3, 12, 4 $\qquad$ d. 2, 9, 6, 5

**15.** Which of these subtractions would never occur in a division computation, except with this subtrahend used as the divisor?

$$\begin{array}{r} 76 \\ -65 \\ \hline \end{array} \quad \begin{array}{r} 84 \\ -81 \\ \hline \end{array} \quad \begin{array}{r} 29 \\ -17 \\ \hline \end{array} \quad \begin{array}{r} 46 \\ -31 \\ \hline \end{array} \quad \begin{array}{r} 94 \\ -85 \\ \hline \end{array} \quad \begin{array}{r} 67 \\ -62 \\ \hline \end{array}$$

$$\begin{array}{r} 58 \\ -54 \\ \hline \end{array} \quad \begin{array}{r} 38 \\ -32 \\ \hline \end{array} \quad \begin{array}{r} 59 \\ -48 \\ \hline \end{array} \quad \begin{array}{r} 87 \\ -79 \\ \hline \end{array} \quad \begin{array}{r} 95 \\ -83 \\ \hline \end{array} \quad \begin{array}{r} 46 \\ -36 \\ \hline \end{array}$$

**16.** Which of these numbers is divisible by 2? By 3? By 5? By 6? By 9?

| | | | |
|---|---|---|---|
| 421 | 754 | 247 | 1604 |
| 168 | 680 | 672 | 2538 |
| 936 | 405 | 906 | 6143 |
| 210 | 999 | 275 | 2700 |

**17.** Which of the following numbers are prime numbers:

| | | | |
|---|---|---|---|
| 69 | 108 | 164 | 19 |
| 17 | 77 | 109 | 37 |
| 42 | 217 | 875 | 137 |

**18.** What is the greatest common divisor of each group of numbers?

a. 16, 24, 8, 72 c. 14, 21, 84, 42
b. 15, 75, 3, 30 d. 12, 18, 42, 24

**19.** Express as fractions in their lowest terms:

| | | |
|---|---|---|
| $16 \div 48$ | $14 \div 35$ | $24 \div 60$ |
| $12 \div 42$ | $10 \div 90$ | $11 \div 88$ |
| $8 \div 44$ | $20 \div 100$ | $18 \div 63$ |
| $9 \div 45$ | $21 \div 49$ | $36 \div 66$ |

**20.** Simplify:

$$\frac{2 \times 6}{4} \div 3 \qquad \frac{9 \div 3}{3} \times 85 \qquad \frac{4 \times 8}{2 \times 4} \times 20$$

$$\frac{5 \times 10}{2} \times 4 \qquad \frac{27 \div 3}{3 \times 1} \times 33 \qquad \frac{7 \times 5 \times 2}{10 \times 7}$$

**21.** $\frac{3}{4} = \frac{?}{20}$ $\qquad \frac{4}{5} = \frac{20}{?}$ $\qquad \frac{5}{6} = \frac{?}{72}$

$\frac{7}{9} = \frac{28}{?}$ $\qquad \frac{3}{11} = \frac{?}{44}$ $\qquad \frac{3}{19} = \frac{?}{57}$

$\frac{9}{16} = \frac{36}{?}$ $\qquad \frac{7}{25} = \frac{28}{?}$ $\qquad \frac{5}{20} = \frac{4}{?}$

**22.** Reduce to lowest terms:

$$\frac{147}{210} \qquad \frac{150}{250} \qquad \frac{19}{38} \qquad \frac{17}{51} \qquad \frac{250}{400}$$

$$\frac{45}{200} \qquad \frac{90}{120} \qquad \frac{15}{90} \qquad \frac{36}{108} \qquad \frac{66}{121}$$

**23.** Change to whole or mixed numbers:

$$\frac{78}{6} \qquad \frac{121}{10} \qquad \frac{75}{200} \qquad \frac{39}{7} \qquad \frac{99}{12}$$

$$\frac{142}{14} \qquad \frac{100}{8} \qquad \frac{100}{30} \qquad \frac{175}{25} \qquad \frac{100}{33\frac{1}{3}}$$

$$\frac{200}{33\frac{1}{3}} \qquad \frac{89}{89} \qquad \frac{48}{3} \qquad \frac{393}{39} \qquad \frac{400}{8}$$

**24.** Add:

$$\frac{1}{3} + \frac{1}{4} \qquad \frac{7}{10} + \frac{1}{5} \qquad \frac{8}{9} + \frac{1}{2} \qquad \frac{6}{15} + \frac{1}{3}$$

$$\frac{7}{12} + \frac{1}{4} \qquad \frac{1}{16} + \frac{3}{8} \qquad \frac{7}{8} + \frac{3}{4} \qquad \frac{5}{8} + \frac{3}{16}$$

**25.** Subtract:

$$3 - \frac{7}{16} \qquad \frac{7}{8} - \frac{1}{16} \qquad 7 - \frac{7}{8}$$

$$2\frac{1}{2} - 2\frac{1}{4} \qquad 6 - 5\frac{1}{8} \qquad 4\frac{1}{5} - 3\frac{2}{5}$$

$$10 - 6\frac{3}{4} \qquad 12 - \frac{7}{16} \qquad 8\frac{1}{2} - 7\frac{1}{4}$$

**26.** Add:

$$\begin{array}{cccc}
6 & 2\frac{1}{8} & 4 & 5 \\
8\frac{1}{5} & 9 & 2\frac{1}{7} & 9\frac{1}{6} \\
7 & 6 & 8 & 6 \\
4\frac{2}{5} & 2\frac{7}{8} & 7\frac{2}{7} & 3\frac{5}{6} \\
6 & 5 & 3 & 7 \\
3\frac{3}{5} & 8\frac{3}{8} & 9\frac{4}{7} & 8\frac{5}{6} \\
+2 & +7 & +4 & +4 \\
\hline
\end{array}$$

**27.** Give the products:

$$\frac{7}{8} \times 160 \qquad \frac{4}{5} \times 300 \qquad \frac{5}{6} \times 240$$

$$\frac{3}{4} \times 88 \qquad \frac{11}{12} \times 120 \qquad \frac{3}{4} \times 48$$

$$\frac{1}{15} \times 300 \qquad \frac{1}{7} \times 52 \qquad \frac{1}{2} \times 8722$$

**28.** Give the products:

| | | |
|---|---|---|
| $50 \times 47$ | $150 \times 18$ | $16 \times 150$ |
| $25 \times 800$ | $20 \times 45$ | $75 \times 400$ |
| $33\frac{1}{3} \times 72$ | $2.5 \times 100$ | $1.642 \times 100$ |
| $66\frac{2}{3} \times 90$ | $.42 \times 1000$ | $.45 \times 200$ |

**29.** Give the quotients:

| | | | |
|---|---|---|---|
| $\frac{4}{5} \div \frac{5}{4}$ | $\frac{8}{9} \div 4$ | $\frac{36}{17} \div \frac{9}{17}$ | $\frac{3}{7} \div 15$ |
| $\frac{4}{6} \div \frac{2}{6}$ | $\frac{7}{12} \div \frac{1}{2}$ | $\frac{15}{16} \div \frac{3}{8}$ | $\frac{5}{9} \div 25$ |
| $\frac{3}{8} \div 4$ | $\frac{7}{15} \div 14$ | $\frac{4}{25} \div 12$ | $16 \div \frac{4}{5}$ |

**30.** a. How many times is $\frac{1}{6}$ of a dollar contained in 1 dollar?
b. $\frac{1}{8}$ of a qt. in $\frac{7}{8}$ of a qt.?

**31.** Read as per cents:

| | | |
|---|---|---|
| .40 | 2.50 | .375 |
| .025 | 1.00 | .125 |
| $.33\frac{1}{3}$ | $.00\frac{2}{5}$ | 6.5 |
| .005 | $.16\frac{2}{3}$ | .3125 |

**32.** Give the products:

| | | |
|---|---|---|
| $6 \times .003$ | $.001 \times .001$ | $7.5 \times 1.00$ |
| $.12 \times .04$ | $.005 \times .011$ | $20 \times 2.43$ |
| $.06 \times .09$ | $.21 \times 10{,}000$ | $1000 \times 6.155$ |

**33.** Give the quotients:

| | | |
|---|---|---|
| $720 \div 1000$ | $48 \div .24$ | $2.48 \div 20$ |
| $.045 \div 5$ | $160 \div 1.6$ | $700 \div .7$ |
| $.0021 \div 21$ | $240 \div 100$ | $16 \div 1000$ |

**34.** Read as decimals:

| | | | | |
|---|---|---|---|---|
| $\frac{3}{8}$ | $\frac{4}{50}$ | $\frac{28}{200}$ | $\frac{1}{50}$ | $\frac{25}{200}$ |
| $\frac{4}{5}$ | $\frac{1}{25}$ | $\frac{7}{8}$ | $\frac{9}{50}$ | $\frac{5}{8}$ |
| $\frac{2}{5}$ | $\frac{3}{20}$ | $\frac{2}{3}$ | $\frac{1}{4}$ | $\frac{3}{4}$ |

**35.** How many $\frac{1}{4}$'s in $12\frac{1}{2}$?

**36.** 28 is $\frac{4}{5}$ of what number?

**37.** Read as decimals:

| | | | |
|---|---|---|---|
| 31.5% | 250% | 200% | $56\frac{1}{2}$% |
| $6\frac{1}{4}$% | $16\frac{1}{2}$% | .05% | 1% |
| $\frac{1}{2}$% | .1% | $25\frac{3}{4}$% | 4.2% |

**38.** Read as common fractions in the lowest terms:

| | | | |
|---|---|---|---|
| 45% | 98% | $16\frac{2}{3}$% | 60% |
| 20% | 75% | 35% | 40% |
| $87\frac{1}{2}$% | $62\frac{1}{2}$% | 8% | 69% |
| $33\frac{1}{3}$% | $6\frac{1}{4}$% | $12\frac{1}{2}$% | 55% |

**39.** What is:

| | | |
|---|---|---|
| 10% of 260? | 8% of 60? | 3% of 1200? |
| 25% of 288? | 50% of 700? | 200% of 16? |
| $66\frac{2}{3}$% of 270? | $\frac{1}{2}$% of 400? | $37\frac{1}{2}$% of 40? |
| 45% of 200? | $62\frac{1}{2}$% of 40? | $\frac{1}{2}$% of 600? |

**40.** Give the number of which

| | | |
|---|---|---|
| 3 is 10% | 20 is $\frac{4}{5}$ | 260 is $\frac{1}{2}$ |
| 4 is $\frac{1}{8}$ | 16 is 10% | 11 is 25% |
| 6 is 200% | 9 is $\frac{3}{7}$ | 9 is 150% |

**41.** What part of

| | | |
|---|---|---|
| 16 is 12? | 120 is 6? | 20 is 8? |
| $\frac{2}{3}$ is $\frac{1}{3}$? | $3\frac{1}{2}$ is $\frac{1}{2}$? | $12\frac{1}{2}$ is $6\frac{1}{4}$? |
| 1000 is 10? | 21 is 14? | 65 is 5? |

**42.** 20 is $\frac{1}{5}$ less than what number?
15 is 25% more than what number?
60 is 20% more than what number?
20 is $\frac{1}{3}$ less than what number?

**43.** What number is

10% less than 70?
25% more than 80?
75% less than 36?
40% more than 100?

**44.** Give the square of:

| | | | | |
|---|---|---|---|---|
| 12 | 11 | .6 | $\frac{1}{4}$ | $\frac{9}{10}$ |
| 10 | 8 | .9 | $\frac{1}{20}$ | $\frac{3}{12}$ |
| 9 | 20 | .12 | $\frac{2}{3}$ | $\frac{7}{8}$ |
| 100 | 200 | 1.2 | $\frac{5}{6}$ | $\frac{9}{2}$ |

**45.** Give the square root of:

| | | | |
|---|---|---|---|
| 121 | 10,000 | 1600 | 3600 |
| 100 | .49 | 6400 | .36 |
| 16 | 225 | 64.00 | .81 |
| 49 | 400 | .25 | 8100 |

**46.**

| | | | |
|---|---|---|---|
| $3^3 = ?$ | $2^4 = ?$ | $10^{10} = ?$ | $14^0 = ?$ |
| $5^2 = ?$ | $6^2 = ?$ | $6^0 = ?$ | $200^1 = ?$ |
| $10^3 = ?$ | $10^6 = ?$ | $3^1 = ?$ | $65^0 = ?$ |

**47.** Express the following ratios as fractions:

| | | | |
|---|---|---|---|
| 4 to 16 | 14 to 16 | 21 to 5 | .5 to .05 |
| 8 to 21 | 17 to 4 | $\frac{1}{6}$ to $\frac{3}{6}$ | 1.5 to 15 |
| $1\frac{1}{2}$ to 6 | 9 to 15 | .7 to .70 | .9 to 9 |

**48.** Give the formula for each of the following:

a. Area of a rectangle.
b. Area of a triangle.
c. Area of a parallelogram.
d. Area of a trapezoid.
e. Area of a circle.

**49.** Give the formula for each of the following:

a. Volume of a cube.
b. Volume of a rectangular solid.
c. Volume of a cylindrical solid.
d. Volume of a cone.
e. Volume of a pyramid.
f. Volume of a triangular prism.

**50.** a. $6 + 4 \div 2 - 3 \times 25 \times 2 - 99 = ?$
b. $4 \times 8 - 2 \div 10 + 17 \times 2 + 5 - 25 = ?$
c. $60 \div 5 \times 2 - 4 + 8 \div 7 \times 1000 = ?$

**51.** Round 2,986,425,729,412

a. to tens; to hundreds; to thousands; to ten thousands.
b. to hundred thousands; to millions; to billions.
c. to ten billions; to trillions.

section **B**

# Application of Processes

## Set I. Percentage and Its Applications

1. In our school 459 pupils, which is 85% of those in school, reported that they had started savings accounts. How many pupils are there in our school?
2. If \$400 earns \$20 interest in a year, at what per cent is it invested?
3. Find the interest on \$800 at $5\frac{1}{2}\%$ for 1 yr. 6 mo.
4. How long will it take \$400 invested at 4% to earn \$64 interest?
5. Find the rate of interest on an investment of \$2000 which earned \$60 in a year.
6. Find the interest on \$2400 at $4\frac{1}{4}\%$ for 1 yr. 3 mo.
7. What tax will be due on property assessed at \$16,000 if the tax rate is 19 mills?
8. A certain city wants to raise \$1,861,800 by taxes. Its assessed valuation is \$107,000,000. What will its tax rate be?
9. After deducting his exemptions, a man has a taxable net income of \$6400. If he pays at the rate of $1\frac{1}{2}\%$ on the first \$4000 and 3% on all over that amount, what will his tax be?
10. The list price of a chair is \$79, but the dealer says, "I'll make it \$75 cash." What per cent discount is he offering?
11. On a small patch of .4 acre Mr. Hyde raised 50 bushels of potatoes. How many bushels can he expect to get from a 5-acre field?
12. A house was sold for \$8000. The buyer paid a real estate dealer $4\frac{1}{2}\%$ commission on the sale, then paid \$600 for repairs on it. He rented the house for 6 months at \$70 a month, and then sold it for \$9400. What was his per cent of profit or loss on the house?
13. Write a problem that can be solved by equation (a) and one that can be solved by (b):
    a. $i = \$900 \times .05 \times 2\frac{1}{2}$
    b. $i = \$1375 \times .045$

14. At what rate of interest must \$200 be invested to earn \$15 interest in a year and a half?
15. If 4900 equals 100% of $N$, 49 is what per cent of $N$?
16. Mr. Addison received \$420 as a year's income on money invested at 6%. How much did he invest?
17. In a certain election a candidate must poll 60% of the votes to be elected. Of the two candidates, $A$ got 88,642 votes and $B$ got 35,196 votes. Was either one elected?
18. What is the total commercial interest time on a note made Feb. 13, 1957, and paid Jan. 6, 1960?
19. Find the time used for computing exact interest from April 28, 1958, to Feb. 18, 1959.
20. Compute the proceeds of a promissory note for \$400 for 9 months, discounted at 6%?
21. What is the interest on a promissory note for \$400 for 18 months with interest at $6\frac{1}{4}$%?
22. Smithville had a tax rate of $23\frac{1}{2}$ mills in 1960, on an assessed valuation of \$1,500,000. What will the rate have to be in 1961 to get \$15,000 more in taxes without raising the valuation?
23. In a certain school 60 pupils were under the average weight. The nurse said this was 12% of the total number of pupils. What was the total school enrollment?
24. If a \$5000 investment earns \$550 in 2 years, what is the rate of interest on it?
25. Find the interest on \$1350 at $4\frac{3}{4}$% for 2 yr. 8 mo.
26. An article that cost \$5.25, with \$1.75 overhead, sold for \$9.50. What per cent of the \$9.50 was profit?
27. A bank told Mr. Alexander they would lend him 60% of the value of the property he offered as security. They lent him \$7200. What value did they place on his property?
28. An appliance company bought a supply of automatic dishwashers for \$3500 wholesale, with discounts of 20% and 8%. They estimated the cost of handling the goods at \$560. The entire lot was sold for \$5475.50. What was the profit?
29. Mr. Elliott bought some rubber company stock when it was selling at 117. The first year it paid 8% in dividends. At the same time his wife bought oil company stock at 107; it paid 7%. Who got the better rate of income on his investment?
30. Dale Brown bought 50 shares of common stock in the Midland Power Copmany at \$25 a share. After holding the stock for 18 months, he sold it at \$28.50 a share (net after paying the commission). Dividends of $2\frac{1}{2}$% (on \$100 par) were paid at the end of each six-month period. Did he

have a profit or a loss? What per cent of the cost price was the profit or loss?

31. An article that cost a retailer \$10 had a catalogue list price of \$12. What rate of discount did he get?

32. A merchant bought a bill of goods priced at \$540 at discounts of 25% and 10%. He sent a check for \$351 and then was advised that he had made an error in the amount due. What error did he made, and in whose favor was it?

33. A merchant buys coffee listed at 60 cents a lb. at a 15% discount and sells it at 75 cents a lb. What is his margin on a pound?

34. A rule says that a single discount equal to two successive discounts can be found by taking the sum of the two discounts less their product. Do the following problem by the usual method and check it by the rule: Find the cost of an article listed at \$80 less discounts of 30% and 10%.

35. Jim and Nancy want a new davenport. They find one they like for \$240 cash, or without down payment for \$45 a month for six months. Nancy's father offers to lend them the money for the davenport at 8% with six months to pay. Which plan will cost them less?

36. Mr. Young wants to carry enough life insurance to provide an income of \$1800 a year for his family in the event of his death. How much insurance must he carry to provide an amount which could be invested at 6% interest with \$1800 annual income?

37. A tax rate of \$14 on each \$1000 of assessed valuation means a tax rate of what per cent? Of how many mills on the dollar?

38. a. 8 is what per cent of 175?
    b. 8 is what fractional part of 175?
    c. 8 is what decimal part of 175?

39. 33.75 is what decimal part of 750?

40. 142 is $16\frac{2}{3}$% of what number?

41. To what per cent of 170 is 280 equal?

42. An agent working on a 6% commission got \$34.50 on a sale. What was the amount of the sale?

43. What number is 15% more than 60?

44. During a sale coffee sold for 81 cents a pound; this was advertised as a 10% discount price. What was the regular price?

45. If a grocer sells a crate of peaches for \$1.65 and has 20% of that for margin, what does he pay for the peaches?

46. The owner of a hatchery counts on 80% of the eggs hatching healthy chicks. How many eggs must he set to expect to fill an order for 500 chicks?

47. A clerk's salary was increased from \$65 to \$72 per week. What was the per cent of increase?

48. At a clearance sale a girl bought a suit for \$54; this was 75% of the regular price. What was the regular price?

49. A salesman receives \$250 a month basic salary plus $2\frac{1}{2}$% commission on his sales. What was his year's pay in a year during which he sold \$20,875 worth of goods?

50. An agent sent his firm \$5725.50 after deducting his commission of 3% for the sale, and \$465.80 for expenses. For what amount were the goods sold?

51. A merchant spent \$56,245 for goods one year and his operating expenses were \$10,465. His year's sales amounted to \$72,269. What per cent of his sales was profit?

52. A dealer sold two cars for \$2675 each. On one he made 10% and on the other he lost 10%. What was the net amount of his profit or loss?

53. A house valued at \$9000 is in a high-risk neighborhood and is insured for three-fourths of its valuation. What will the premium for 3 years be at 75¢ per hundred per year?

54. If I borrow \$1000 from a bank for 90 days, and the bank deducts the interest at 7% and pays me the proceeds, how much money will I get? How much will I owe the bank at the end of the 90 days?

55. A loan company uses a table of interest rates which designates, for a \$50 loan, 4 monthly payments of \$13.46 each. What annual interest rate is being paid on unpaid balances at this rate?

56. A chap who needed money pawned his watch for \$40 and at the end of a month redeemed it for \$42.50. What rate of interest did he pay?

57. Find the cost of 50 shares of Standard Oil of Indiana stock bought at $90\frac{3}{4}$ with brokerage 35¢ a share.

58. A stock paid 5% on the investment when the dividend was \$4.50 per share. What did it cost?

59. Last year the rainfall in a certain area was 15 in. This year it was 12 in. What was the per cent of decrease?

60. A collector received \$100 for collecting bills; his commission was 5%. How much did he collect?

61. A farmer sends 800 bu. of wheat to a commission merchant who sells it at \$1.25 a bu. and charges 2% commission. How much money does the farmer receive for the wheat?

## Set 2. Measurement

1. What part of a $1\frac{3}{4}$-inch square is a $\frac{7}{8}$-inch square?

2. Find the area of a parallelogram whose base is 5 yd. 2 ft. and whose altitude is 4 ft.

3. Find the area of a trapezoid whose bases are 8 ft. and 10 ft. and whose altitude is 6 ft.

4. What is the difference between the base of a rectangle and the base of a rectangular solid? Between the base of a triangle and the base of a triangular prism?
5. A common brick is 8 in. by 4 in. by 2 in. How many of these bricks will make a pile 3 ft. by 6 ft. by 12 ft.?
6. A cylindrical tank is 24 in. in diameter and 84 in. long. How many gallons of water will it hold?
7. Write the formula for the volume of a cone.
8. Write the formula for the volume of a pyramid.
9. What is the volume of a rectangular solid whose base is 1 sq. in. and whose altitude is 6 in.?
10. What is the volume of a 12-in. cube?
11. What is the total area of all the sides of a cube whose base is 36 sq. in.?
12. Draw a gas meter that registers 49,000 cu. ft.
13. A triangle containing a 90°-angle is called a ______________________.
14. The diameter of the earth at the equator is about 8000 miles. What is the approximate circumference of the earth at the equator?
15. A wheat bin which is 5 ft. deep, 8 ft. wide, and 9 ft. long is filled with wheat to an average depth of 3 ft. If 1 bu. of wheat occupies $1\frac{1}{4}$ cu. ft. and weighs 60 lb., how much is the wheat in the bin worth at $1.90 a bushel?
16. A dealer was billed for an order of $380 worth of goods on June 1. The bill allowed three discounts: 2% for cash in 30 days, 40% trade discount, and 5% quantity discount. If he writes a check in payment on July 5, what amount should he pay?
17. Jane Addison, traveling in Europe, asked the distance from where she was to Paris and was told it was about 200 kilometers. How many miles is this?
18. a. What part of a square foot is a square inch?
    b. What part of a square decimeter is a square centimeter?
19. Find the volume of a circular hat box 12 in. in diameter and 10 in. deep.
20. The length of a rectangle is 6 ft. and the width is *w*. How can its perimeter be expressed?
21. A stockman sold a carload of 26 cattle averaging 1210 lb. each. He received $23.50 per cwt. for them. What was the average price per animal?
22. Draw a circle with a radius of 2 in., and another with a radius of $2\frac{1}{2}$ in. By how much does the area of the larger circle exceed that of the smaller?
23. a. Draw two circles whose diameters have a 3 to 5 ratio.
    b. What is the ratio of their areas?
24. Draw a 3-in. line and draw a 2-in. line perpendicular to it.

25. Using a carpenter's square as a model, make a cardboard square and demonstrate its use in drawing perpendicular and parallel lines.

26. Show that if we know the size of one angle of a parallelogram, we can find the size of each of the other angles. (All the angles of a parallelogram together equal 360°.)

27. Show that if we know the size of one of the acute angles in a right triangle we can find the size of each of the three angles. (All of the angles of a triangle together equal 180°.)

28. Draw figures and write a proportion to illustrate that pairs of corresponding sides of similar triangles have the same ratio.

29. What period of time is five times as long as 6 min. 25 sec.?

30. What is the difference in weight between 4 lb. 15 oz. and 2 lb. 9 oz.?

31. How many tiles 8 inches square will be required to cover a floor 16 ft. by 20 ft.? Will there be any waste? Explain.

32. How many tiles 8 inches square will be required to cover a floor 13 ft. by 22 ft.? Will there be any waste? Explain.

33. A war relic cannon was placed in a public park in a 20-foot square enclosed by an iron fence. A sidewalk 6 ft. wide was laid around the square. How many square feet of sidewalk had to be laid?

34. Illustrate by drawings the effect upon the area of a rectangle of multiplying its length by 2; of multiplying both length and width by 2.

35. What will be the cost of 78 two-by-fours 9 ft. long and 24 two-by-eights 12 ft. long at $250 per thousand?

36. About how many acres are there in a vacant lot 100 ft. by 300 ft.?

37. How many rods of fence are needed to fence a square field containing 160 acres?

38. Which will require more fence, fencing a field of 160 acres in a square, or fencing the same area in a rectangle that is twice as long as it is wide? How much more?

39. How many posts are needed for a 360-ft. fence if the posts are set 12 ft. apart?

40. How many rods of barbed wire are needed to put a 4-wire fence around a field 30 rd. by 40 rd.?

41. If excavation costs $10 a cubic yard, what will it cost to excavate a basement 50 ft. by 40 ft. by 8 ft.?

42. How many half-pint cartons can be filled from 6 gal. of milk?

43. Make a diagram and set up a problem to show that the diagonals of a rectangle are equal.

44. A half-gallon of paint covers a 15-ft. square. How much will be required to cover a building 80 ft. by 60 ft., with eaves 20 ft. above the ground and a gable roof with the ridgepole 18 ft. above the eaves?

45. a. Find the area of the largest circle that can be cut from a piece of cardboard 9 in. wide and 15 in. long.
b. What is the area of the remaining cardboard?

46. *AB* is 7 in.

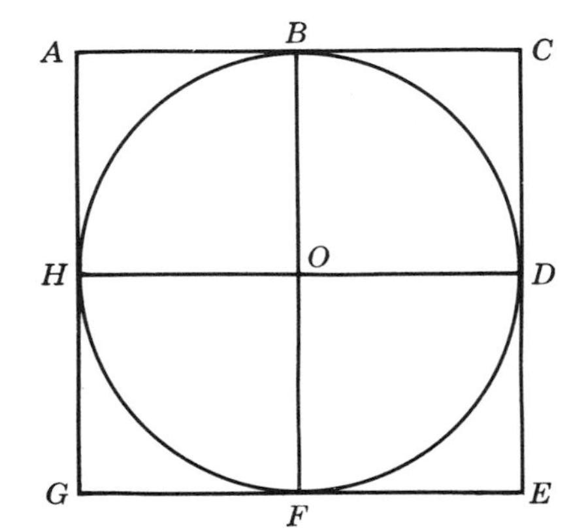


a. Find the area of the square *ABOH*.
b. Find the area of the square *ACEG*.
c. Find the area of the inscribed circle.
d. Circumscribe a circle about the square *ACEG* and find the approximate area enclosed by it.

47. Find the area of the part of the circle that is shown.

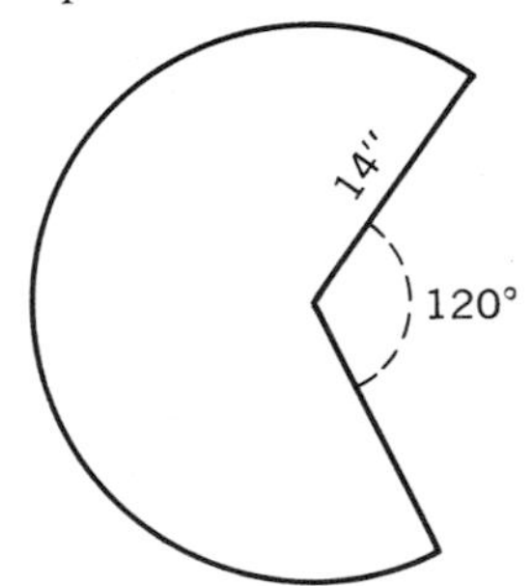


48. Find to the nearest inch the diameter of a circle whose area is equal to that of an 8-in. square.

49. Find the area of a 5-ft. sidewalk around a circular pool 20 ft. in diameter.

50. How many square feet of surface need to be painted to cover the outside of a cylindrical tank 6 ft. long with a diameter of $2\frac{1}{2}$ ft and closed at both ends?

51. How many gallons will an oil drum that is 18 in. in diameter and $3\frac{1}{2}$ ft. high hold?

52. A cylindrical cistern 9 ft. in diameter and 10 ft. deep will hold how many barrels of water?

53. Show why the area of the lateral surface of a regular pyramid equals one-half the product of the perimeter of the base and the slant height.
54. Find the volume of a prism whose base is a square with 6-in. sides and whose altitude is 12 in.
55. Find the altitude of a pyramid whose volume is 240 cu. in. and whose base is 16 sq. in. in area.
56. Find the volume of a cone if the radius of its base is 6 in. and its altitude is 9 in.
57. The surface of a sphere $= 4\pi r^2$. Find the surface area of a globe $2\frac{1}{2}$ ft. in diameter.
58. What is the surface of the largest sphere that can be cut from a 12-in. cube?
59. Find the volume of the largest cylinder that can be cut from a 12-in. cube.
60. What is the volume of the largest cube that can be cut from a block 6 in. by 8 in. by 10 in.?
61. If the edge of a cube is doubled, what is the change in its volume?
62. How many cubic yards of concrete are needed to build a foundation for a building 20 ft. by 35 ft., the foundation being 2 ft. deep and 8 in. thick?
63. If 200 cu. ft. of air space is required per pupil, how many pupils may occupy a classroom 20 ft. by 20 ft. by 12 ft.?
64. Compare the area of a right triangle whose sides are 6 in., 8 in., and 10 in. with that of a square having the same perimeter.
65. How many ties 2 ft. 5 in. long can be cut from a spool of ribbon that is 8 ft. 6 in. long?
66. In a certain state an error of 1% in weights in retail stores is permissible. If sugar labeled 5 lb. actually weighs 4 lb. 14 oz., is it within the law?
67. If $\frac{2}{3}$ ton of hay costs $16, what will 3 cwt. 75 lb. cost?
68. What is the length of a line that is $\frac{3}{4}$ as long as a $\frac{1}{2}$-in. line?

## Set 3. Work and Rate-Time-Distance Relationships

1. Using *d*, *r* and *t* as symbols, write the formula for problems involving rate, time and distance.
2. Suppose two persons, A and B, 850 miles apart, set out to meet on an agreed-upon route. A travels 48 mi. an hour and B 37 mi. an hour. When will they meet?
3. If A can fold a certain number of bulletins in 2 hr. and it takes B 3 hr. to do the same number, how long will it take both working together to fold this number?
4. If Ted works only half as fast as Tom, how long will it take both of them working together to do a task Ted can do alone in 4 hr.?

5. How long will it take A and B working together to do a job for which A requires $2\frac{1}{2}$ hr. and B $4\frac{3}{4}$ hr.?
6. If a "souped-up" car travels at the rate of $1\frac{3}{4}$ mi. per minute, how long will it take to do 1 mi.? What is its speed (m.p.h.)?
7. Bad roads permitted a speed of only 40 mph. for the first 80 mi. of a 320-mi. trip. If the entire trip took 6 hr., what was the average speed on the good part of the road?
8. If it takes 8 men 24 days to do a certain job, how long will it take one man working alone to do it?
9. A can do a job in 2 days, B in 3 days, and C in 6 days. How long will it take the three working together to do it?
10. A can dig a pit alone in $2\frac{1}{2}$ days; B digs one just like it in $3\frac{1}{3}$ days. How long will it take them working together to dig a pit of the same dimensions?
11. If 5 men can do a job in 18 days, how many men will it take to finish it in 9 days?
12. If 3 men do a job in 4 days, working 10 hr. a day, how many days will it take 8 men working 6 hr. a day?

## Set 4. Ratio and Proportion

1. Explain the statement, "The value of a ratio is the quotient of the first term divided by the second."
2. If one principle of budget making is that the ratio of rent to earnings should not exceed 1:4, is a man who pays $60 a month rent and is paid $150 every other week exceeding that ratio? Explain.
3. If a certain quantity of milk tests 4% butterfat, what is the ratio of butterfat to milk of that quality?
4. a. Mr. A gardens 15 acres and Mr. B 9 acres. They agree to hire a man and pay him on the basis of the ratio of their acreage. What is the ratio of A's land to B's?
   b. What amount will each pay on the first $100 the man earns?
5. What number has a 5 to 1 ratio to the number 10?
6. What is the ratio of the side of a square to the perimeter?
7. What is the ratio of the diameter of a circle to the circumference?
8. What is the ratio of 9 in. to 2 ft.?
9. What is the ratio of Dick's height, 4 ft. 6 in., to Jim's, 5 ft. 3 in.?
10. Alice uses a cake recipe that calls for $1\frac{1}{2}$ cups of flour and serves 8 people. Increasing the recipe to serve 12 people will take how much flour?
11. When a post 6 ft. high casts a shadow $4\frac{1}{2}$ ft. long, how high is a flagpole which casts a shadow $31\frac{1}{2}$ ft. long at the same time?

12. Find the length of $AB$, if triangle $abc$ and triangle $ABC$ are similar triangles.

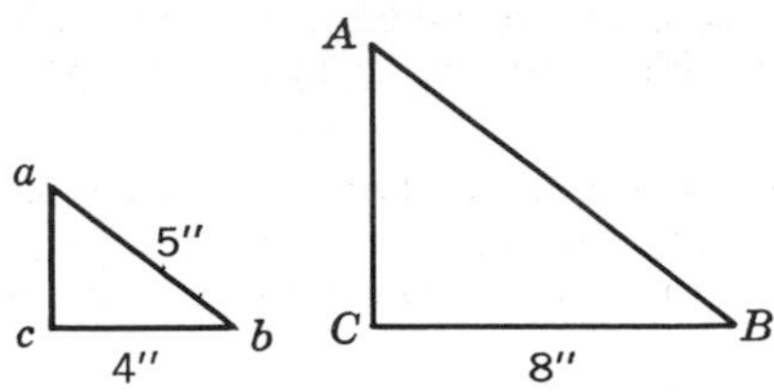


13. What is the ratio of the area of a rectangle 3 in. by 5 in. to that of a rectangle 4 in. by 8 in.?
14. If 4 apples cost 25¢, what will 18 apples cost at the same rate?
15. The ratio of the weight of a given substance to that of the same volume of water is called its *specific gravity*. A cu. ft. of water weighs $62\frac{1}{2}$ lb.; what is the weight of a cu. ft. of ice (specific gravity .92)?
16. What does 1 cu. ft. of gold weigh (specific gravity 19.21)?
17. A man traveled 30 mi. in $3\frac{3}{4}$ hr. At that rate, how far can he go in $7\frac{1}{4}$ hr.?
18. In a classroom of 35 pupils, there are 2 boys to 3 girls. How many boys and how many girls are there in that room?
19. Divide 28 into 2 parts so that one part will be to the other as 3 is to 4.
20. Divide 16 apples between Frank and Bob in the ratio of $1\frac{1}{2}$ to $2\frac{1}{2}$.
21. Divide 14¢ between Ann and Ruth so that Ann has $1\frac{1}{3}$ times as much as Ruth.
22. If 9 men finish a certain job in $2\frac{1}{2}$ hr., how long will it take 5 men to do it?

### Set 5. Approximation, Estimation, and Rounding Off Numbers

1. The radius of a circle is 12 ft. 5 in. Find its circumference correct to the nearest inch.
2. A rectangle is $4\frac{3}{4}$ in. wide and $6\frac{1}{2}$ in. long. Find its area correct to the nearest square inch.
3. If the gasoline used on a 600-mi. trip measured 34 gal., what mileage, correct to the nearest mile, was the driver getting?

### Set 6. Graphs and Scale Drawings

1. Make a graph showing the length of the four longest rivers in the United States, and explain the scale used.
2. Keep a record of hourly temperatures for 15 hr. on a certain day and record the data on a line graph.

3. Show on a circle graph the proportionate expenditures of a farmer who spends 26% of his year's income for equipment and materials, 11% for wages, 6% for taxes, 5% for interest, 28% for family living expenses, and 8% for rent, with the rest as savings. What per cent of his income does he save?

4. Mr. Billings tries to operate his shoe store on a general pattern of 60% for cost of goods, 25% overhead, and 15% profit. Make a circle graph to show that pattern, and indicate what part of the circle represents margin.

5. Make a graph showing the comparative production of lumber, gold, wheat, and beef in your state.

6. Draw a right triangle 8 ft. by 6 ft. by 10 ft. to scale, using $\frac{1}{2}$ in. to 1 ft.

7. On a scale drawing where 1 in. represents 12 ft., what length of line will represent 28 ft.? $4\frac{1}{2}$ ft.? 8 ft.?

8. On a house plan where 1 in. represents 15 ft., what does 5 in. represent? $3\frac{1}{2}$ in.? $\frac{1}{4}$ in.?

9. In the above plan where 1 in. represents 15 ft., what length on the drawing will represent 40 ft.? 60 ft.? 10 ft?

10. Make a scale drawing of a basketball court 40 ft. by 80 ft., using a scale of 1 in. to 8 ft.

11. Rounding the diameter of the earth to 8000 mi. and that of the sun to 866,000 mi., if a ball 1 in. in diameter represents the earth, what will be the diameter of a ball representing the sun on the same scale?

**Set 7. Powers and Roots**

1. Find the side of a square whose area is

   a. 324 sq. in. b. 441 sq. in. c. 289 sq. rd.

2. How long is one side of a square field which contains 10 acres?

3. Find the side of a square that contains 400 half-inch squares.

4. Demonstrate the Pythagorean theorem.

5. Find the hypotenuse of a right triangle whose sides are 12 ft. and 35 ft.

6. Find the diagonal of a rectangle 8 in. by 15 in.

7. Find the length of side *bc* in triangle *abc*.

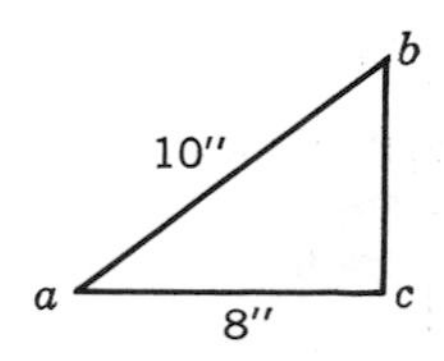

8. A ladder 24 ft. long is placed against a house with its base 8 ft. from the wall. How far from the ground is the top of the ladder?

## Set 8. Miscellaneous Processes

1. Mr. Davis paid $2650 for a new car. He used it three years, during which time he spent $528 for gas, oil, repairs, and other expenses for it. When he turned it in for a new car, he was allowed $975 for it. What did it cost him to own and operate the car for three years?
2. The temperature in St. Paul on one day was 8° below zero at 7:00 A.M. and 14° above at 4:00 P.M. What was the average hourly rise in temperature that day?
3. The maximum temperatures for our city for a ten-day period in early autumn were 75, 72, 65, 60, 69, 77, 76, 70, 71, and 68. What was the average daily maximum temperature for that period?
4. A clerk is now receiving $55 a week; this is $\frac{1}{10}$ more than his last year's salary per week. What was his weekly salary last year?
5. After spending $\frac{3}{5}$ of her monthly allowance, Janice had $8 left. What was her allowance?
6. A gasoline tank registered $\frac{3}{4}$ full. When 4 gal. were added, it was full. What was the tank's capacity?
7. If $\frac{2}{3}$ of a month's salary is $150, what is the rate of pay per month?
8. Square 43 using the formula $a^2 + 2ab + b^2$.
9. Dave has to travel a certain distance. After going 35 mi., he still has $\frac{2}{7}$ of the total distance to go. When he has gone $\frac{3}{7}$ of *that* distance, how far does he still have to go?
10. How many times $\frac{3}{11}$ of 44 is twice that number of which $\frac{4}{5}$ of 30 is $\frac{4}{9}$?
11. A boat worth $864, of which $\frac{1}{8}$ belonged to A, $\frac{1}{4}$ to B, and the rest to C, was burned. If the boat was insured for $500, what was each man's individual loss?
12. If 8 children spend $400 for bus fare in 5 months, what would the bus fare cost for 8 months if 3 more children were added to the group?
13. A and B enter into a gardening partnership for one year. A puts in $600, and B $900. After paying $150 expenses, they have a profit of $450. What is each one's share of the gain?
14. Five times a certain number is 16 more than 3 times the same number. What is the number?
15. If $\frac{3}{4}$ of James' money is increased by $6, the sum equals what Bruce has. Both together have $34. How much has each?
16. A man had three sons, A, B, and C. He willed $\frac{2}{7}$ of his estate to A, $\frac{1}{3}$ to B, and the remainder to C. The difference between the legacies received by A and C was $160. What amount did each son receive?

## Set 9. Miscellaneous Mental Exercises and Mathematical Information

**1.** Linear measure is used to measure ____________, and is concerned with ____________ dimensions.

**2.** Square measure is used to measure ____________, and involves ____________ dimensions.

**3.** Cubic measure is used to measure ____________, and involves ____________ dimensions.

**4.** To find the area of a square, we must know ____________ .

**5.** To find the area of a rectangle, we must know ____________.

**6.** To find the area of a triangle, we must know____________.

**7.** To find the area of a parallelogram, we must know ____________.

**8.** To find the area of a trapezoid, we must know ____________.

**9.** To find the area of a circle, we must know ____________.

**10.** To find the volume of a cube, we must know ____________.

**11.** To find the volume of a rectangular solid, we must know ____________.

**12.** To find the volume of a cylinder, we must know ____________.

**13.** To find the volume of a cone, we must know ____________.

**14.** The formula $A = ab$ is used to find ____________.

**15.** The formula $A = \frac{ab}{2}$ is used to find ____________.

**16.** Gas used in homes is measured in units called ____________.

**17.** The amount of electricity used is measured in units called ____________.

**18.** Temperature is measured in units called ____________.

**19.** In a rectangle the angles are all ____________ angles.

**20.** Circles and angles are measured in units called ____________.

**21.** Angles $m$ and $n$ each have ____________ degrees, and are called ____________ angles.

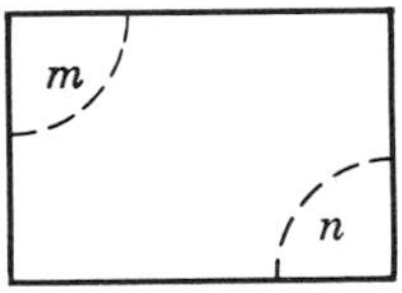

**22.** Line $ab$ is said to be ____________ to line $bc$.

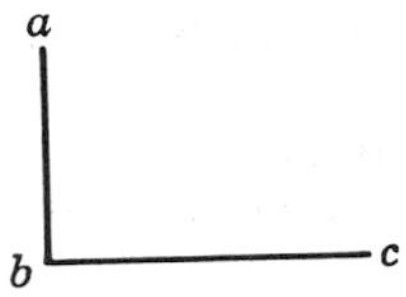

23. We cannot find the area of triangle $ABC$ because we do not know its ________.

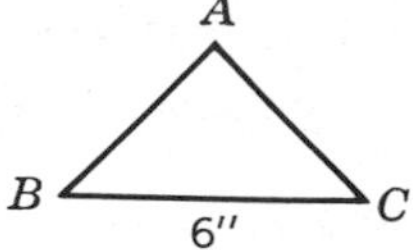


24. Point out the radius, the diameter, and the circumference of a circle.
25. If we know the diameter of a circle, we can find the radius by ________, and the circumference by ________.
26. If we know the dimensions of a rectangular farm in rods, how do we find its area in acres?
27. Knowing the circumference of a circle, how do we find its area?
28. How do we find how many bushels a given box will hold?
29. When we put money in a bank in a checking account, we must make out a ________.
30. The bank furnishes each person who has a checking account a ________, which shows all amounts deposited.
31. The monthly statement for a checking account shows ________.
32. Before a check can be cashed, it must be ________.
33. A tax rate on 20 mills on a dollar means ________ on $100.
34. Knowing how many hits a batter has made during the season, and how many times he has been at bat (chances to hit), how would you compute his batting average?
35. If John gets 8 out of 10 problems correct on a sample test, how many out of 150 problems of equal difficulty can he expect to have correct?
36. In what time will any principal at 5% yield the same interest as it would yield in 4 yr. at 10%?
37. One parcel post package weighs $2\frac{3}{4}$ lb., another $3\frac{1}{2}$ lb., and a third one $4\frac{1}{2}$ lb. What is the total weight?
38. A house valued at $12,000 was insured for $\frac{3}{4}$ of its value. What was the insurance on it?
39. If oranges sell at 4 for 25 cents, what will two dozen cost?
40. If Don earns $7.50 for 10 hr. of work, what will he earn in 40 hr.?
41. What is the perimeter of a field that is 40 rd. by 60 rd.?
42. What would fence for the above field cost at $2.50 per rod?
43. How many gross in 2880?
44. How many square feet in a triangle whose base is 10 ft. and altitude 10 ft.?
45. If the edge of a cube is doubled, how does the volume of the larger cube compare with that of the smaller?

46. When a post 8 ft. high casts a shadow 10 ft. long, how tall is a tree that at the same time casts a shadow of 40 ft.?

47. What will $2\frac{1}{2}$ dozen cookies cost at 32 cents a dozen?

48. How many cartons holding $\frac{3}{4}$ pt. each will be needed for 12 pt. of orange juice?

49. If a car travels at the rate of $\frac{3}{4}$ mi. per minute, how many minutes does it take to go a mile? 3 miles?

50. How many half-yards in 45 ft.?

51. If a 5-lb. chuck roast costs $4.25, what is its cost per pound?

52. The diagonal of a square is 1.1412 times the length of its side. What is the diagonal of a 10-ft. square?

53. What is the circumference of a circle whose diameter is 100 ft.? (Use decimal computation.)

54. What is the circumference of a circle whose diameter is 21 ft.? (Use common fraction computation.)

55. A does a piece of work in 2 days. B can do it in 3 days. How long will it take them working together?

56. A piano that cost $800 was sold at 8% above the cost price. What was the selling price?

57. What is the interest on $100 at $6\frac{1}{2}$% for 1 year?

58. What is the interest on $40 at 5% for 2 years?

59. What is the cost of 100 shares of Milling Company stock that sells at 135?

60. What is the volume of a pyramid if the area of its base is 25 sq. in. and its altitude is 9 in.?

61. How many board feet in a board 4 in. wide, 2 in. thick, and 9 ft. long?

62. What is the area of the lateral surface of a cylinder whose circumference is 15 ft. and whose altitude is 10 ft.?

63. A man walking at the rate of 5 mph meets a bicycle rider going 9 mph. How far apart will they be in 2 hr, if they continue traveling at the same rate?

64. a. What is the volume of a rectangular solid 3 in. by 8 in. by $2\frac{1}{2}$ in.?
 b. What is the area of a circle with a radius of 7 in.?
 c. What is the volume of a 10-in. cube?
 d. What is the volume of a box 10 in. by 8 in. by 6 in.?

# APPENDIX

# Tables of Measure

1. *Linear Measure* (length)

| | | |
|---|---|---|
| 12 | inches (in.) | = 1 foot (ft.) |
| 3 | feet (ft.)[1] | = 1 yard (yd.) |
| $16\frac{1}{2}$ | feet | = 1 rod (rd.) |
| $5\frac{1}{2}$ | yards (yd.) | = 1 rod |
| 320 | rods (rd.) | = 1 mile (mi.) |
| 5280 | feet | = 1 mile |

2. *Square Measure* (area)

| | | |
|---|---|---|
| 144 | square inches (sq. in.) | = 1 square foot (sq. ft.) |
| 9 | square feet | = 1 square yard (sq. yd.) |
| $30\frac{1}{4}$ | square yards | = 1 square rod (sq. rd.) |
| 160 | square rods | = 1 acre (A.) |
| 640 | acres | = 1 square mile (sq. mi.) or 1 section |

3. *Cubic Measure* (volume)

| | | |
|---|---|---|
| 1728 | cubic inches (cu. in.) | = 1 cubic foot (cu. ft.) |
| 27 | cubic feet | = 1 cubic yard (cu. yd.) |
| 128 | cubic feet | = 1 cord (cd.) (wood measurement) |
| $24\frac{3}{4}$ | cubic feet | = 1 perch (p.) (stone masonry) |
| 1 | cubic yard | = 1 load (sand or soil) |

[1] Accepted practice is to use the same abbreviation for both the singular and plural forms; e.g., in. for both inch and inches.

4. *Liquid Measure* (fluid contents)

| | |
|---|---|
| 4 fluid ounces (fl. oz.) | = 1 gill (gi.) |
| 4 gills | = 1 pint (pt.) |
| 2 cups | = 1 pint |
| 2 pints | = 1 quart (qt.) |
| 4 quarts | = 1 gallon (gal.) |
| $31\frac{1}{2}$ gallons | = 1 barrel (bbl.) |
| 2 barrels | = 1 hogshead (hhd.) |

1 gallon contains 231 cubic inches
1 cubic foot contains $7\frac{1}{2}$ gallons

5. *Dry Measure*
(Grains, Vegetables, and Fruits)

| | |
|---|---|
| 2 pints | = 1 quart |
| 8 quarts | = 1 peck (pk.) |
| 4 pecks | = 1 bushel (bu.) |

1 bushel contains 2150.42 cubic inches

6. *Avoirdupois Weight*
(Common Commodities)

| | |
|---|---|
| 16 ounces (oz.) | = 1 pound (lb.) |
| 100 pounds | = 1 hundredweight (cwt.) |
| 2000 pounds | = 1 ton (T.) |
| 2240 pounds | = 1 long ton (used in customs and mining) |
| 7000 grains (gr.) | = 1 pound |

7. *Troy Weight*
(Precious Metals)

| | |
|---|---|
| 24 grains | = 1 pennyweight (dwt.) |
| 20 pennyweight | = 1 ounce (oz. t.) |
| 12 ounces | = 1 pound (lb. t.) |
| 5760 grains | = 1 pound |

8. *Apothecaries' Weight*
(Drugs)

| | |
|---|---|
| 20 grains | = 1 scruple (s. ap.) |
| 3 scruples | = 1 dram (dr. ap.) |
| 8 drams | = 1 ounce (oz. ap.) |
| 12 ounces | = 1 pound (lb. ap.) |
| 5760 grains | = 1 pound |

9. *Angles and Arcs*

| | |
|---|---|
| 60 seconds (″) | = 1 minute (′) |
| 60 minutes | = 1 degree (°) |
| 90 degrees | = 1 right angle |
| 90 degrees | = 1 quadrant |
| 180 degrees | = 1 straight angle |
| 360 degrees | = 1 circle |

10. *United States Money*

| | |
|---|---|
| 10 mills | = 1 cent (¢) |
| 10 cents | = 1 dime |
| 10 dimes | = 1 dollar ($) |
| 5 cents | = 1 nickel |
| 25 cents | = 1 quarter (dollar) |
| 50 cents | = 1 half-dollar |

(The mill is not coined, but is frequently used in computation, especially in taxes.)

11. *Time*

| | |
|---|---|
| 60 seconds (sec.) | = 1 minute (min.) |
| 60 minutes | = 1 hour (hr.) |
| 24 hours | = 1 day (da.) |
| 7 days | = 1 week (wk.) |
| 30 days | = 1 commercial month (mo.) |
| 52 weeks | = 1 year (yr.) |
| 12 months | = 1 year |
| 360 days | = 1 commercial year |
| 365 days | = 1 common year |
| 366 days | = 1 leap year |
| 10 years | = 1 decade |
| 100 years | = 1 century |

The time from vernal equinox to vernal equinox is a year containing 365 days, 5 hours, 48 minutes, and 45.92 seconds, or about $365\frac{1}{4}$ days. For this reason the calendar has an extra day (February 29) every fourth year. This 366-day year is called a *leap year*. It is always a year whose number (e.g., 1960) is divisible by 4. However, the first year of a century is not a leap year unless the number is divisible by 400; thus 1600 was a leap year, but 1900 was not.

12. *Table for Counting Objects*

| | |
|---|---|
| 12 units | = 1 dozen (doz.) |
| 12 dozen | = 1 gross (gro.) |
| 12 gross | = 1 great gross (gr. gro.) |
| 20 units | = 1 score |

13. *Table for Counting Paper*

| | |
|---|---|
| 24 sheets | = 1 quire |
| 20 quires | = 1 ream |
| 2 reams | = 1 bundle |
| 5 bundles | = 1 bale |
| 500 sheets | = 1 ream |

14. *Other Measures in Common Use*

| | | | |
|---|---|---|---|
| Land: | 640 | acres | = 1 section |
| | 36 | sections | = 1 township (twp.) |
| Sea: | 6 | feet | = 1 fathom |
| | 6080.20 | feet (in U.S.) | = 1 nautical mile |
| | 1 nautical mile per hour | | = 1 knot |
| Miscellaneous: | 40 | yards | = 1 bolt (cloth) |
| | 120 | yards | = 1 skein (yarn) |

## The Metric System

(**indicates basic units; *indicates commonly used units.)

1. *Length*

| | | | |
|---|---|---|---|
| 1 millimeter (mm.) | = | .001 | meter |
| *1 centimeter (cm.) | = | .01 | meter |
| 1 decimeter (dm.) | = | .1 | meter |
| **1 meter (m.) | = | 1. | meter |
| 1 dekameter (dkm.) | = | 10. | meters |
| 1 hectometer (hm.) | = | 100. | meters |
| *1 kilometer (km.) | = | 1000. | meters |

2. *Area*

| | | |
|---|---|---|
| 1 sq. centimeter (cm.$^2$) | = | 100 sq. millimeters (mm.$^2$) |
| 1 sq. decimeter (dm.$^2$) | = | 100 sq. centimeters |
| 1 sq. meter (m.$^2$) | = | 100 sq. decimeters |
| 1 sq. decameter (dkm.$^2$) | = | 100 sq. meters |
| 1 sq. hectometer (hm.$^2$) | = | 100 sq. decameters |
| 1 sq. kilometer (km.$^2$) | = | 100 sq. hectometers |

3. *Capacity*

| | | | |
|---|---|---|---|
| 1 milliliter (ml.) | = | .001 | liter |
| 1 centiliter (cl.) | = | .01 | liter |
| 1 deciliter (dl.) | = | .1 | liter |
| **1 liter (l.) | = | 1. | liter |
| 1 dekaliter (dkl.) | = | 10. | liters |
| 1 hectoliter (hl.) | = | 100. | liters |
| 1 kiloliter (kl.) | = | 1000. | liters |

4. *Weight*

| | | | |
|---|---|---|---|
| 1 milligram (mg.) | = | .001 | gram (g.) |
| 1 centigram (cg.) | = | .01 | gram |
| 1 decigram (dg.) | = | .1 | gram |
| **1 gram (g.) | = | 1. | gram |
| 1 dekagram (dkg.) | = | 10. | grams |
| 1 hectogram (hg.) | = | 100. | grams |
| *1 kilogram (kg.) | = | 1000. | grams |
| 1000 kilograms | = | 1. | metric ton (T.) |

5. *Volume*

| | |
|---|---|
| 1 cubic centimeter ($cm.^3$) | = 1000 cubic millimeters ($mm.^3$) |
| 1 cubic decimeter ($dm.^3$) | = 1000 cubic centimeters |
| 1 cubic meter ($m.^3$) | = 1000 cubic decimeters |

6. *Metric Equivalents*

| | |
|---|---|
| 1000 cubic centimeters | = 1 liter (basic relationship) |
| Weight of 1 cubic centimeter of water | = 1 gram |
| Weight of 1 cubic decimeter of water | = 1 kilogram |

# Easily Made Aids for Teaching Arithmetic

1. *Number Counter*

Use a board 1 in. by 6 in., 22 in. long. Drill 10 holes in it and insert in them 8- to 10-in. dowel pins over which carem rings, metal washers, or large spools cut in half will slip. This may be used to count to 10 or to 100.

2. *Card Holder*

Use a smooth two-by-four 12 in. long. Cut a very thin groove through the middle of one of the 4-in. sides. This will hold cards for counting or for matching with number cards or for practice in reading numbers.

3. *Hundred-Square Peg-Board*

Make an 11-in. square of $\frac{3}{4}$-in. plywood with holes 1 in. apart. Insert kindergarten pegs—ten rows with ten in each row—for learning to count or for finding parts of 100.

4. *Show-Us Pocket*

Use cardboard 6 by 8 in. Staple across the bottom of it a strip of oak-tag 2 in. by 6 in. Ask the pupil to select, from a row of cards on the chalkboard ledge, a mixed number, a fraction equal to 1, and so on, and place the cards in the pocket. Or place such cards in the pocket and ask the pupil to tell what they are as he removes them.

5. *Place-Value Pockets*

Use oak-tag or oilcloth for the back and the pocket strip. Sew or staple the pocket strip onto the back, and stitch the pocket partitions.

Label the pockets with place values. Use cards of suitable size for numbers; place them in the pockets for number reading. For more convenience in handling, thumbtack the back to a piece of wallboard.

6. *Combination Practice Cards*

Use any convenient size cards made of oak-tag. Pupils may make sets of small cards for themselves for practice at their desks. With a felt-point pen, put a combination on one side and the combination with the answer on the other. Cutting one corner off: $\begin{array}{r} 4 \\ +3 \\ \hline \end{array}$ permits ready arrangement of cards with the same side (combination or answer) up.

7. *Review Book*

Fasten sheets of Bristol board, 24 in. by 30 in., together with rings like pages in a notebook. As important principles, generalizations, and formulas come up, put them one on a page, in manuscript writing using a felt-point pen. Be sure they are large enough to be read by the entire class. Use for review in applying the principles, etc.

8. *Flannel Board*

A flannel board is easily made by covering a piece of wallboard of suitable size, or any type of bulletin-board material, with cotton flannel. Thumbtack the flannel neatly on to the back of the board. Neutral colors such as gray or tan are best.

9. *Flannel Board Pictures*

From oak-tag make an adequate number of small chicks, kites, pumpkins, or whatever is seasonable, and color with crayola or tempera. A small square of sandpaper pasted on the back of each picture will hold it to the flannel. Numbers can be cut from old first-grade workbooks or from old calendars. Use in counting to 10.

10. *Circles for Fractional Parts*

Cut several circles, 6 to 12 in. in diameter, into various equal parts. Use on the flannel board for equivalent parts in work with fractions.

# Suggested Equipment for an Arithmetic Laboratory

## Primary Grades

1. Number concepts—counting, group recognition, place value, etc.

    Abacus
    Balls (bouncing)
    Bean bags
    Calendar
    Checkers
    Cuisenaire rods
    Date stamp
    Disks (plastic)
    Dominoes
    Flannel board and pictures
    Inch-cube blocks
    Jumping-rope
    Meat skewers
    Sticks (colored, counting)
    Tongue depressors
    Toothpicks (round)

2. Measurement

    Beans, pebbles, and sand for weighing
    Egg cartons
    Measuring spoons and cups
    Pint, quart, and gallon measures
    Ruler and yardstick
    Scales
    String
    Tape measure
    Thermometer

3. Geometric concepts

    Circle (8-in. Bristol board)
    Compass for chalkboard
    Square (8-in. Bristol board)
    Triangle (8-in.)

4. Miscellaneous

    Clocks (movable hands)
    Coin chart (see Chap. 20)
    Games and puzzles
    Practice cards
    Telephone and directory
    Toy cash register
    Toy money

### Intermediate Grades

1. Measurement

    Beans, pebbles, and sand for weighing
    Egg cartons
    Gill, pint, quart, and gallon measures
    Inch-cube blocks (1728 of them)
    Ounce and pound weights
    Pint, quart, peck, and bushel measures
    Rectangular pattern
    Rectangular solid model
    Ruler and yardstick
    Scales
    Square-inch, square-foot, and square-yard patterns
    Tape measure
    Thermometer

2. Miscellaneous

    Circle and fractional parts of circle
    Compass for chalkboard
    Flannel board and pictures
    Games and puzzles
    Practice cards
    Road maps
    Triangle patterns

### Upper Grades

1. Measurement

    Angle aid (yardstick type; see Chap. 20)
    Boards (1 × 4, 1 × 6, 1 × 12, 2 × 4, 2 × 6, each 2 ft. long)
    Carpenter's square

Circle (21-in., marked in degrees)
Compass for chalkboard
Cone model
Cubic-inch, cubic-foot, and cubic-yard models
Cylinder model
Electric meter
Gas meter
Meter stick, yardstick
Parallelogram pattern
Pyramid model
Rectangular solid
Rulers with small divisions
Speedometer
Thermometers (room, clinical, and cooking)
Trapezoid pattern
Triangle patterns

2. Miscellaneous

Bank forms (checks and stubs, deposit slips, bank statements, pass book, savings account book, promissory note)
Games and puzzles
Road maps
Sales slips
Slide rule (simple type)
Time tables

# Answers to Odd-numbered Problems in Part Two

## SECTION A—COMPUTATION

**Set 1 (page 349)**

**1.** a. 21,703
b. 19,435
c. 95,438
d. 24,318

**3.** $19\frac{19}{24}$

**5.** 31.205

**7.** $1\frac{7}{8}$

**9.** a. $76\frac{1}{36}$
b. $113\frac{2}{15}$
c. $27\frac{1}{20}$

**11.** a. 31,452
b. 32,974
c. 35,145

**Set 2 (page 350)**

**1.** 5,963,010

**3.** a. 6.945750
b. 1,201.256875

**5.** $\frac{2}{5}$

**7.** a, b, c, f.

**9.** $1\frac{11}{24}$

**11.** a. 1
b. 8.6394
c. .0228

**Set 3 (page 351)**

**1.** $2\frac{38}{47}$

**3.** 192

**5.** .012

**7.** divisor; quotient; dividend.

**9.** No.

**11.** 4

**13.** 20%

**15.** 2

**17.** $129\frac{17}{93}$

**19.** a. $3556\frac{4}{9}$

b. $813\frac{3}{5}$

**21.** a. .65
b. .04002
c. .008
d. .05125
e. .4267
f. 1.0069

**23.** $\frac{3}{8}$

**25.** $\frac{40}{1}$

**27.** 30

**29.** .3

**Set 4 (page 352)**

**1.** a. $\frac{3}{4}$; .75; 75%

b. $\frac{1}{6}$; $.16\frac{2}{3}$; $16\frac{2}{3}$%

c. $1\frac{8}{25}$; 1.32; 132%

d. $\frac{3}{50}$; .06; 6%

e. $\frac{2}{3}$; $.66\frac{2}{3}$; $66\frac{2}{3}$%

f. $\frac{13}{200}$; .065; $6\frac{1}{2}$%

g. $\frac{17}{400}$; .0425; $4\frac{1}{4}$%

h. $\frac{1}{7}$; .14285+; $14\frac{2}{7}$%

i. 250; 250.; 25,000%

j. $2\frac{1}{2}$; 2.5; 250%

k. $\frac{9}{200}$; .045; 4.5%

l. $\frac{5}{6}$; $.83\frac{1}{3}$; $83\frac{1}{3}$%

m. $\frac{1}{400}$; .0025; $\frac{1}{4}$%

**3.** 1500

**5.** .045

**7.** $4\frac{1}{4}$%

**9.** $176

11. $18\frac{3}{4}$ mills

13. $198

15. 20%

17. 101%

19. 371.25

21. a. $\frac{1}{4}$; .25; 25%; 1:4

b. $\frac{7}{32}$; .21875; $21\frac{7}{8}$%; 7:32

c. $\frac{4}{1}$; 4.; 400%; 4:1

d. $\frac{3}{4}$; .75; 75%; 3:4

23. 9

25. a. $1\frac{71}{124}$ b. $\frac{25}{56}$ c. $\frac{1}{15}$

27. $\frac{7}{8}$

29. 25,000

31. 77

33. a. $\frac{3}{16}$ b. $\frac{3}{40{,}000}$ c. $\frac{59}{2500}$ d. $\frac{3}{1000}$ e. $\frac{1}{3}$ f. $\frac{1}{150}$

**Set 5 (page 354)**

1. 13 ft. 1 in.

3. 2 lb. 8 oz.

5. 11 gal. 1 qt.

7. 0 cu. yd., 3 cu. ft., 1073 cu. in.

9. 1 sq. mi.

11. 2 lb. $8\frac{2}{3}$ oz.

13. 14 ft.; 168 in.

15. 1 ft. 9 in.

**Set 6 (page 354)**

1. For 126: 2, 3, 7
For 241: none
For 165: 3, 5, 11
For 732: 2, 3, 61
For 110: 2, 5, 11
For 316: 2, 79

3. a. 192
b. 495
c. 180

5. a. 4
b. 15
c. 6

**Set 7 (page 355)**

1. 9; 8; 7; 10; 20

3. a. $10^{-2}$ b. $10^{-3}$ c. $10^{-4}$
d. $10^{-6}$ e. $10^{-9}$

5. a. $10^5$ b. $10^4$ c. $10^8$d. $10^8$

7. a. 672,000 b. 1465

9. a. 7; 18; 4 b. 9; 11; 15
c. 13; 12; 25

11. a. 36(9 × 4); 30(3 × 10); 26(2 × 13)
b. 39(3 × 13); 72($2^3$ × 9); 50(2 × $5^2$)

13. $\frac{7}{12}$; $\frac{4}{9}$; $\frac{20}{25}$

15.
$$\begin{aligned} 6 \times 1 &= 6 \\ 2 \times 10 &= 20 \\ 1 \times 100 &= 100 \\ 2 \times 1{,}000 &= 2{,}000 \\ 4 \times 10{,}000 &= 40{,}000 \\ 6 \times 100{,}000 &= 600{,}000 \end{aligned}$$

17. $10^{11}, 10^{10}, 10^{9}, 10^{8}, 10^{7}, 10^{6}, 10^{5}, 10^{4}, 10^{3}, 10^{2}, 10^{1}, 10^{0}$

19. 103,854

**Set 8 (page 356)**

1. 74

3. a. 50,000,016,420,063
   b. 1,000,016,480,000,000,000,000,300
   c. 9,000,009,000,000,000,000,000,009,000,000,009

5. a. 75.004241
   b. 8001.08001

7. $h = \frac{3V}{B}$

9. 10,000 times as big

**Set 9 (page 357).** The answers to the odd-numbered problems in Set 9 are found in *Answers to Even-numbered Problems in Part Two*, published as a separate booklet.

## SECTION B—APPLICATION OF PROCESSES

**Set 1 (page 364)**

1. 540
3. $66
5. 3%
7. $304
9. $132
11. 625 bu.
13. a. What will the interest be on $900 at 5% for $2\frac{1}{2}$ years?
    b. What will the interest be on $1375 for 1 year at $4\frac{1}{2}$%?
15. 1%
17. *A* was. He had 71% of the votes.
19. 296 days
21. $37.50
23. 500 pupils
25. $171
27. $12,000
29. Mr. Elliot
31. $16\frac{2}{3}$%
33. 24 cents
35. Borrowing from Nancy's father will cost them $20.40 less.
37. 1.4%; 14 mills.
39. .045
41. $164\frac{12}{17}$%
43. 69

45. $1.32

47. $10\frac{10}{13}\%$

49. $3521.88

51. 7.6+%

53. $151.89

55. 38.6%

57. $4555

59. 20%

61. $980

**Set 2 (page 367)**

1. $\frac{1}{2}$

3. 54 sq. ft.

5. 5832 bricks

7. $V = \frac{Bh}{3}$

9. 6 cu. in.

11. 216 sq. in.

13. right triangle

15. $328.32

17. 125 mi.

19. $1131\frac{3}{7}$ cu. in.

21. $284.35

23. a. Various possible solutions.
    b. 9 to 25 or $\left(\frac{3}{5}\right)^2$

25. No specific answer.

27. 180°–90° (angle $A$) equals 90° for $C$ and $B$. Subtract the known angle from 90° to find the third angle.

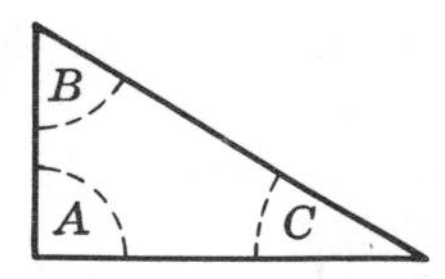


29. 32 min. 5 sec.

31. 720 tiles; no waste

33. 624 sq. ft.

35. $213

37. 640 rd.

39. 31 posts

41. $592.59

43. Two sides and the included angle of triangle $BCD$ are equal to two sides and the included angle of triangle $CAD$; hence the two triangles are equal, and their respective sides, $BD$ and $AC$, are equal.

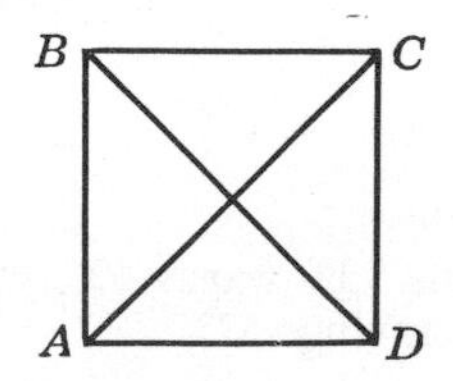

45. a. $63\frac{9}{14}$ sq. in.

b. $71\frac{5}{14}$ sq. in.

47. $410\frac{2}{3}$ sq. in.

49. $392\frac{6}{7}$ sq. ft.

51. 46.28 + gal.

53. It is the sum of the area of four triangles. The slant height is the altitude of triangles taken at the middle of each face.

55. 15 in.

57. $19\frac{9}{14}$ sq. ft.

59. $1357\frac{5}{7}$ cu. in.

61. 8 times as large

63. 24 pupils

65. 3

67. $4.50

**Set 3 (page 371)**

1. $rt = d$

3. $1\frac{1}{5}$ hr.

5. $1\frac{37}{58}$ hr.

7. 60 mph.

9. 1 day

11. 10 men

**Set 4 (page 372)**

1. A ratio may be written 1 to 4, 1:4, or $\frac{1}{4}$. $\frac{1}{4}$ is $1 \div 4$.

3. $\frac{1}{25}$

5. 50

7. 1 to $3\frac{1}{7}$ or $\frac{7}{22}$

9. $\frac{6}{7}$

11. 42 ft.

13. $\frac{15}{32}$

15. 57.5 lb.

17. 58 mi.

19. 12 and 16

21. Ruth has 6 cents; Ann, 8 cents.

**Set 5 (page 373)**

1. 78 ft. 1 in.

3. 18 mi. per gal.

**Set 6 (page 373)**

1. Various possible solutions.

3. Equipment and materials 93°, wages 40°, taxes 22°, interest 18°, living expenses 101°, rent 29°, savings 57°.

**5.** Various possible solutions.

**7.** $2\frac{1}{3}$ in.; $\frac{3}{8}$ in.; $\frac{2}{3}$ in.

**9.** $2\frac{2}{3}$ in.; 4 in.; $\frac{2}{3}$ in.

**11.** $108\frac{1}{4}$ in. or 9 ft.

**Set 7 (page 374)**

**1.** a. 18 in. b. 21 in. c. 17 rd.

**3.** 10 in.

**5.** 37 ft.

**7.** 6 in.

**Set 8 (page 375)**

**1.** \$2203

**3.** 70.3°

**5.** \$20

**7.** \$225

**9.** 8 mi.

**11.** A, \$45.50; B, \$91.00; C, \$227.50

**13.** A, \$180; B, \$270

**15.** James \$16; Bruce, \$18.

**Set 9 (page 376).** The answers to the odd-numbered problems in Set 9 are found in *Answers to Even-numbered Problems in Part Two*, published as a separate booklet.

# INDEXES

# Index of Names

# Index of Subjects